07724

STRAND PRICE
$ 5.00

W9-DBT-836

# THE

# CAPTIVE

# SEA

"CAROLINA SNOWBALL"

# THE

# CAPTIVE

# SEA

*Life Behind the Scenes of the*

*Great Modern Oceanariums*

**CRAIG PHILLIPS**

*With More than 125 Original Illustrations by the Author*

**CHILTON BOOKS**
**A Division of Chilton Company**
**Publishers**
Philadelphia and New York

Copyright © 1964 by
Craig Phillips
First Edition
*All Rights Reserved*
Published in Philadelphia by Chilton Company,
and simultaneously in Toronto, Canada,
by Ambassador Books, Ltd.
Library of Congress Catalog Card Number 64-11425
Designed by Edwin Bookmyer
Manufactured in the United States of America by
Quinn & Boden Company, Inc., Rahway, N. J.

# DEDICATION

*To Fanny*

## ACKNOWLEDGMENTS

To ERNEST A. LACHNER of the U.S. National Museum who painstakingly reviewed this manuscript as it went to press; to my wife FANNY for her many thoughtful suggestions and criticisms during its preparation; to BURTON CLARK and W. B. GRAY of the Miami Seaquarium; to BOB HINES of the U.S. Fish and Wildlife Service; and to my fellow aquarists from Maine to California, who generously provided me with countless valuable notes, reprints, and pictures, I extend my heartfelt appreciation.

## PUBLISHER'S NOTE

A note seems indicated to explain the absence of a bibliography in this book. The main theme of this work is the origin and organization of great aquariums and this is covered nowhere else. On the other hand, any listing of works pertaining to the animals mentioned would be altogether too extensive and detailed to serve any purpose in this context. Zoologists are acquainted with this technical literature or know very well how to trace it.

# CONTENTS

# LIST OF ILLUSTRATIONS

# THE

# CAPTIVE

# SEA

# CHAPTER 1

# THE SEAQUARIUM IS BORN

*A Blob Comes to Life. A New Type of Aquarium Is Begun at Miami. Invaded by Tree-Climbing Crabs. My Seaside Laboratory. Never Look a Gift Shark in the Mouth. "Stew," the Pampered Loggerhead. Hauling a Giant Turtle Across the Everglades*

The bulldozer rattled past my temporary laboratory building on the shore of Biscayne Bay, pushing before it a heap of mud and mangrove roots, and as I watched I saw a strange shapeless blob stir at the top of the growing mound, wrench itself free with convulsive movements, and tumble into the wake of the 'dozer, where it lay on the sand, making an odd, bobbing motion from time to time. As I approached to investigate, two shiny black eyes rose on stalks from the center of the muddy blob, and a stream of small bubbles was projected in my direction to the accompaniment of a hissing sound.

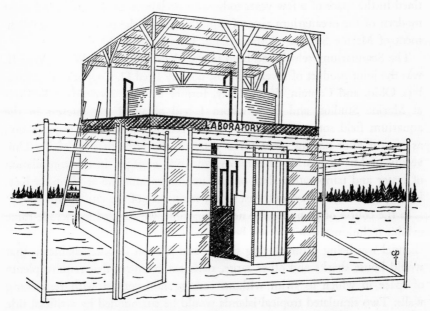

SEAQUARIUM pilot plant in summer of 1953.

This was a giant purple land crab, but a crab the like of which I had never seen before. It stood well off the ground on long, jointed legs ending in hairy brushes like a miniature Percheron horse. Its hard back was sculptured with deep grooves and raised designs, and, most singular of all, its heavy porcelain-like pincers were both the same size, whereas in most land crabs I had observed previously, one claw is noticeably smaller than the other. The crab was now moving away toward the protecting tangle formed by the aerial roots of some as yet unbulldozed mangroves, and I knew that, should the creature attain his goal, he would disappear for good down one of the many muddy holes that exist in great numbers in such locations.

The crab was moving faster now, brandishing his claws and sputtering more bubbles in my direction whenever I got too near. I saw that now I would have to move quickly if I were to take him alive as a specimen, so, running past him, I reached the mangroves first, where I quickly broke off a section of one of the curving, aerial roots which the trees send down into the mud. With this I held the crab down firmly against the ground, and with my free hand I seized him by the back of his shell, out of reach of the waving claws. A short time later I had my captive in a wire cage under the laboratory shelter where I could observe him at my leisure.

The time was the summer of 1953, when groundbreaking operations were under way on the new and as yet unnamed Miami Seaquarium. It was destined in the space of a few years to become acclaimed as the finest and most modern of the oceanarium type of aquarium since the pioneering establishment of Marine Studios at Marineland, Florida, in 1937.

The Seaquarium, which had been in the planning prior to World War II, was the joint product of several minds, notably Fred D. Coppock of Columbus, Ohio, and Captain W. B. Gray, former head of specimen collections at Marine Studios, and from whom I had obtained my interest in the aquarium field some years earlier. I had recently joined the organization as curator after having spent three years on the research staff of the University of Miami Marine Laboratory, and was engaged in the compilation of water and temperature data on the new aquarium site at Virginia Key, located in Biscayne Bay southeast of the main part of the city of Miami.

In the course of planning the new aquarium, we decided to include some exhibit techniques that had not been tried before. A gigantic circular shark channel was being planned, ring shaped and 750 feet in outer diameter, that would house sharks and other large, swift sea creatures that require plenty of space in which to swim without coming into contact with restraining walls. Two simulated tropical islands would be surrounded by artificial tide pools connected to the ocean by means of an underground pipe so that when the tide rose and fell in the sea, it would do likewise in the pools. This would give us an area in which to exhibit inshore creatures such as mollusks; crustaceans, including giant spider crabs and tropical lobsters; starfishes, sea urchins, sea cucumbers, sea anemones; and shallow-water fishes. The islands themselves would be landscaped with palm trees and various other tropical plants and be inhabited by land crabs, tree-climbing hermit crabs, and large iguana lizards.

A special sea-show arena with stadium was to be built, where trained dolphins, sea lions, and other creatures could be put through their paces at specified times, and a special outside tank was planned for the exhibition of sea cows, or manatees. There would also be two giant, 3-level circular tanks in the main building, an 80-foot one for dolphins, nurse sharks, sawfishes, giant rays and other large fishes, and a 50-footer for the display of the smaller, brightly colored fishes of the coral reefs.

Finally, there was planned a series of 26 individual tanks of up to 500 gallons each arranged in circular fashion around the corridor surrounding the main 80-foot tank for the display of individual species and habitat groups of fishes and invertebrates.

The Virginia Key site included a 55-acre tract of land adjacent to the Marine Laboratory buildings of the University of Miami. At the outset of the planning, most of the key, although covered by a dense growth of mangrove trees, was actually under a foot or so of water at high tide. Therefore, in order to prepare the land for the new aquarium, the trees had to be removed by a dragline and the land then dredged in to a height of 6 feet above tide level. This meant that the entire south portion of the key, which was bisected by the Rickenbacker Causeway, had to be first leveled and then filled, and during this process virtually the entire animal population of this typical south Florida mangrove swamp was uncovered. As a result, a number of interesting discoveries came to light.

The first of these was the remarkable brush-footed, purple land crab, which proved to be a West Indian species, *Ucides cordatus,* up to this time unknown to the Florida mainland. Since about a dozen additional specimens of this crab were literally and figuratively flushed from their burrows when the fill-in by dredging began, it is likely that these creatures have always been a part of the normal key fauna, hiding under the very noses of local biologists up to the time that we rooted them out of the mangrove muck.

Land crabs are perhaps the most typical inhabitants of the mangrove communities of south Florida. The largest and most abundant of these is the blue land crab, *Cardisoma guanhumi,* also found in abundance in the

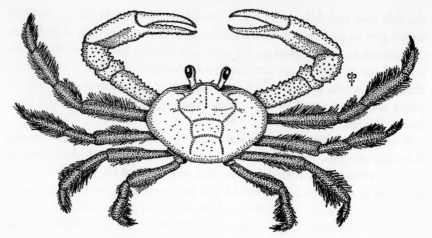

Brushfooted Land Crab, *Ucides cordatus.*

Bahama Islands and in the West Indies. The males attain a length of about a foot between the outstretched walking legs and are of a clear powder-blue color with one pincer greatly enlarged for digging and fighting. The females are slightly smaller and vary from purplish to mauve-gray to nearly white or yellowish. During the late summer months they swarm about the mainland from Miami southward, where great numbers are squashed by cars along the highways. Although edible, they have a bit of an iodine taste due to their fondness for marsh grass, but in the Bahamas and elsewhere these crabs are penned up by the natives, who feed them fresh vegetables for a time, considerably improving their culinary qualities.

The 2- to 3-inch climbing mangrove crab, *Sesarma,* is swift-moving and sure-footed, climbing up the face of vertical seawalls and pilings and, in the swamp, ascending many feet to the very tops of the mangrove trees, where they feed on any small insects they can catch, in addition to plant material. While making my way through a mangrove thicket, I once heard a 17-year locust or cicada calling in an odd manner, and on tracking down the source of the sound, I discovered the hapless insect on a twig about 10 feet from the ground and held firmly in the pincers of a *Sesarma* crab no larger than itself! The crustacean released the cicada as I ascended the branches, but undoubtedly would have eaten it had I not interfered.

A crab of gaudy coloration, not often seen, is the large red-legged mangrove crab, *Goniopsis,* which is found along both coasts of Florida from the center of the state southward. The body of this crab is purplish black marked with a profusion of white dots, the pincers are cream yellow, and the flattened legs bright crimson with stiff black hairs. Considerably larger than the

Arboreal crab (*Sesarma*) capturing cicada in a mangrove tree.

*Sesarma,* the red-legged variety is adept at dodging from one side of a tree trunk to the other, and is exceedingly difficult to capture alive. When it is cornered at the end of an overhanging branch, I have seen it drop like a plummet into the water and swim rapidly into the shelter of an overhanging bank.

Finally, we must mention the large land hermit crab, *Cenobita,* whose habits are in marked contrast to its many water-dwelling relatives. This red and blue creature climbs trees slowly and deliberately, dragging along its borrowed seashell which protects the soft coiled abdomen. Clinging to the bark with great tenacity with all its legs as well as its pincers when disturbed, it is frequently difficult to dislodge by hand. During the daylight hours one can often find a hollow in a tree closely packed with colorful seashells; on closer inspection each shell is seen to contain a resting hermit crab.

On some occasions I have picked up a hollow driftwood log from the shore above the high tide line, shaken it, and seen a small bucketful of crab-packed shells come clattering out. Since these crabs must constantly find larger quarters as they grow, empty shells are at a premium in some areas and it is not unusual to find an occasional "slum dweller" whose eroded shell exposes parts of the crab in inappropriate places. Sometimes substitute homes, such as enameled cups, discarded pipe bowls, and the like are adopted for shelter purposes. While serving with the Navy in the Pacific I once saw a number of small hermit crabs on Guadalcanal Island wearing empty brass 30-caliber cartridges, certainly an easily obtained commodity at the time. I can't help but wonder if, given sufficient time, a new race of straight-tailed crabs might have evolved as a result of this habit.

As the dredging progressed at Virginia Key and the remains of the mangroves gradually became submerged in a constantly widening slurry of mud and sand deposited by the dredge pipes inside the continuous retaining dike which ringed the area, other swamp denizens continued to make their appearance. Raccoon tracks appeared nightly, giving evidence of these animals' discovery of a larder of crabs and other food to be had at little effort, and by day a host of shore and wading birds patrolled the area, concentrating near the dredge pipe outlets, as these in turn provided a bounty of small worms and other invertebrates sucked up along with the mud and sediment from the floor of Biscayne Bay.

The dikes and other high-ground areas soon began to virtually swarm with armies of dispossessed land crabs, which were soon pressing at the portals of my small pilot plant laboratory which was located behind a wire fence. Crabs worked their way over, under, and between the wires, and my worktable was soon covered with the little gray mangrove crabs, who would crawl and scuttle in and out of the maze of water pipettes, beakers, and Erlenmeyer flasks, and occasionally pause and regard me with bobbing eyestalks and strangely petulant expressions while I analyzed water samples. One night I forgot to fasten the case of my Beckmann pH meter with which I tested the alkalinity of seawater, and on arriving next morning I found that several mangrove crabs had invaded its internal workings. I had to remove the back of the case in order to get them out, but aside from nipping the insulated wires here and there, they had done no damage to the machine.

Since these crabs lose their legs easily, it is difficult to capture one by hand and have it remain intact. The appendages can be instantly dropped by means of the sudden contraction of a special muscle at the point where the limb joins the body; at the same time the crab automatically applies a sort of tourniquet action, which protects it from losing more than a tiny amount of its body fluids. Should a crab be restrained in any way, two or three legs are frequently thus autotomized simultaneously, and these will continue to flex spasmodically for a time. There is a somewhat parallel situation in regard to several species of small lizards inhabiting the same area. Certain lizards are well known for their ability to autotomize their tails should these be seized and, as the lizard scurries to safety, the detached tail thrashes about violently on the ground. This is commonly thought to be an attention distracting device which allows the lizard to escape. In due time it regenerates a new tail.

A regrown lizard tail is never quite as long or as flexible as the original, but in the crab, a more primitive beast, a replaced limb is identical to the member lost, though usually requiring at least two successive moults of the shell to attain full size. On one occasion I saw a *Sesarma* hitching himself along a mud flat by means of only one leg. A series of new pink leg-buds were already developing, showing that, barring further misadventures, this temporarily crippled individual would not be handicapped for long.

The pilot plant itself was a wooden structure contained in an area approximately 12 feet square. Besides the worktable which held my instruments and a cabinet for chemical reagents, there were two electrical water pumps that supplied a 200-gallon reservoir and a gravity filter containing sand and gravel. After filtering, this water was pumped to a roof tank, circular in shape, 8 feet in diameter and 16 inches deep. This was a one-tenth scale model of our projected 80-foot tank, and held about 500 gallons of water. From the circular roof tank, which was reached by climbing a ladder, the overflow water returned by gravity through the filter and into the collection reservoir below. New water for the system was drawn through a 1-inch plastic line connecting with the intake located near the bottom of the sea, 50 feet offshore.

One of the important things we were attempting to learn was how to maintain high standards of water clarity within our tanks. Seawater with little or no preliminary filtration can be used in tanks of up to a thousand gallons capacity, but beyond that, apparent cloudiness or turbidity increases very rapidly, depending on the horizontal depth of the tank. For instance, a gallon of seawater that cannot be distinguished by eye from a 1-gallon container of distilled water (the ultimate standard of clarity), may begin to show a slight haziness when you are looking through 5 feet of it. Through 10 feet, it will be definitely cloudy, at 20 feet objects will appear quite hazy, and at 40 feet, nearly invisible.

Thus, water suitable for viewing the specimens in a huge tank of the oceanarium design must be considerably clearer than normal seawater or that which comes from the average home water faucet. In order to maintain a high standard of clarity, large aquariums find it best to refilter and re-use the same water over and over, constantly aerating it and adding new ocean water only to make up that which is lost in the course of normal handling and when the filters are periodically backflushed. This process results in a small but constant turnover which prevents the buildup of harmful chemicals that might result from decomposition of fish wastes, uneaten food, etc., as well as the products of the gradual but inevitable corrosive action of salt water upon pipe fittings, pump impellers, and other metallic parts of the water system.

Another factor affecting underwater visibility is color. Pure water is colorless, and the apparent blue of very clear, deep water is due entirely to the absorption of the red side of the daylight spectrum by the water itself, so that only the shorter wavelengths of blue light are reflected upward from the depths. The apparent blue of the daytime sky is caused in much the same way.

Whereas pure offshore ocean water may appear blue, the water near shore may appear green or even brownish due to the presence of certain pigments produced by microscopic plant and animal life which grow abundantly in shallow coastal waters where rivers and other run-off from the land enrich the sea with dissolved chemical nutrients and suspended matter. When these plants and animals in turn die off, their body pigments tend to go into solution and discolor the water, and this minute though discernible coloration is exceedingly difficult to remove. Filtering the water does not help any more than the filtering of a cup of tea would remove the brown color, and most bleaching agents, such as chlorine, are highly toxic to living animals. As yet, no practical way has been developed to remove dissolved color on a large scale, so at the present time this factor has to be tolerated, though it is seldom a serious one.

I was once able to demonstrate in quite a dramatic way the part that color or the apparent lack of it plays in our illusion of underwater clarity by the following experiment: in one of two large adjoining tanks having an average degree of turbidity and in addition a considerable amount of green color at the time, I placed a spoonful of methylene blue powder, a dye that permeates water quickly. Within a couple of minutes the greenish water in the treated tank was completely masked by a clear light blue, and the effect was most dramatic. Virtually everyone who was asked to comment on the comparative appearances of the two tanks insisted that the water in the treated tank was "clear," while in the untreated one it was "cloudy," and some observers even insisted that the dye must in some way have precipitated out the turbidity. Comparisons with a light meter showed this to be definitely not the case, and in fact, by adding the colored dye, I had actually cut down the visibility by a slight amount! This illustrates the considerable degree to which our eye can be deceived by our unconscious associations in regard to water clarity.

The model tank on the pilot plant roof contained a small assortment of brightly colored reef fishes, and a partial canopy was erected over them to protect them from the heat and brightness of the noonday sun. They were fed daily on fresh shrimp and cut fish fillets, and water samples were taken periodically for the testing, among other things, of oxygen content, pH, turbidity, and color. The two latter tests were taken by placing samples in 3-foot-long glass tubes, viewing them through the open tops, and comparing them with standards of known quality.

One problem with which we had to contend at this time was unforeseen. The public, having heard that an aquarium was being built on Virginia Key, almost immediately started bringing us specimens which we could neither keep nor care for in this early stage in the operations. Hardly a day went by without someone arriving on the scene with a freshly caught fish, sometimes of considerable size, a sea turtle, octopus, or the like. Since these gifts were almost always well intended, I made it a practice to accept or reject them as graciously as possible, especially as the donor had often gone to considerable effort to bring them to us. On one occasion two fishermen came bouncing up to the door of the pilot plant in an open-bed truck of doubtful vintage, in the back of which lay a violently thrashing and thoroughly miserable 4-foot blacktip shark. There was nothing to do but carry the shark up the

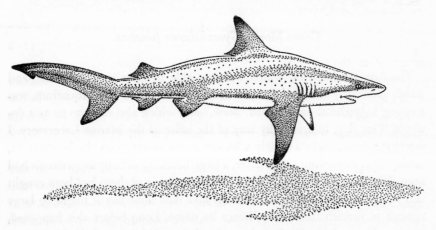

Blacktip Shark, *Carcharhinus limbatus*.

ladder by the tail and deposit him in the tank in order to try to save and eventually return him to the sea, but he expired before the gentlemen had taken their departure.

Eventually a large tidal lake was dug as part of the aquarium plan, and connected with the sea at each end by means of a screened culvert, and this served as a repository for many of our advance specimens, while those of special scientific interest were usually preserved and donated to the University of Miami Marine Laboratory, which was situated adjacent to the aquarium property on the key. Although the newly excavated lake remained too turbid for visibility for a considerable period, the specimens soon learned to come close to shore at feeding time. One of these was a 5-foot green moray eel whom we soon dubbed affectionately "Old Blood-and-Guts" because of his fondness for the less inspiring portions of fish viscera, a commodity easily obtained from the nearby Crandon Park fishing docks.

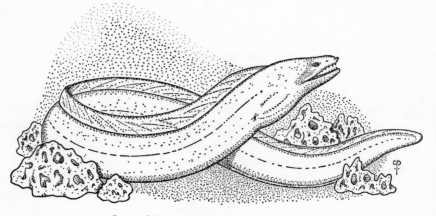

Green Moray, *Gymnothorax funebris.*

The first specimen on which we were able to keep permanent tab, and which eventually was placed in the main tank of the finished aquarium, was a young loggerhead turtle called "Stew," and which also came to us as a donation. One day, indirectly by way of the office of the Marine Laboratory, I received a letter from a couple who ran a tourist camp on the beach at Ft. Lauderdale. According to the letter, a large hatching of baby loggerheads had been discovered on the beach a year before, and one of them had been caught and raised in a large dishpan with the idea that some day it might be large enough to furnish turtle soup, hence its name. Long before this happened, quite understandably, the little loggerhead came to be regarded with increasing affection by its owners, until the very notion of eating it was unthinkable. Since "Stew" by now had grown so large as to completely fill the dishpan, the letter said, it was earnestly hoped that somebody known to the Marine Laboratory personnel would be interested in giving him a permanent home.

Ordinarily loggerhead turtles, especially young ones, are so easily obtained that the drive to Ft. Lauderdale for this one was not worth the trouble, but it so happened that I was to drive to that area shortly thereafter on business, and besides, there was something so charming in the tone of the letter that I penned an acceptance reply at once. When I called for the turtle I was impressed by both its size and its extremely healthy condition, and was told that, since the tourist court also maintained a restaurant, "Stew" had been reared on a diet of choice meat scraps, including chicken, liver, beef, and fish. During the turtle's subsequent tenure at the Seaquarium on a fare consisting of fish fillets, I can't help but wonder if he ever longed for his former epicurean life.

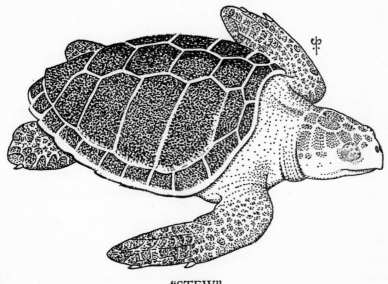

"STEW"

Another loggerhead of special significance was obtained about a year after "Stew." This one was also a gift, this time from Mr. Jack Hurlibut who owned and operated an aquarium in St. Petersburg. One day Jack called me on the phone and said he had a female turtle of unusually large size which he would be glad to give us if we cared to come after it. I accepted, and for this job I borrowed an ancient jeep station wagon owned by one of the company employees and drove the 200-mile distance across the Florida Everglades to the Gulf.

Next morning, with the aid of half a dozen helpers, Jack and I turned the 400-pound loggerhead on her back and slid her along two heavy planks onto a mattress in the back of the jeep. During the moving process the turtle offered little resistance, but once in the jeep she commenced wildly flailing her flippers as overturned sea turtles frequently do, beating a pounding tattoo on her bony plastron. Moreover, the stout curved basal claw on each flipper was beginning to snag in and tear what remained of the jeep's upholstery. To forestall this, I ordered a hacksaw and armed with this instrument, I seated myself astride the protesting turtle's middle and manicured the tip of each claw, placing the jeep's upholstery out of danger for the time being.

Since the turtle was to remain in this position for a 24-hour period, we sought to make the creature as comfortable as possible for the trip. We placed a pillow beneath its head and covered the body, neck, and flippers with a heavy cotton blanket for protection, because when dried out, a turtle's skin areas can become windburned and chapped from prolonged exposure.

The return trip to Miami proved to be less routine than I had anticipated. With the extra load the jeep seemed to be feeling its years, tending to labor when shifted into high. Perhaps the periodic rockings administered to it by the struggles of the turtle had shaken something loose, for without warning the front hood suddenly snapped up in the wind, obscuring all vision as I was driving down the highway. I managed to stop the car without mishap and replaced the faulty catch with one fashioned from a coathanger, but five minutes later the radiator noisily boiled dry. Although I was some miles away from a service station, there was a canal along the roadside, and from this I managed to obtain some brackish but usable water. Since the radiator continued to leak, it was necessary to repeat this performance every few miles until I could have it repaired.

By now the turtle itself was becoming a problem. So long as I continued driving or while the jeep was parked it lay quietly, but whenever I stepped on the starter, the beast would erupt in a frenzy of activity, its head bobbing about on the pillow and the great flippers flailing about wildly, flinging off the blanket, and on one occasion hurling it completely out of the car. After a brief time the turtle would again become placid, and I would then replace the blanket, adjust the pillow, and we would resume our Miami-ward journey.

Although this became a routine and not particularly troublesome incident, another situation rapidly became intolerable from my standpoint. The turtle's head was located against the front seat immediately behind my back, which

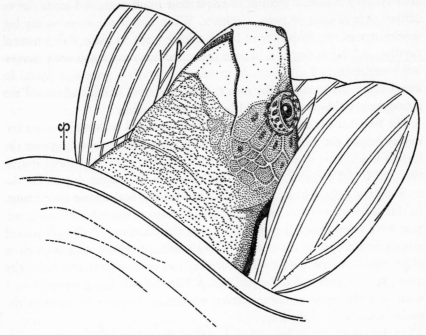

Loggerhead riding in comfort in the back of a jeep.

proved to be a discouraging proximity, as at intervals its breath would be expelled with a deep sigh, and for some reason nature has bestowed upon sea turtles a phenomenal case of halitosis.

In my past association with various air-breathing marine animals I have noted that seals, sea lions, and dolphins have a somewhat fishy quality to their breath, that of a manatee or sea cow is fresh and clovery like that of a young calf, but a large sea turtle's exhalation reminds me of rancid fat with an indeterminable something added, and it is one of the most disagreeable odors I know. No other reptile to my knowledge has anything to compare with it, and I cannot correlate it with anything specific in the turtle's diet, so it must be just part of the intrinsic nature of this otherwise affable beast.

When resting motionless on the bottom, sea turtles do not have to rise to breathe at all. Instead, they fill their throats with water and expel it with a slow, continuous pumping action, absorbing oxygen through the highly convoluted and blood-supplied tissues of the throat, which serve as a sort of gill. This habit is shared with certain freshwater turtles as well, and in this manner they are amphibians in the true sense of the word, although scientifically they don't belong to this class. However, when moving about actively, they find this method of respiration insufficient, and must rise to "blow" at least once or twice a minute. When out of the water as my big specimen was, the frequency of breath-taking tends to maintain its natural rhythm, and the timing of it became impressed upon my senses with increasing forcefulness as I drove on. At measured intervals a great sigh would be heard above the sound of the motor, and for several seconds afterward the atmosphere inside the car would become unendurable.

The fact that the day was hot and the air saturated with midsummer humidity helped not a bit. At length I tried placing a large paper bag over the turtle's head. This was loose enough to allow it to breathe without restriction and it did seem to cut down the effluvium to a slight degree, besides muffling the sighs, which in themselves had become bothersome after a time. In this manner, and still making occasional stops to quench the hissing engine with canal water, I proceeded across the Tamiami Trail and arrived shortly before dusk at the town of Everglades City, within a hundred miles of Miami. At a service station I had the radiator trouble diagnosed as a leaky hose gasket, which had to be replaced. While this was being attended to, I went to a restaurant across the street, neglecting, however, to mention the turtle in the back of the jeep.

On my return a half hour later, I noticed the two colored station attendants peering curiously through the dusty windows at the blanket-shrouded form in the back. On my approach, one of them turned to me, and, indicating the rear compartment with a jerk of his thumb, inquired: "Somebody sick back there?" Meanwhile, the other attendant had entered the driver's seat and, after glancing nervously behind him, started the engine. Instantly the blanket was hurled partly out the window and the jeep bounced on its springs as the loggerhead thrashed about in its confined space, followed by the rapid exodus of the attendant who had pressed the starter. After the commotion had subsided I persuaded both attendants to return for a closer look, and they erupted in gales of laughter. I was told that, as they were working on the jeep, they became increasingly aware of muffled sighing in the back, as if "somebody was dyin', like." Looking through the window into the dimly lighted interior only reinforced their suspicions, as all they could discern was a bulky form beneath a blanket with the head resting on a pillow.

In the early evening I drove the remaining distance to Miami, where I left the turtle in the jeep until morning when I could obtain the assistance necessary to move it into the shark channel, which at that time served as our repository for sea turtles. Apparently none the worse for its long trip, this particular specimen remained our largest loggerhead for several years.

Back at the pilot plant, our water tests continued and further data were recorded as the new aquarium slowly began to take shape. What had once been a flourishing tidal mangrove swamp was now a gleaming expanse of white sand raised several feet above its original level; on this, reinforced concrete piles were being poured, later to be water-jetted into the hardening substrate and serve as the foundation for the massive circular tanks. The shark channel was gradually walled in by a series of interlocking concrete wall slabs, and the tide pools were already dug and various palms and other tropical plants had been set in the mounds of earth that were to be the center islands. Large boulders of weathered coral limestone rock had been obtained from a quarry south of Miami, and these lay in a great pile near the area of construction until they could be used, both for landscaping the tide pool islands and aquascaping the floor of the main tanks. All these vast changes had been wrought within the space of a short year, and only the little gray mangrove crabs, which still swarmed about my laboratory cubicle in the pilot plant, served as a reminder of the former wildness of Virginia Key.

# CHAPTER 2

# INVERTED FISH AND AN ORPHANED SEA COW

*The Strange School of Upside-Down Fish. Coral Rock Stow-aways. Building the Tide Pools. Fish that Construct Sleeping Bags. Spiny Lobsters and Fiddler Crabs. A Manatee Waif. The Inhumanity of Man to Manatee. Sea Cow Lore*

The school of upside-down fish appeared in the newly dredged boat harbor which formed a part of our new aquarium facilities in the spring of 1955. This was a sight the like of which I had never seen before (nor have I since), and to this day I have no explanation for it. It was just one of those baffling things that one occasionally encounters in nature, and I confess that, had the scene been described to me by a local fisherman or casual observer, I would either have thought the man was pulling my leg or else misinterpreting what he saw. The fact that the same or a similar phenomenon had been witnessed a day earlier by at least one other person is reassuring, although I wish that circumstances had permitted me an opportunity for a more thorough observation at the time.

On this particular day the sky and sea had a leaden overcast and no wind was stirring. I was working alone aboard our collecting barge the *Sea Cow*, which lay at anchor in the harbor. The bilges were half filled with accumulated rain water from a copious downpour that had occurred during the previous night, and my arm and shoulder were sore from making endless but futile tugs on the starter cord of the sodden, obstinate gasoline engine that operated the bilge pump. Taking a breather from my work, I seated myself on the gunwale, lit my pipe, and, silently cursing all temperamental gas engines and bilge pumps in general, I directed my gaze across the harbor.

During the past few days dense schools of little anchovies had made their way into the shallower parts of Biscayne Bay, and a large number of them were swarming about on the surface of the harbor, rippling the surface here and there like patches of rain on water. Now and then the surface would be cut to foam as blue runners (*Caranx fusus*), active members of the jack family, attacked the densely packed anchovies from below. Close to the barge the water was clear enough to permit a view of these larger fish as they rushed upward from the depths to feed on the anchovies.

Suddenly before my startled gaze, a pack of about fifteen blue runners appeared from under the barge and charged at a group of anchovies at the surface nearby, vanishing an instant later into the depths below, and *I saw that every one of them was swimming upside down!* Hardly before I recovered from my initial surprise they reappeared, and I watched them closely for a period of about a minute before they were finally out of sight. During this time they steadfastly retained their belly-up position. They swam, as all

Upside-down school of Blue Runners, *Caranx fusus,* chasing Anchovies.

blue runners do, in close formation, speeding, turning, and now and then breaking the surface as they snapped at the anchovies. I noted that their pelvic and anal fins occasionally showed above the water surface as their dorsals would have done, had they been swimming upright. In short, their actions were so normal in every respect as to rule out any possibility that these might be sick or injured fish. For some reason they were apparently deliberately choosing to swim in this manner!

As a normally swimming fish will sometimes turn on its side briefly when changing direction, these did from time to time, only instantly to resume swimming belly up. The thing that clinched my opinion that their inverted position was at the time "normal" insofar as the school was concerned was the fact that during the time I watched them they were joined briefly by another group of slightly larger individuals swimming in the usual fashion, and, despite the strong follow-the-leader tendencies of most schooling fishes, this affected their behavior not one whit. After making a concentrated pass at a school of anchovies during which time the two groups of blue runners mingled freely, the right-side-uppers and the upside-downers parted company, and I couldn't help but wonder whether, somewhere in the primitive brains of both parties, there may have existed a ghost of a feeling that somebody wasn't quite with it. Sometime later I was forcibly reminded of this incident on seeing a magazine cartoon where one school of fish meets another school swimming toward them upside down in mid-water, each viewing the other in disapproval with the joint caption: "No, fellows, THIS way!"

Fishes that do swim upside down occasionally, and certain Mochokid catfishes of India that normally swim in this fashion exist, but this trait is invariably connected with some mode of behavior such as feeding or protection, and in the case of the reversed catfishes it is accompanied by physiological changes such as a dark-colored belly and light upper sides. However, this sort of activity is, to my knowledge, unheard of in blue runners or any related Carangid fishes.

Several days following this incident, I was discussing what I had seen with one of the biologists at the Marine Laboratory of the University of Miami and learned that he had seen a similar, if not the same, school of inverted blue runners in another harbor a half mile away on the day previous to my own sighting. To date no further reports of this phenomenon have come to my attention, and while I have no present theory to account for it, there exists a possible clue in the similar swimming behavior of certain mullet (*Mugil*) that have been seen in the Biscayne Bay area.

For some years prior to the blue runner incident I had heard various fishermen report seeing an occasional mullet swimming upside down in a school of normal individuals. None had actually been captured so far as I could ascertain, and although I myself had seen many schools of mullet in the area, nothing of this sort had ever met my eye. Frankly, I was dubious about the existence of these inverted mullet until a close acquaintance of mine who is an ornithologist and a trained scientific observer saw one and tried unsuccessfully to capture it along the shore of Crandon Park, three miles from the aquarium site. According to his account, he watched it at close range for several minutes before it finally eluded him by making for deeper water, and according to him it swam about with great rapidity, never once deviating from its belly-up position.

Finally, in October of 1952, an upside-down mullet was seen and caught by Dr. Don de Sylva of the Marine Laboratory, and was studied for some time in an aquarium tank before it died. An account of its behavior is given by Dr. de Sylva in the 1953 No. 4 issue of COPEIA, The Journal of the American Society of Ichthyologists and Herpetologists.

I describe this behavior in the mullet as merely a "clue" because I am not convinced that inverted swimming in de Sylva's mullet and my blue runners was necessarily caused by the same factor. The reversed mullets may possibly be genetically variant individuals with their sense of balance askew, since in nearly all cases they have been seen in schools of otherwise normal fish. To consider all of the 15-odd blue runners in the school to be individually reversed is too great a coincidence to be tenable, and instead appears to be an instance of group behavior and orientation, though to what end or purpose, I cannot possibly guess.

The barge on which I was working at the time was then being used to transport weathered coral rock from the windward side of the upper Florida Keys to the aquarium site for use in decorating the future individual tank displays and also to line the shores of the two tide pools. A vast amount of this rock was required, and many barge loads were brought back and piled on the grounds, later to be sorted and set in place by hand. Loading it on the barge was an arduous task as paths had to be cut through the undergrowth on the Keys and the rocks, some weighing up to 300 pounds, were ferried in a flat-bottomed skiff from the shore to the barge.

The limestone rock which forms the substrate of the southern tip of Florida and the chain of Keys themselves represents the remains of fossilized coral reefs which were long ago buried under sediments and much later slowly uncovered as geological changes caused the land to rise. In certain places this rock, called "Key stone," is quarried in large blocks and sawed into slabs for decorative facings on buildings, and in these slabs can clearly be seen cross sections of individual corals, shells, worm tubes, and many other individually recognizable fossils. When freshly cut, the Key stone is soft and chalky, but on prolonged exposure to the air it becomes considerably hardened. When the rock is gradually exposed and broken up due to wave action and other forces of natural weathering along the shoreline, the individual chunks tend to become pitted like meteorites, the outer surface gradually acquiring a very hard, glasslike veneer and the mass giving out a ringing or metallic clanging sound when struck.

It was the stone in its latter form that we were after, as rocks in this condition could be fitted and cemented together in a continuous mosaic to duplicate a natural weathered shoreline in appearance. In selecting and gathering up the individual loose rocks, we encountered many interesting items of litter that had floated ashore and been cast up well above the tideline by past storms and hurricanes. There were bottles of all shapes and sizes, many of otherwise clear glass having gradually acquired a purple tint as glass will do after prolonged exposure to the sun. Bits of rope, net floats, and various poles, boards, and timbers were scattered about in the undergrowth, and it always surprises me to find numbers of discarded electric bulbs completely intact among the jagged rocks, often with their copper bases almost completely corroded away, showing that they had been lying in this position for quite some time.

The rocks themselves often harbored various forms of life in their pitted and hollowed recesses. Among the "stowaways" that were carried back to the aquarium site inside the rocks were enormous scorpions, large, hairy wolf spiders, centipedes, land crabs, tree snails, and occasional small lizards and snakes. Most representative of the lizards was the diminutive 2-inch reef gecko, *Sphaerodactylus notatus*. These tiny creatures would often appear clambering about the walls of the barge and on the dock as the rocks were being unloaded, their robust shape being somewhat reminiscent of scale-model crocodiles. Like most true geckos they have no eyelids, their eyes being covered by a transparent scale as in the case of snakes, and as many geckos do, these have the interesting habit of now and then protruding their pointed tongue from the corner of the mouth and delicately licking the surface of the eyeball, presumably to remove dust or perhaps to keep it slightly moist, since the covering scale is not so thick or so well developed as in the case of snakes.

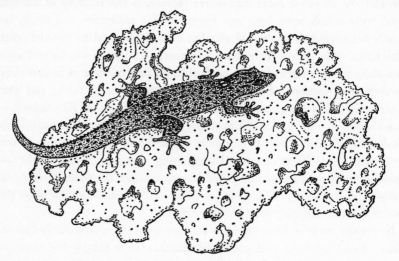

Reef Gecko, *Sphaerodactylus notatus*.

From one barge load of rocks emerged two tiny ringnecked snakes, *Diadophis punctatus*, each about 5 inches long. In common with the geckos, these are a secretive and nocturnal species, hiding in the rocks by day and coming forth at night to feed. These were sooty-black above, the only visible marking being the coral-red ring at the back of the head which gives them their name. Beneath, they are brilliant orange with a row of round black spots down the center of the belly, while the underside of the tail is colored bright red. When disturbed, these little snakes have the habit of curling their tails in the form of a flat spiral, and then inverting the disk thus formed so that the red shows from above. This habit of flashing so-called warning colors by means of the tail is shared by the cylinder snakes of Asia and certain South American coral snakes, though the ringneck is otherwise quite innocuous in habit.

Since the Virginia Key site had previously been cleared of all its natural shrubbery and attendant animal life, the vacated niches were taken over in part by these newcomers arriving in the daily barge loads of rock. The geckos particularly started turning up in corners of the new buildings, and today their descendants form a thriving colony on the Seaquarium grounds.

The first loads of rock were used in the tide pools, which were newly dug. These "pools" actually consisted of two oval channels about 15 feet wide and from 2 to 3 feet deep, surrounding man-made center islands decorated with large limestone boulders and planted with palms, sea grapes, mangroves, fig trees, cacti, Spanish bayonets, and many other tropical shrubs in preparation for the iguanas and other unusual creatures who would eventually inhabit this area.

Besides starfishes, sea urchins, spiny lobsters, crabs and a host of other local invertebrates, the tide pools were designed to exhibit specimens of multicolored parrot fishes (Family *Scaridae*) which are particularly suited to a shallow-water habitat. The parrot fishes receive their name from the form of their jaws, in which their teeth are fused into a remarkably good imitation of a parrot's beak. They are largely omnivorous in habit, feeding extensively on algae as well as living coral which they break up with their strong jaws. Often while skindiving on the reefs I have heard the sharp crunchings and munchings as a school of "grazing" parrot fishes pauses to make a concentrated assault on a particular coral head, and the sound can be startlingly loud when heard underwater at close range.

Not only do these fishes have beaks that resemble those of parrots, but their scales are unusually large and their colors in some cases strikingly imitate the hues of tropical macaws. Not long ago it was discovered that these fishes in many cases show a phenomenon peculiar to many fishes and also many groups of birds, that of sexual dimorphism, where the males and females may be colored totally unlike one another. When this fact was learned by ichthyologists, the number of supposed parrot fish species was greatly reduced; certain ones having originally been described as separate species being found to be two color forms of the same fish. This introduced a further complication in the manner of common names, since many species had been named for their dominant color, such as red, green, blue, purple, emerald, scorched, rainbow, etc., parrot fish, and in some cases a name highly appropriate for one sex can be quite misleading when applied to the other. To further complicate this situation, some parrot fishes undergo various color changes as they grow from young to adults.

Quite recently it was also discovered that certain parrot fishes spend the night in "sleeping bags" in the form of mucous envelopes which are secreted by the fish especially for this purpose. Apparently these mucous sleeping bags serve some protective function, possibly making the fish undetectable or distasteful to a would-be predator.

Largest and most striking in appearance of the Florida species is the rainbow parrot fish, *Scarus guacamaia,* which has been reported to reach a weight of more than 50 pounds, though most specimens seen are considerably smaller. The head is orange and the scales brilliant green with orange borders, and the color of the beak makes it appear exactly as if the fish were wearing bright blue lipstick, giving it a highly ludicrous appearance. The purple parrot fish, *Scarus coelestinus,* often schools with the rainbows under natural conditions, and it has been suggested that it may be merely a color variation of the latter. These fish are a deep indigo purple all over with a few scattered bright blue scales on the top of the head. Another large species is the blue parrot fish, *Scarus coeruleus,* which is a beautiful sky blue all over with its beak outlined in pale pink. These three species form the bulk of

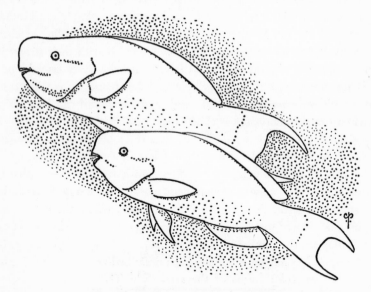

Blue Parrotfishes, *Scarus coeruleus.*

the parrot fish population in the tide pools along with a fourth, the green parrot fish, *Sparisoma viride.* This latter species has a slender tail prolonged into upper and lower filaments, and for some reason this particular one is often accompanied by a small remora, or suckerfish, which clings to its side.

One of the most striking characteristics of the parrot fishes, and one which they share with certain other fishes of the coral reefs, is the manner in which they swim. This I call "rowing," and it consists of rhythmic strokes of both pectoral or side fins in unison, the tail being dragged behind limply and serving only as a rudder. There is nothing quite so splendid as the sight of a group of large parrot fishes swimming along in formation in shallow water, their large pectorals flashing in this unique rowing motion, reminding one somehow of a flock of swallows in flight. When frightened or in a hurry, the fish bring their tails into action in the normal way, but at such times the majestic grace of their leisurely rowing is lost.

When we first introduced the parrot fishes into the tide pools, the bright sun had already caused a heavy growth of green algae on the rocks and the pool floors themselves, but within a few days this disappeared completely under the grazing activity of these fish. They soon became quite accustomed to our presence and would on occasion venture into water so shallow that their backs were exposed in order to rasp seaweed tidbits growing in barely accessible places on the rocks.

While the parrot fishes in the tide pools invariably did well, those later kept in the individual corridor tanks did not, as the fare of cut fish which they received did not seem to satisfy their dietary requirements. Adding boiled spinach proved messy and expensive, and although slices of raw potatoes were greedily accepted, the specimens continued to remain thin and their colors progressively faded. We were on the point of excluding parrot fishes from the indoor tanks entirely when, by chance, we discovered that they would thrive beautifully on a well-known brand of kibbled dog food!

Along with the parrot fishes we introduced a number of spiny lobsters,

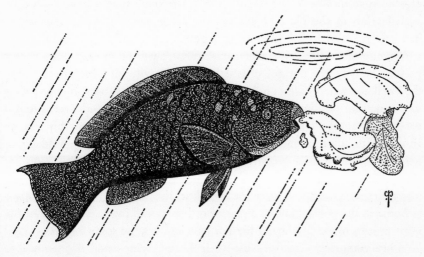

Purple Parrotfish, *Scarus coelestinus,* eating cabbage leaves.

*Panulirus argus,* and on the islands themselves we placed a horde of little fiddler crabs *(Uca)* which we had rounded up on nearby tidal flats. "Rounding up" fiddler crabs was a trick I had learned, incidentally, during my boyhood in St. Petersburg, Florida. At high tide these little crabs enter their holes or seek shelter among clumps of grass and mangrove roots, but as the tide recedes they will swarm about on the open flats, seeking food.

In order to catch them for bait or other purposes, one starts running around a swarm in a great, wide circle, narrowing this a bit on each go-around. If this is done properly, the fiddlers will eventually compact themselves into a central mound which is several crabs deep. As soon as the runner has narrowed his circle sufficiently and the crabs are satisfactorily compacted, they may be scooped into a bucket by the double handful. This latter performance requires a certain amount of nerve, but oddly enough, I don't recall ever having had a finger pinched in the process. On the other hand, when trying to catch an individual fiddler by hand, I almost invariably get pinched. Also, I might add, the above method is not recommended to those who are prone to dizziness, unless they are capable of changing direction abruptly without causing the flock to scatter.

The fiddler crabs adapted themselves to the islands almost at once and set about digging burrows at the water's edge. The male has one immense claw, longer than the body, which gives the crab its name, while in the female both claws are small and of equal size. As is usual with crustaceans whose pincers are of unequal size, should the large claw be lost in a mishap, as frequently occurs, the smaller claw will grow into a large claw in a couple of successive moults of the shell, while at the same time a new small claw will develop in the place of the missing large one. For this reason right-handed and left-handed crabs occur together quite indiscriminately.

A group of fiddler crabs, when undisturbed, will often engage in a most peculiar activity, the purpose of which remains mysterious. In perfect unison they will alternately stand on "tiptoe" with their pincers thrust upward, drop to a squatting position, and then repeat the process over and over. From a concealed vantage point I have often watched them perform this strange ritual for minutes on end, and when doing this they always remind me of nothing so much as a group of army trainees performing their morning calisthenics.

While the fiddlers took over the shoreline, the "lobsters" made themselves at home in the pools. Having a pair of ordinary walking legs in place of the great pincers found on the northern or true lobsters, the spiny lobsters (called in other countries, crawfish) use their heavy, spine-studded antennae to fend off molesters. The base of each antenna is joined to the head by means of three flexible joints, and the basal one of these bears a projection that can be rubbed against a filelike stridulating ridge under the eye, producing a harsh, rasping sound whenever the lobster is disturbed.

During the day these creatures kept mostly under the shelter of large, loose rocks provided for the purpose, but on the approach of dusk they would set out, often four, five, or more traveling in single file like a chain of circus elephants, the head of one individual being directly over the tail of the one before him. In this manner they would move about actively throughout the night, returning to the rocks by morning.

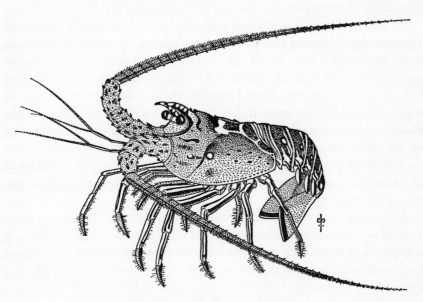

Spiny Lobster, *Panulirus argus.*

Occasionally we would obtain a female lobster with what resembled a small lump of black clay plastered to the underside of the body. This was a spermatophore or sperm capsule, placed there by the male at the time of mating. This would be carried about for some time previous to egg-laying by the female, and then as the eggs were extruded and cemented to leaflike appendages on the underside of the abdomen, she would scrape at the spermatophore with her legs, thus freeing the microscopic motile sperm and fertilizing the eggs. Later on, we observed a number of egg hatchings in the individual corridor tanks. While the young of the northern lobster are a fairly reasonable duplication of the parent when they hatch, baby spiny lobsters are so bizarre as to be almost beyond belief. They are flat, spidery, and quite leaflike, with their eyes placed at the end of long stalks. The larvae, called *phyllosomas,* are usually carried great distances by wind and tide before they transform, in a single moult, into perfect replicas of the adult.

During the time that we were setting up the tide pool exhibit, I received a phone call from a resident of Key Biscayne, several miles away, informing me that there was what appeared to be a motherless baby manatee, or sea cow, swimming about the boat harbor there. The caller wondered if we might be able to capture and care for it. On being told that it was very tiny, just over 3 feet long, and that it was staying close to the side of a boat tied to a dock, I got together with Captain Gray, who headed our collecting operations, to make plans for the little creature's capture.

We placed a large mattress and a blanket in the back of our truck, and I donned my swimming trunks while Gray selected an oversize dipnet with heavy mesh and a long handle. On arriving at the dock in the truck, we saw that the little manatee was in bad shape; it was quite emaciated from lack of food and its back showed injuries where some senseless person had tried unsuccessfully to spear it. On becoming aware of our presence, the manatee dove beneath the boat, and we presumed that it would soon surface on the other side. Since we lacked access to that side of the boat it was decided that I would enter the water a short distance away and would swim as carefully as possible toward the boat from the far side, herding the manatee within range of the net.

When I approached the boat, however, the manatee was nowhere in sight. I called to Captain Gray who was on the dock beyond my sight, asking if it might have swum back under the boat, but he saw no sign of it. I decided to explore beneath the boat, and so, adjusting my face mask and taking a deep breath, I submerged slowly so as to create as little disturbance as possible. The water was fairly clear, and although I could easily see along the keel of the boat and beyond its stern, there was no sign of the little sea cow.

Slowly I turned around to face toward the bow of the boat, and suddenly there was the padlike, bristly snout of the manatee, as it looked straight at me with a slightly quizzical Weakeyes-Yokum expression, not 6 inches from my face mask! It seemed quite unafraid; and so, rather than attempt to drive it out into the open where it might conceivably escape, I decided to try to capture it myself. With a sudden motion I flung both arms around its middle and hugged it tightly against my chest. Since it was noticeably weak and starved, I had little trouble holding it, and I recall that it emitted several tiny plaintive squeaks as it struggled underwater. Breaking surface on the dock side with the little manatee held securely in my arms, I shouted to Gray, who reached down and hoisted it up by its flippers. We laid the manatee down carefully on the mattress, covered it with a wet blanket, and drove back to the aquarium, where we placed it for the time being in a large wooden tank filled with seawater.

I have always loved manatees because, although they do not have a high intelligence, they are friendly, inoffensive, thoroughly charming beasts, with their caterpillar-like snouts and tiny, myopic eyes that shed protective gluey tears on the slightest provocation. Along with the dugong, these beasts are a vanishing race of mammals that have no close relatives, but in their skeletal and other internal structure they indicate a remote kinship with the elephant. Their hide is very thick and roughened and bears scattered silky hairs like a burlap bag, and heavy bristles surrounding the mouth assist the creatures in obtaining aquatic vegetation, their natural food. Although somewhat seal-like in shape, they have no hind limbs, and the body ends in a great horizontally flattened paddlelike tail.

The breasts of the female are situated forward on the chest, close to the juncture of the flippers, and, despite what I have heard from other sources, were small and quite inconspicuous on the few lactating females I have seen. The flippers have an elbow and a wrist joint and are quite mobile, used both for swimming and for conveying grass to the mouth, and their movements, when viewed from the side underwater, are surprisingly human. There are several flattened nails on each flipper, and the creature does not seem to have regular eyelids, the eyes being closed by a sort of sphincter muscle.

Manatees feeding at the surface always remind me of fat brownish caterpillars, since the muscular upper lip is two-lobed, each lobe working sideways against the other like the jaws of an insect, and caterpillar-like, they tend to sway the body from side to side while grazing, and the general effect is further heightened by the ringlike wrinkles on the head and neck. They have no front teeth, chewing their food by means of heavy flattened molars in the rear of the jaws.

When viewed from beneath, the sexes are easy to distinguish, since the genital opening of the male is located very far forward, close to the middle of the belly, while that of the female is next to the anal region. Only one young is born at a time, and the babies appear to start nibbling at algae and soft grasses while only a few weeks old.

The American manatee, *Trichechus latirostris,* and its West African twin, *T. senegalensis,* have a smaller relative, *T. inunguis,* which is confined to fresh water in certain rivers in northern South America. In the Pacific and Indian oceans we find the dugong, *Halicore dugong,* the males of which have downward directed tusks. Unlike the manatee, the dugongs have visible ear-holes and a crescent shaped tail much like a porpoise or whale. Another species, the enormous Steller's sea cow, *Rhytina (Hydrodamalis) stelleri,* of

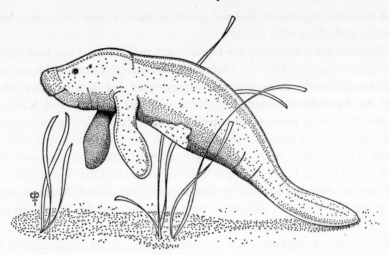

Amazonian Pink-Breasted Manatee, *Trichechus inunguis.*

the Bering Sea, was extensively hunted for its meat and oil and became extinct during the eighteenth century.

Since they have delicious flesh and are comparatively easy to kill, the manatees in Florida were hunted for a time and might eventually have gone the way of the Steller's sea cow, had they not been finally placed under rigid protection. Now they are by no means rare, especially in Biscayne Bay where they swim in and out of the Miami River in considerable numbers. Recently, however, they have met with a new and dangerous enemy in the form of speedboats. Being sluggish, manatees are often struck and killed or seriously injured as they rise to breathe, and it is difficult to find a large individual that does not bear at least one or two scars from an encounter with a boat keel or a propeller.

Our little manatee, a female, had quite likely lost her mother in this way, and her emaciated condition told us that chances of saving her life were none too good. I had no idea of the nutritional or physical qualities of manatee milk, but I promptly sent for a veterinarian in the hope that between us we could think of something in the way of a substitute diet. While I was awaiting his arrival a most fortunate coincidence occurred.

I had lifted the little manatee from its tank (it weighed only 27 pounds) and set it on a mattress, where I carefully painted each spear wound with antiseptic. I was bending over it feeling relieved that its injuries appeared to be merely superficial, thanks to its tough hide, when I gradually became aware that two people were standing beside me, watching. Looking up, I saw Dr. de Sylva of the Marine Laboratory and beside him stood an attractive young woman with dark hair. "Craig," said de Sylva, "I want you to meet Eugenie Clark."

Here was the one person who could help me! Dr. Clark, whose famous book *Lady with a Spear* I had recently read, is an eminent marine biologist who had made an extensive study, among other things, of dugongs in the Red Sea. She told us that the milk of the dugong, and almost certainly that of the manatee, was extremely thick in consistency, in fact, nearly a solid. This was something to go on, and in consulting with the vet, I decided to try condensed milk thickened with Pablum, with a little cod-liver oil and corn syrup mixed in.

The manatee had shown a willingness to suckle from the first, when I experimentally poked my finger in its mouth, and I noticed that on capture its nose was reddened with copper paint, where it had repeatedly nuzzled the bottom of the boat.

We gave it its first meal from a baby's nursing bottle which I had purchased from a nearby pharmacy, and, although it readily took the nipple, it

Baby Manatee, *Trichechus latirostris,* feeding from nursing bucket.

seemed to have difficulty in drawing the thick liquid through, even though we had enlarged the hole. My solution was to obtain a calves' nursing pail from a local dairy supplier, and to this was attached a specially large nipple with a check valve inside. I had a 10-inch length of pipe welded on between the nipple attachment and the pail outlet, and this made it possible for the baby to nurse underwater and at the same time breathe when the pail was fastened to the edge of the tank, since its valvular nostrils were located on the very top of its snout.

Thanks to this feeding device and to Dr. Clark's helpful advice, our manatee continued to get milk regularly, although after a week's time it was still very thin and had gained weight only slightly. Then it abruptly ceased feeding, and although we continued to give it vitamin injections and attempted to force milk into its stomach through a tube, it died 10 days after we had caught it.

Of course, attempting to raise an animal about which so little is known to date would be tricky business under the most favorable conditions, but I still feel that our chances of success would have been much better had we been able to capture it a little sooner. However, during the brief time it survived in our care I was able to learn a little concerning its habits, and this information, along with additional observations I was able to make on captive manatees elsewhere, later proved highly useful when we eventually obtained an adult female for the Seaquarium two years later.

# CHAPTER 3

# THE PREFABRICATED HYDROSEAL TANK

*Evolution of the Aquarium Tank. Open and Closed Water Systems. Circulation and Filtration. Problems Arise. The Breakthrough. Optics and Illusions. The Compensationally Illuminated Diorama, a New Concept in Exhibit Technique*

Attendant on the planning of exhibits for the future Seaquarium, we succeeded in developing an entirely new kind of aquarium tank, the body of which was prefabricated entirely of laminated fiberglass with the viewing panes held in place by internal water pressure alone when the tank was filled—a device I call the hydroseal principle. Drained of its water, the tank could be quickly disassembled by hand.

For the back of the tank was designed a new type of optically curved and lighted diorama that increased the apparent internal size of the tank itself through putting to use certain natural principles of light refraction and the absorption of certain wavelengths by the water. This is the story of how this invention came about: but first, let me outline some of the basic principles of the construction and running of a modern aquarium.

The prototype of all aquariums was probably a pool or a pond, either natural or artificially dug, where fish were kept for food, rearing, or just plain enjoyment. The next step was the portable aquarium which had to be much smaller, consisting of some sort of jar, bowl, or other vessel that could be moved about. Finally, with the invention of glass, came the great change. Now, for the first time, a person was permitted a "fish-eye view" of underwater life, and a great new era of visual interest was opened. The first crude glass vessels must have offered a cloudy and distorted view of their contents, but their effect on the imagination must have been considerable. Today people are still looking at fishes through glass, and the aquarium has proved to be one of the most universally popular exhibits ever devised by man.

The simplest type of aquarium is, of course, an ordinary fishbowl or tank where the water is periodically changed. If sufficient surface area is present to permit a natural interchange of oxygen and carbon dioxide between the air and the water and if the tank is not overcrowded, the frequency of necessary water change is very slight. Natural bacteria "burn up" the fish's metabolic waste products to a considerable extent, and the constant turbulence of the water caused by the fish's swimming activities speeds up the natural interchange of gases at the water surface. Also, the fish, by his metabolic activity "conditions" the water in some way that is not well understood, so that a well-lived-in aquarium is healthier to a fish than one containing "raw" or new and unconditioned water. (On the other hand, water conditioned by one kind of fish may not always be beneficial to other species suddenly introduced into the tank.)

The next step is the so-called balanced aquarium which contains living aquatic plants along with the fish. This is an attempt to duplicate a natural lake or pond in miniature, and it is frequently quite successful. Again, if the tank is not overcrowded, a balanced aquarium may maintain itself for one or two years without a water change, though water lost due to evaporation has to be replenished from time to time, and the constantly growing plants likewise must be periodically thinned out. Contrary to popular opinion, the plants' main function is not to restore oxygen—more enters the water surface naturally than is ever replaced by the plants—but to absorb the various nitrogenous and other waste products of the fish that tend to accumulate in solution.

If one wishes to keep a large number of fishes, or fishes of large size, in a limited area for exhibition or other purposes, then some mechanical means must be resorted to to keep a sufficiently large volume of good quality water circulating through the tank or tanks. This is the principle upon which the modern aquarium building is run. (At this point I wish to point out that the word "aquarium" is ambiguous—it can mean either a tank or enclosure where aquatic life is kept, or it can mean a building or institution housing a number of such enclosures. In referring to the first definition in the plural, I prefer to use the term "aquaria," and in the second case, "aquariums.")

Modern aquariums may be divided into two main categories, those employing the "open" and the "closed" system of water circulation respectively; and, of these two systems, the closed, though more complex, is most frequently used. In the open system, which is illustrated by Fig. A, water is

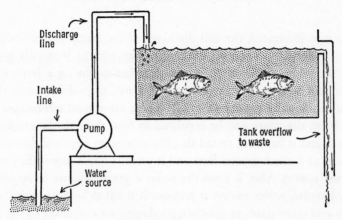

**Discharge line**

**Intake line**

**Pump**

**Water source**

**Tank overflow to waste**

A. Aquarium with open water system.

obtained from a suitable source, such as a well, spring, stream, bay, or reservoir, run through the tanks, and discharged to waste. Aeration and filtration may be used or not, depending on circumstances. Fish hatcheries, which are usually located at the site of a river or spring, usually use the open system, as well as do many small seaside aquariums. However, since quality and clarity of the available water often change with weather conditions this system may be unreliable and ideal sites for an open system are limited.

In the closed system (Fig. B) the water is used over and over, being filtered and aerated each time it is recirculated, with a certain amount of makeup water added from time to time to replace that lost to evaporation or spillage. The advantage of this system is that the water quality, if well handled, tends to remain fairly constant and the entire supply can be insulated from outdoor weather changes or contamination.

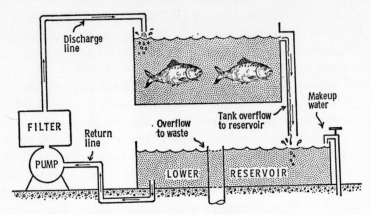

Discharge line

FILTER

Return line

PUMP

Overflow to waste

Tank overflow to reservoir

Makeup water

LOWER    RESERVOIR

B. Aquarium with closed water system.

In the case illustrated, the full discharge of the pump is delivered to the tank, with the pump running constantly. However, it is usually preferred to have the pump work on an intermittent basis, moving a large quantity of water at a time to a reservoir situated above the exhibit tanks through which it can flow by gravity (Fig. C). There are several advantages to this system. First, the water can be regulated to flow through the exhibit tanks as desired, and it has been found that the minimum required flow is just as satisfactory as a much greater flow and it permits much more efficient operation of the system. Also, it gives the water a greater chance to settle; for, if water is handled under too great pressure it tends to become saturated with nitrogen and other gases in solution, producing air embolism in the fish. In severe cases of this, the eyes will bulge due to air pockets behind the eyeball, and froth may also appear under the skin and fin membranes. Some of this air may be released by using a small hypodermic needle, but relief is only temporary unless the conditions that cause air saturation in the water are corrected. If the water has sufficient time to settle in a reservoir before flowing by gravity to the tanks, no air embolism problems will occur.

As shown in the diagram, the pump may be controlled by means of a float switch located in either the upper or the lower reservoir, depending on whether it is "off" or "on" in the low position. (It should be noted here that when the water rises in one reservoir, it falls in the other, and vice versa.)

In Fig. D is shown a modified form of this system that I designed while at the Seaquarium. I call this the "Self-Improving Continuous-Flow Closed Aquarium System" because the longer it runs, the clearer the water becomes. This is due to the fact that the water is actually filtered and aerated at a

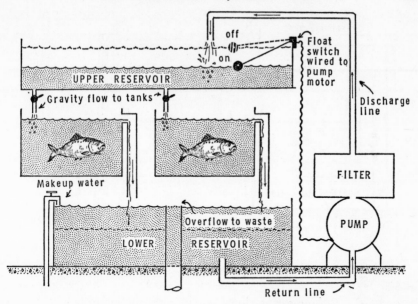

C. Closed system with intermittent flow.

faster rate than it is used in the exhibit tanks, owing to the surplus water flow taking a shortcut back to the filter pump by way of an overflow bypass installed in the upper reservoir. This results in a constant improvement of its condition.

By installing a float switch in either reservoir, this system may be converted at once into an intermittent-flow system at the flick of a master switch. Either system may then be used optionally, depending on the operator's preference.

The rate of flow, and hence water replacement, in an aquarium tank varies considerably due to its particular conditions but ranges, roughly, between one volume replacement (which means one-half the total water change, due to continuous intermixing) every half hour to every four hours. As a rule, replacement must be carried out more rapidly in salt water than in fresh and more rapidly in warm than cold water, since both seawater and warm water tend to carry less oxygen in solution.

By bubbling air through porous airstones in the bottom of the tank the oxygen level is raised and water replacement can be cut down accordingly, but this procedure usually creates an artificial appearance which I find somewhat disturbing, and it tends to detract from the life and decorations of the tank. If airstones are used in this manner, the best place for them is on either side of the front of the tank in the space between the glass and the corner

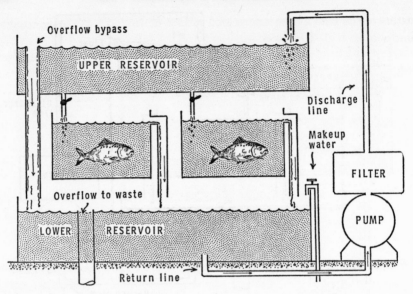

D. Self-improving closed system with continuous flow.

of the side wall. Here the bubbles may rise to the surface in a position where they are least likely to be noticed by the viewer.

For small tanks, from 50 gallons capacity down, and especially for tanks in the "tropical aquarium" class (both freshwater and salt) the sub-sand filter works best, either with or without supplemental water replacement. In fact, for tanks of 25 gallons or under, I recommend this as the *sole* means of keeping the water conditioned, from the standpoint of aeration and filtration. If properly maintained and the specimens are properly cared for and the pH (degree of acidity or alkalinity) kept within the proper range, the tank will have to be cleaned and the water replaced only once in a great while. It is not uncommon to see a tank that has run continuously with a sub-sand filter for one, two, or three years, or even longer, with the specimens in good health and the tank clean and tidy in appearance.

In the sub-sand filter, of which there are several kinds on the market, a spacer, usually a finely perforated plastic plate, supports the sand about a quarter of an inch off the bottom of the tank, as shown in Fig. E. An air-lift tube attached through a larger hole in one or two corners of the plate draws the water up from beneath it, and this is constantly replaced by new water percolating down through the sand. In time, each grain of sand presumably acquires a coating of beneficial aerobic bacteria (those that live in the presence of oxygen), and these condition the water by converting poisonous waste products into harmless compounds. Due to the finely divided nature of the sand a tremendous total surface of aerobic bacteria are brought into contact with the water.

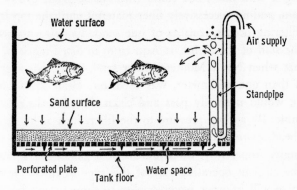

E. Sub-sand filter.

For larger tanks of several hundred to several thousand gallons capacity, a sub-sand filter of the type just described is impractical because of the difficulty and expense in securing plastic or other suitable perforated sheets of large size, besides the great weight of the sand in such a tank and the difficulty of supporting it. However, other methods, such as a perforated plastic hose looped back and forth and buried under the sand and attaching the ends to air-lift pipes set in the front corners of the tank on either side of the glass, have been used with varying degrees of success. I believe a combination of this sort of filtering, along with water replacement, to be ideal for tanks of intermediate range capacity, although most of them seem to work very well on water replacement alone, provided this has a sufficient rate of flow.

No type of bottom filter has as yet to my knowledge been devised or suggested for extremely large tanks of the oceanarium type, and it is unlikely that they would be practical, considering the probable difficulties of installing and maintaining them. To date, these giant community tanks are run on a series of large sand-filter beds of the type used by city water plants, as a tank 80 feet in diameter and 16 feet deep requires a constant flow of about 3,000 gallons a minute and a 50-foot tank of the same depth 2,000 gallons a minute.

The two main Seaquarium tanks are of the dimensions just mentioned, and eight filter beds are used to recirculate the required 5,000 gallons a minute. Backwashing, which is done each evening, requires from five to ten minutes per bed, and considerable amounts of saline water from well points sunk deep underground are required for this process. Despite the large amount of water required for their backwash, sand filters of this type are extremely reliable and comparatively simple to maintain, frequently functioning for years without need of overhaul or repair.

In building a sand filter, one starts with coarse grade gravel or pebbles on the bottom, adding successively finer material until the top layer, where the actual filtering occurs, consists of fine sand. Experiments recently conducted by the staff of the Steinhart Aquarium in San Francisco, California, indicated that when No. 1 Monterey filter sand, which has a grain size of slightly less than one millimeter, was used, one clean square foot of this filter surface would normally pass and clean three-fourths of a gallon of water a minute. By adding pressure to the filter, such as by increasing the hydrostatic head, more water would pass through but its quality would drop correspondingly. Apparently, three-fourths of a gallon per square foot per minute is the efficient operating rate of this type of filter. Decreasing the sand grain size will improve water quality to some extent, but the flow is correspondingly decreased. The same thing happens when the filter surface becomes "dirty," that is, clogged with filtered sediment. The longer a filter runs, the more it clogs, and hence, it will filter smaller particles from the water, but at a slower rate. In order to keep a filter in efficient operation, it must be backwashed at intervals to float off the accumulated sediment.

During backwash the sand and some of the lighter gravel are lifted in suspension, but when the water stops rising the larger and heavier particles settle first, so that this type of filter "re-grades" itself automatically. Increasing the thickness of the filter bed has little or no effect in increasing its efficiency, since the actual filtering action takes place in the top layer of sand.

In using a sand filter, it is usually necessary to "break it in." This process may require from several days to several weeks or even months, depending on circumstances. This phenomenon is believed due to the necessity of acquiring a coating of "resident" bacteria on each sand particle; once these are established they appear to condition the water by converting impurities into harmless substances.

One type of filter which was originally designed for swimming pools is now beginning to find application in various aquariums. This device makes use of a series of hollow "sandwiches" of screen covered with cloth, usually in the form of disks strung along a central hollow pipe. Diatomaceous earth, a finely divided substance, is usually employed to precoat the cloth surface, and the water to be filtered is then run through it under pressure. The main advantage of this type of filter over the sand filter is compactness, where a great deal of square footage of filter surface is convoluted into a comparatively small unit. Also, it has to be backwashed much less frequently, and, since the backwash process consists simply of draining the tank that encloses the unit, much less water is required for the process.

Other materials frequently used in filtering, particularly in small tanks, are glass wool, asbestos fiber, and charcoal. Charcoal comes closest to being the ideal filtering material, but its expense and the fact that it must be periodically "reactivated" or replaced, prohibit its extensive use in large aquarium setups.

In designing aquarium tanks, those of large size are usually made of poured concrete with the front viewing pane set in a watertight frame, either wedged or bolted against a gasket, or set in semiflexible cement of firm consistency, or both. Reinforced concrete is a durable material; properly made it lasts as long as the building, and its low coefficient of expansion due to temperature changes or the filling and emptying of the tank tends to keep the glass firmly sealed at all times. Most aquarium tanks are made of concrete, but in designing the Seaquarium, we were after a new kind of tank.

Instead of conventional tanks of poured concrete, we were looking for a portable type that could be set above a continuous drain trough and against framed window openings in the wall that divided the public gallery from the work area in back. At first we had thought of making the tanks of solid welded copper alloy steel with a curved back, making them less boxlike and with more room for the specimens and decorations, and protecting the metal from corrosion with a tough plastic coat.

However, there was the ever-present danger that in one way or another this coating, no matter how impervious to abrasion or prolonged water soaking, might break through in places, and once the seawater came into contact with the bare metal, points of corrosion would develop, weakening the tank and releasing harmful ions into the water, thus endangering the specimens. Also, metal tanks would weigh a great deal even when empty, making them difficult to remove or replace in front of the wall openings, should this ever become necessary.

For a time we thought we might build them of marine plywood supported by metal frames. Then I got an idea that was later to prove a most fortunate one. Visiting a local Miami boat show, I observed a number of small craft that were made of laminated sheets of fiberglass impregnated with a type of epoxy resin, built up in layers over a wooden mold. These boats were so impervious to water and tough and resilient as to be nearly indestructible, so the manufacturer claimed. It occurred to me that if they were impervious from the outside they should be impervious from the inside as well, and an aquarium tank made in this manner should come very close to answering the ideal requirements, combining indestructibility with very light weight when empty.

For several days I worked on a number of rough sketches, and when I had completed my final drawings, I went to a local boat fabricator and showed him what I wanted. He looked over my drawings and said he thought he could build such a tank with little difficulty, and within a short time we had our first trial model, 7 feet 4 inches long by 3½ feet high by 3 feet in width. The tank was fitted with an overflow drain and set up on concrete blocks in one of the work buildings near the pilot plant.

I ordered the viewing panes—two of them for each "window"—of a special tempered kind of plate glass ¾ inch thick. The reason for having two glasses was that I had decided that these tanks would be of the look-through type with an artificial dry diorama behind them. I had experimented with such dioramas on a small scale at Marine Studios and later at the Marine Laboratory of the University of Miami, and they seemed to offer a tremendous potential for varying and improving each exhibit without the necessity of increasing the size of the tank where the specimens were kept.

The interior of the tank was colored a pastel blue-green, this hue being incorporated into the resin as the tank was built. The viewing panes were attached to the inside of the tank body with an aquarium cement carefully colored to match the tank itself, and wooden braces inserted to hold the glass in place until the cement hardened. After several days, the tank was pumped full of water. Although the cement was well placed and no leaks were observed, several days later the cement began to flow from between the glass and the tank frame, so the tank was quickly emptied and allowed to set for a week.

Again the tank was filled and again the cement began to flow. This was maddening, as I was losing time and I had to decide very shortly as to whether we would order more of these prefabricated tanks. With considerable difficulty the glass was removed and it as well as the tank frame scraped free of all cement, and a new type of cement applied in its place. After several days following the filling of the tank, the new cement also began to flow. It seemed that, once the almost imperceptible oozing began, it remained like a fluid river in slow motion and so long as there was pressure against it, the flow just would not stop.

Apparently the main trouble was the small size of the ¾-inch retaining lip on the frame and the great amount of pressure the glass exerted against it. Since the tank frame itself was slightly flexible there was no way of bolting or wedging the glass in place as may be done with a concrete tank, and it began to look as if the fiberglass tank just wasn't practical—unless I could find a cement that would set up more firmly!

I was contemplating using a thicker kind of cement with less tendency to flow when an idea struck me. Why not use some sort of spacer between the glass and the tank lip to separate them at the proper distance and thus stop the squeezing action that caused the cement to flow? For this I tried a continuous strip of rubber welding hose glued to the tank lip and applied the cement directly over it. This plan worked; the cement flow stopped, and I was in business at last.

A hard plastic ½-inch line was run out into the sea, and through this water was delivered to the tank by means of a small centrifugal pump after shunting it through the sand filters at the nearby pilot plant. Another plastic line was attached to the tank overflow and returned to the filters so that the entire system could be recirculated as long as desired. A number of fish were then placed in the tank and experiments conducted on various types of lighting, decoration, and background. By this time the fiberglass tank had proved its merit as a practical innovation. Besides weighing only 40 pounds when empty, this 500-gallon tank was totally unaffected by prolonged contact with seawater and the hard, smooth interior surface resisted algae growth much better than tanks made of concrete or wood; and, unlike metal, it would never corrode or rust.

Before ordering additional tanks I decided to cut down the vertical height by 6 inches, which would give it a better proportioned appearance and also reduce the water pressure on the glass panes to some extent, as they, despite their ¾-inch thickness, had begun to bow out slightly at the top, where their support was the weakest. (Here I should mention that water pressure against the glass is proportional to the water depth alone, *not* to the total volume of water within the tank. A glass of given size backed by a column of water a foot or so in horizontal thickness has just as much pressure against it as if it were set in the side of a swimming pool, or for that matter, as if it had the entire Atlantic Ocean behind it.)

Since this pressure would always remain constant so long as the tank was full, it suddenly occurred to me that I might put this pressure to good use. Why not, I asked myself, dispense with the cement altogether and simply let the internal water pressure force the glass against a rubber gasket, thus making a tight seal? The main advantage of this idea, aside from its comparative simplicity and the ease of installing the glass initially, was the fact that the tank could easily be disassembled whenever desired merely by removing its contents and drawing the water down.

On subsequent tanks I had the rubber hose gasket glued to the tank lip with waterproof cement along its inner side. Both sides of the tank receiving glass were treated in this manner and the glass panes were pressed firmly against the gaskets by means of wooden braces which spanned the center of the tank. When the tank was filled, the glasses were pressed firmly in position by the water as planned, and all leakage stopped when the water rose to a height of about a foot.

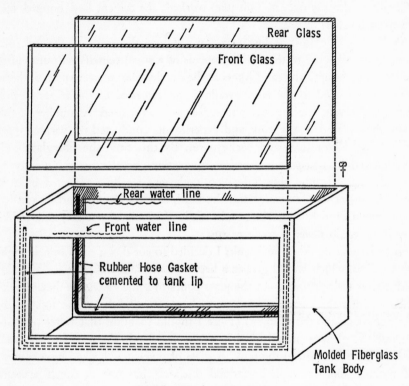

F. The Hydroseal Tank.

Filled for several weeks, the tank panes became even more firmly seated in the frame and I later discovered that the water could, if necessary, be lowered to about 8 inches without danger of leakage. In actual operation we never drained the tanks more than halfway. I have since found that it is easier on the specimens to leave them in the tank during all scrubbing and cleaning operations; even though the water may become extremely cloudy with mud and sediment at such times, it does not appear to bother the fish and invertebrates to any extent. On the other hand, to move them to another tank while the cleaning is going on can often be harmful as, no matter how carefully they are handled in a net, their fins and scales are likely to be injured and the protective coat of mucus rubbed from their bodies in the process.

In cleaning a tank, we use a long-handled scrub brush and a bundle of steel wool on the end of a stick. After all accumulated algae and other sediment is worked loose, it is siphoned from the bottom of the tank as the sand is turned over and smoothed with a small rake. During this process the ¾-inch siphon tube (covered with a screen to keep fish from getting caught in it) is left in place and the incoming water turned on full force to maintain the proper depth inside the tank.

Now that the design of the hydroseal tank was satisfactory (see Fig. F), it was necessary to design a proper background for it. I had experimented for some time with dioramas of the flat sort, but for a tank of this size it appeared that a curved one would serve the purpose much better, being both less cumbersome and creating the illusion of more spaciousness, and getting away from the boxlike shape of conventional aquarium tanks, besides.

Just how effective this sort of background really is cannot be appreciated by anyone who has not actually seen it, as its unique effect is created only when the tank is filled with water, due to the principles of light refraction.

As everyone has noticed at one time or another, a straight stick thrust underwater at an angle appears to be bent at the point where it enters the surface. Also, when a vessel is filled with water, its bottom appears to rise by about one-fourth the distance to the surface. Likewise, when a rectangular aquarium is filled with water, its back will appear to come forward by one-fourth the horizontal distance. Thus, an empty tank with a horizontal depth of 4 feet will appear to be only 3 feet from front to back when filled. I have seen aquariums of this sort that *appeared* to lack sufficient space for large specimens to swim freely and turn about, although this was actually not the case. Oddly enough, when an aquarium is backed by a dry diorama, the space apparently lost within the tank becomes visually added to the diorama space, as illustrated in Fig. G. This illusion permitted the design of a comparatively narrow diorama, with a resultant saving of space in the work area behind the tanks.

For the diorama for the fiberglass tank, I started with a crescent-shaped base of heavy plywood, its flat edge cut just slightly longer than the back side of the tank itself. To this was attached a sheet of curved untempered Masonite bent so that its hypothetical radius fell a foot or so in front of the tank. (The Masonite was actually doubly curved, with its upper radius shorter than the lower. The result of this was that the curved background

leaned forward at the top so that it was impossible to see over its upper edge
by looking through the tank from the front.)

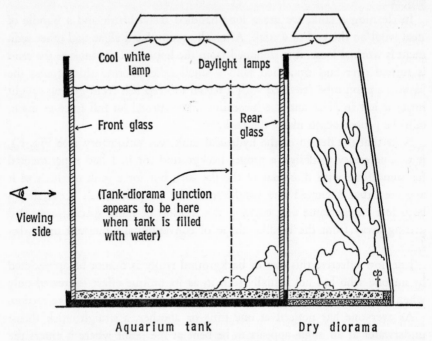

**Aquarium tank**          **Dry diorama**

G. Aquarium showing use of double glass and dioramic background.

When the dioramas were completed, I called on Frank McConnel, then
director of the Junior Museum of Miami, to design aquascapes on their
inner surfaces. Frank, who is also a skindiver and a skillful artist (and a former art teacher of mine) worked painstakingly with an airbrush, and using
actual sea fans, sponges, seaweeds, and corals, for a stencil effect, created
26 different designs in front of which we later constructed our backgrounds
using these actual materials, besides driftwood, rock, etc. The sand that
covered the base was carefully blended to match that inside the tanks.

After our fiberglass technician had constructed the first twenty 500-gallon
tanks using the same mold, this mold was cut down and the remaining six
tanks, of 300 gallons capacity each, were then built. The tanks and their
dioramas were then set in place in front of the window frames that lined
the public corridor encircling our main 80-foot Seaquarium tank, and lighted
from above with fluorescent tubes.

When the tanks were filled the effect was that of spacious tanks with
the decorations inside gradually receding into the dioramas. However, there

was still a noticeable transition between the tank space and that of the dioramas themselves, the tanks appearing "wet" and the dioramas "dry." I soon saw that this was due to the quality of the light over each. Although each space was being illuminated by a type of lighting known as "warm white" (which had been previously found to best simulate conditions of natural daytime undersea illumination and showed the colors of the specimens to best advantage), the lighting within the tanks had a noticeably cooler tone than the dioramas, giving an unnatural appearance to the latter. This was due to the fact that water rapidly absorbs the "warmer" colors (red, orange, yellow) from the spectrum, and any light passing through it will appear bluer the deeper one goes. To compensate for this, I decided to light the diorama separately from the tank, using lighting of different quality in each case.

At last, through trying light in various combinations, the solution was found. By using one warm white and one daylight tube (the latter actually gives a bluish light) over the aquarium tank and one daylight tube alone over the diorama, the light-absorption factor in the water was exactly compensated for. The effect of this was more startling than expected, and resulted in the glass pane that divided the tank from the diorama becoming invisible for all practical purposes, so that it actually appeared as if the water inside the tank extended to the back wall of the diorama, and yet the specimens were all in clear view. Had the tanks actually been shaped as they appeared, many of the specimens would have hidden themselves behind or beneath the objects in the background.

As new materials are produced and new aquarium techniques devised, even the most modern tanks are bound to become outmoded in time. Tanks are now being designed with angled side walls that disappear when filled owing to the same principles of light refraction that have been described, and unusual new lighting effects have already been tried on an experimental level. The Seaquarium's dioramic hydroseal tanks, which have been in service since early 1955, represent but one step along a road that promises to bring more and more realism, and the actual feeling of viewing the undersea world as it is, into the purely artificial world of the aquarium.

# CHAPTER 4

# OUT OF THE SEA AND INTO THE TANKS

*Fishing the Florida Keys. Finding the Neon Goby—A Delouser
of Other Fishes. Clam-Crushing Leopard Rays. The Scarlet Sea-
horse and a Fish that Walks. The Stomatopod—A Creature of
Parts. Hunting the Giant River Shrimp. Red Crayfish in New
Orleans. Shrimps that Delouse Fishes. Collecting in the Coral
"Jungles"*

The collection of specimens for a large modern aquarium is a tremendous
task, the magnitude of which can be appreciated only by those who have
engaged in it. Unlike commercial fishermen, aquarium collectors cannot rest
once the specimens have been taken from the sea as these must then be cared
for and constantly watched until they reach their final destination in the

tanks. Getting them back to the aquarium in good condition is often a
delicate operation and one that must be handled by experts, as many speci-

mens are prone to suffer injuries in capture and subsequent handling, and the difficulties involved are usually proportional to the time and distance involved.

The mammoth task of stocking and maintaining the tanks of the newly completed Miami Seaquarium fell to Collections and Exhibitions Director Captain William B. Gray (who has described many of his collecting adventures in his excellent and entertaining book *Creatures of the Sea,* published in 1960), and his assistant, Captain Emil Hanson. It was as assistant to Captain Gray when he held the position of Chief Collector for Marine Studios that I received my first full-time aquarium experience in the summer of 1946, although in 1939 I had served there briefly as a voluntary laboratory assistant to the original Curator, Arthur McBride.

During World War II, Marine Studios had closed down and was now preparing to reopen, so Gray and I spent the entire summer at Tavernier in the Florida Keys living aboard the collecting boat *Beau Gregory,* fishing all day and some nights as well, gathering our specimens together in floating live boxes, and sending them back to Marine Studios by way of a tank truck that made the 700-mile round trip every few weeks. The *Beau Gregory* was a 45-foot cruiser of questionable vintage; the bilges leaked constantly and considerable plain and fancy pumping was required at intervals in order to keep her afloat. Her engine was not only temperamental, it was truly neurotic, and its periodic reluctance to function evoked much picturesque language from both of us. One day, doing a stint at the wheel, I actually did see a rat leap overboard and swim toward shore—an ominous sign to a mariner given to superstition, but nonetheless the *Beau Gregory* continued to remain afloat, performing in her erratic and exasperating fashion, and the collection of specimens at the Studios gradually increased to their former abundance.

Despite the heat, the mosquito swarms, the constant summer rain squalls, and the postwar scarcity of serviceable fishing gear, my memories of that 1946 summer are exceedingly pleasant ones. Here was an entirely new kind of fishing, involving techniques quite new to me. I learned the thrill of gazing through a glass-bottomed bucket at the fantastic wonderland of a coral reef, selecting a particular fish to be caught, placing the appropriate bait on a handline, maneuvering it in front of him, and, once he was hooked, hauling him to the surface to join the other prizes in our live-well.

I recall seeing my first puddingwife, *Halichoeres radiatus,* drifting over a massive coral head one day and wondering then as now, how this magnificent emerald-green, golden, and pearly wrasse ever managed to be saddled with such a nondescript, pointless, and utterly drab name. No hunter ever fumbled his gun with the degree of buck fever that afflicted my trembling fingers as I hastily baited a hook with a portion of fresh conch and dropped it before the fish, some 20 feet beneath our keel. He took it at once, I set the hook, and hauled him to the surface, only to have the line part just above the leader as I prepared to lift him aboard. This was a heartbreaking experience as already I could see him taking his place among the growing throng of colorful fishes in the 100-foot-long reef tank at Marine Studios.

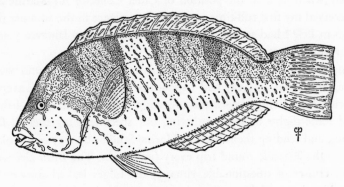

Puddingwife, *Halichoeres radiatus.*

Along toward evening when we were getting ready to quit for the day, we spotted another puddingwife on a reef about a hundred yards away from the original spot, and Gray managed to hook him and bring him aboard, and, as the reader may already have guessed, this turned out to be the original puddingwife, with my hook and leader still in his (or her) mouth.

Gray's extensive knowledge of the finer points of angling never ceased to amaze me. For instance, on one occasion when I spied a hogfish (*Lachnolaimus maximus*), a larger relative of the puddingwife, and failed to tempt the creature with a succulent portion of spiny lobster tail, he tapped the underside of the dead lobster with his bait knife. "Try a piece right there," he said, indicating a solid horny plate from which the bases of the jointed legs arose on either side. Since this part seemed mainly shell and contained very little meat, I was highly dubious over the likelihood of its holding any attraction for the hogfish, but to my surprise, he took it at once. I soon had him aboard, and this particular section of lobster anatomy has never failed to catch hogfishes for me since.

I will mention by the way that in the adult hogfish as in a number of other wrasses the sexes may be easily distinguished. Usually this is simply a matter of pattern and color variation, but in the male hogfish the head is disproportionately large and the tooth-bearing bones of the jaw have a sort of telescopic sliding arrangement whereby they move forward whenever the mouth is opened. This "lazy-susan" device gives the fish a boardinghouse reach that is almost beyond belief, and the tips of the jaws themselves are provided with two pairs of recurved tusks that are particularly useful in holding things. On one occasion one of our collecting crew witnessed a remarkable feeding performance on the part of one of these fish. The man was wearing an aqua-lung and netting small fishes on a reef in about 20 feet of water, when he saw a hogfish extend its jaws and pick up a black needle-spined sea urchin (*Diadema sp.*) and swim with it up against the side of a large coral head. With repeated sideways movements of its head the fish proceeded to bat the urchin against the coral rock until most of its protecting spines were broken off, after which the globular center shell or test was broken between the fish's teeth and its contents swallowed!

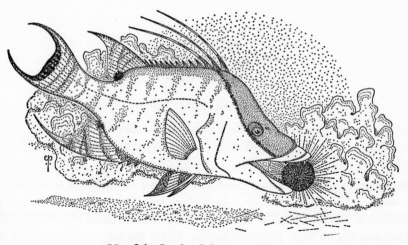

Hogfish, *Lachnolaimus maximus*.

Once in a while we would happen onto something quite new to us. One day we were wading in shallow water next to a deep channel, prodding a pole into a rocky system of holes in an effort to drive out two young queen angelfishes that were hiding there. All at once I saw a tiny fish unlike any I had ever seen or heard of before. This was a 1-inch black sliver of a creature with two lengthwise stripes of brilliant blue whose intensity and hue changed according to the angle from which it was seen. The fish suddenly emerged from one of the holes, skittered about briefly, and then returned to the hole, not to be seen again. From its shape and mode of swimming I correctly assumed it to be a goby—a kind of fish that spends most of its time resting on the sea floor supported by a small fan formed of its united pelvic fins. Words nearly failed me when I tried to describe it to Gray, who hadn't seen it, but not long afterward we caught two of them under a flat piece of loose coral, and I was then able to examine them in more detail.

The blue stripe appears to be a refractive color—one caused by reflection of light of certain wavelengths by crystalline substances in the skin of the fish, as it varies from pale to deep blue, to blue tinged with violet, as the fish turns in relation to the direction of the light source. In a similar manner, light-refractive ridges in their wings account for the intense blue brilliancy

Convergent evolution in cleaner fishes:

(upper) Neon Goby (*Elacatinus*), Atlantic Ocean.
(lower) Neon Wrasse (*Labroides*), Pacific Ocean.

of the tropical *Morpho* butterflies. Eventually I learned that this fish was known as *Elacatinus oceanops,* which Gray and I soon dubbed "neon goby" because of the blue band which is very similar to the markings of the small freshwater neon tetra, *Hyphessobrycon.* Today the fish, which has been extensively collected, is a favorite among fanciers of marine tropicals.

The neon goby has a trait which it shares with a number of other fishes and certain crustaceans of tropical seas—that of picking parasites and other debris from the bodies of larger fish. Certain coral heads inhabited by these fish serve as "cleaning stations" which are deliberately visited by other fishes in order to be serviced by the gobies, and on the reefs I have often seen a large specimen such as a Nassau grouper (*Epinephelus striatus*) getting a going-over by the little neons, who swarm over the body and even into the mouth of the big fish like service station attendants working on a bus. Marine Studios Curator F. G. Wood has reported similar scenes in the large reef tank there.

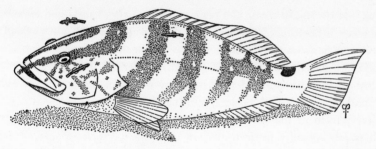

Nassau Grouper, *Epinephelus striatus,* being cleaned by Neon Gobies.

In the Pacific a small wrasse, *Fissilabrus,* which is nearly identical in size, shape, and coloration to the neon goby, performs similar cleaning services, and is in turn mimicked by a small sabertooth blenny (*Dasson*) which takes advantage of its resemblance to the former fish to nip away portions of the fin membranes of the trusting larger fish!

In 1955, nine years after that first summer of collecting, Gray was undertaking the task of stocking a second aquarium of the oceanarium type, only this time with a larger boat, a floating live-barge that could hold a dozen large sharks or an equal number of dolphins (although only small numbers of the latter were collected at any one time), two skiffs, a trawl, a number of large hand-built wire traps, seines, dipnets, harpoons, handlines, trolling lines, rods and reels, and all the various other paraphernalia it takes to be ready for any kind of fishing, anytime, anywhere. The collecting crew at that time consisted of Captain Gray, Emil Hanson, and Woody Woodford, who were assisted occasionally by Reynolds A. Moody and myself. (Moody, who was active at the Seaquarium for a time, was later involved in a tragic accident involving air embolism during a deep dive off Key Largo. Though the experience prevented him from any further diving, he continues to write articles on the subject of the sea and diving in particular.)

The average collecting trip would last from one to several days, and most of the specimens were taken from the upper Keys. The arrival of the collecting boat at the Seaquarium dock was always attended with excitement, as it held an element of the unexpected. To open the lids of the live-wells and gaze at the new specimens was much like opening Christmas presents, and this was always followed by the additional excitement of placing the specimens in their respective tanks and watching their various reactions to their new environment.

Among the early collections of Gray's crew were a number of leopard, or spotted, eagle rays, *Aetobatus narinari,* which were enmeshed in a tangle net set out overnight along the edge of a channel. These great rays, which may reach a breadth of 8 feet across the "wings," which are pointed and move in majestic up and down sweeps in the manner of a bird in slow motion, are nearly black in color, though marked, in youth, with a pattern of close-set, whitish polka dots. As the ray grows in size, the spots enlarge and tend to acquire dark centers, eventually turning into rings as new dots gradually form in the spaces between them. The result of this in the large adult is a beautifully intricate pattern, and the spectacle of several leopard rays traveling along together over a sand flat is a most remarkable thing to behold.

The tail of the leopard ray resembles a slender, black leather thong, and is normally slightly over twice the length of the head and body combined. Several inches from the base of the tail, behind a small erect dorsal fin, are one

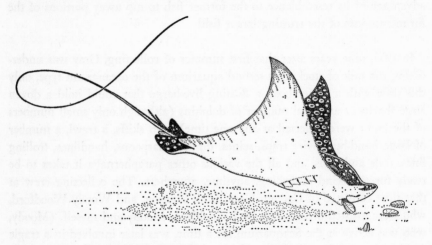

Leopard Ray, *Aetobatus narinari,* eating a clam.

or more serrated stinging spines like those of its cousins the stingrays. Unless a person inadvertently jabs himself while handling the ray there is little danger of injury from this species, as the sting is too close to the body to allow any thrusting movement. (By contrast, the true stingrays normally bear their spines about halfway down on the upper surface of the tail and, if stepped upon, can strike with accuracy and force and may cause a severe wound.) Normally, the stinging spines of all large rays are removed with pliers by the collectors as a safety measure. This procedure causes no harm to the specimen, and a new spine will eventually grow to replace the one lost.

While removing a leopard ray from the net one morning, Hanson suffered an accident which, though painful to him, and disconcerting to those who witnessed it, was fortunately without serious or lasting results. As the specimen was hauled over the gunwale of the skiff, Hanson's foot came down on the spine, which was driven completely through his rubber boot and the fleshy part of his foot between the first and second toes before tearing loose from the tail of the ray. The spine was pulled out in the same direction it had entered, and the injury quickly healed without complications.

Regarding ray stings, a definite poison is present but the virulence of this seems to vary considerably from species to species. From case histories to date the most dangerous species appear to be the round stingrays (*Urolophus*) and the true freshwater stingrays (*Potomatrygon*) of South American rivers, both of which are comparatively small in size. I have twice been stung, once on the hand and once on the foot, by *Dasyatis sabina,* a small stingray common to Tampa Bay and which sometimes enters freshwater creeks, but aside from a fair amount of bleeding and fairly intense pain initially, I had no serious effects from my experiences.

The natural food of the leopard ray consists of small shellfish which it roots out of sandy and muddy bottoms by poking about and applying a suction movement with its flat, padlike snout. (In the related cow-nosed ray, *Rhinoptera bonasus,* two flaplike cephalic fins on the underside of the indented snout accomplish the same thing by means of pistonlike movements.) When a small clam or other mollusk is encountered, it is taken into the mouth and crushed by applied pressure on the part of two hard, pavement-like surfaces composed of fused teeth in both upper and lower jaws.

At Marine Studios I have seen leopard and cow-nosed rays pick clams up off the bottom and then swim about carrying them between their crushers like a nut in a nutcracker, gradually increasing the pressure. Finally the shell would split into fragments with a sharp pop that could easily be heard through the wall of the tank, and then the meat would be swallowed while the spare shell fragments would fall from the mouth of the ray.

Cow-nosed Rays, *Rhinoptera bonasus.*

At the Seaquarium our specimens learned to accept fish and soon became exceedingly tame, following the diver with his feeding basket about on the floor of the tank and accepting food from his hand. One little ray which we named "Bobby" because he had no tail lived for a number of months in the main Seaquarium tank and became a special pet of the divers.

A type of collecting that is highly productive in seahorses and other of the smaller bottom-dwelling creatures is trawling in the beds of *Thallassia* grass that grows in great abundance in lower Biscayne Bay. This straplike green grass forms dense submarine "meadows" on either side of channels and provides a home for a vast array of fishes, crustaceans, mollusks, and other lower forms of life. In open patches in the meadow here and there grow loggerhead and colorful finger sponges which are in turn inhabited by their own specialized residents.

Depending on the speed of the boat and the density of the *Thallassia,* the trawl is dragged along the bottom from 5 to 15 minutes at a time and then hauled aboard by means of a power winch and its contents emptied into a wooden sorting trough by loosing the drawstring attached to the neck of the bag. Sponges, shells, pieces of grass and other debris are thrown aside as quickly as possible so as to recover the specimens alive and in good shape.

Seahorses are frequently the main objective of the trawling runs. The local species (*Hippocampus erectus*) reaches a length of about 8 inches, and many of the males when taken have brood-pouches distended with eggs which are placed there by the female as mating takes place. During the breeding period the skin of the male (which overlies the jointed bony exoskeleton that protects the body from injury) becomes thickened and leathery, and often the color changes to hues different from the normal mottled and patchy pattern of brown and gray. Breeding males living in orange or yellow finger sponges will often have assumed a bright color to match that of their surroundings.

Once in a great while a seahorse of a uniform brilliant red or orange color is taken, this hue interrupted only by the usual black stripe which borders the small dorsal fin. Such aberrant specimens are things of exquisite and striking beauty, but when placed in an aquarium tank their color will rapidly darken unless some similarly colored object, such as a vermilion finger sponge or piece of red coral, be put in with them.

We photographed one such specimen in color along with a nearly black breeding male and another aberrant individual which was so pale as to be almost white. Thinking this picture to be unique, we submitted it to a leading national picture magazine, but it was never published. Quite some time later we learned that the editors of the magazine had checked the photo

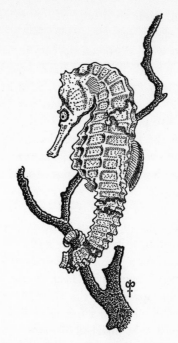

Spotted Seahorse, *Hippocampus erectus*.

with an ichthyologist who, although familiar with preserved museum specimens, had never seen or heard of a red seahorse in life, so our picture was
considered to be a hoax! Unfortunately we were not told of this at the time,
but our efforts were eventually rewarded when another one that was made
at the same time was printed on page 81 of Steinhart Aquarium Curator
Earl S. Herald's excellent book *Living Fishes of the World*, which was published in 1961.

Another veritable prize that turns up in the trawl from time to time is
the splitlure frogfish, *Antennarius scaber*. This creature is one of the angler
fishes, a group so named from their remarkable habit of luring other fishes
within gulping range by waving in front of their heads a built-in device
that consists of a wormlike or moplike "bait" on the end of a slender movable
spine or "pole."

Splitlure frogfishes are very toadlike in shape and grow to a length of
nearly a foot, though most specimens are smaller. Like its near relative the
weed-dwelling sargassum fish (*Histrio*), the paired fins of this fish are fleshy,
jointed and remarkably limblike, and by means of them it walks slowly
along the sea floor, crouching from time to time in the shelter of a sponge
or coral head in its constant search for prey. The color may be nearly jet

black or mottled brown, while the bait is pale flesh-colored and resembles a small, coiled worm in shape. In common with the Plectognath puffers or balloonfishes, sometimes when disturbed the frogfish will commence gulping water until its stomach is vastly distended, its outlines tend to become nearly spherical, and the normally baggy skin turns tight as a drum. Presumably this habit makes the fish more difficult to swallow by would-be predators, and it is a most impressive performance to observe.

The fishing "pole" of the frogfish is actually the first spine of the dorsal fin that, in the course of evolutionary specialization, has become free of the remainder of the fin and has moved to a position on the tip of the snout of the fish. Normally, this spine lies back along the top of the fish's body with the bait rolled up and on one side of the dorsal, but on the approach of a potential fish victim the entire apparatus is swung forward from its jointed base, the wormlike bait unrolls its two ends and is waved about in a series of rapid and lifelike gyrations, a performance that few fish seem able to resist.

When the curious victim approaches near enough, it is swallowed in a tremendous gulp, and so capacious is the elastic stomach that *Antennarius* is quite easily capable of swallowing a fish more than half as large as itself. In fact, unless they are evenly matched size-wise it is impossible to keep two of these fish successfully in the same tank for any length of time, for the larger one will almost certainly swallow or partially swallow the other before long. One splitlure frogfish which Gray caught in the trawl was filmed by nature photographer William A. Anderson, who spent many long and patient hours watching it through the viewfinder of his camera as it moved over the bottom stalking and capturing its prey. The results of his remarkable and revealing film sequences were admired by all who saw them included in the Walt Disney nature film, *Secrets of Life*.

Numerous crustaceans are also obtained by trawling, of which none is more strange than the creature known as the Stomatopod or mantis shrimp. This creature (*Lysiosquilla*), although resembling a shrimp in general form, does not appear to have any close relatives among any of the other crustaceans. A camel has been humorously defined as a horse designed by a committee. A Stomatopod on the other hand might be compared to a lobster built on a Government contract by various companies for final assembly. Truly a creature of parts, this beast seems to be constructed of leftovers and appears to have half again as many appendages as are really necessary.

The cephalothorax or unjointed forepart of the body is quite small and flattened, while the stalked eyes are peanut-shaped, oval, and slightly constricted in the middle, besides being placed so close together as to give the creature a definitely cross-eyed appearance. The name "mantis shrimp"

Splitlure Frogfish, *Antennarius scaber,* capturing young Porkfish,
*Anisotremus virginicus.*

comes from the enlarged forward pincers, which, instead of operating like
tweezers or tongs as in the case of ordinary shrimps, crabs, and lobsters, are
folded back against the basal joints as in the praying mantis. The terminal
joint, or dactylus, is provided with a fringe of narrow, comblike spines which
fit into deep perforations in the basal joint, forming quite a fearsome instrument for the capture of food. On either side of the mouth and behind the
first pair of claws are several others, smaller and hooklike in shape. In the
center of the body are three pairs of slender walking legs which appear
totally inadequate for supporting its weight on the bottom. The tail or
abdomen, which has ten movable joints instead of the usual seven found in
ordinary shrimps, is exceedingly flexible and is terminated by a heavy telson
or end joint that is armed with sharp spines.

When interfered with, the Stomatopod will flip its tail in such a way
that the armored telson delivers a blow something like the sudden crack of
a whip—a painful experience for an unprotected hand—earning it the name
of "thumb-splitter" among shrimp fishermen. At least one species of large

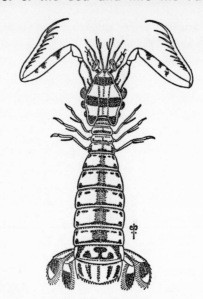

Stomatopod, *Lysiosquilla maculata.*

Stomatopod found in the Pacific Ocean has its telson so armored with spines that it resembles a Lochaber—that spike-bearing metal ball on the end of a short chain used as a weapon in medieval times, and probably wielded almost as effectively.

In captivity Stomatopods are hardy and will thrive for considerable periods of time in a tank also inhabited by fish, apparently since they are so well protected by nature. Occasionally they will swim about rapidly, but most of the time they rest on the floor or in the corners of the tank, sometimes upside down, where the rhythmic shuffling movements of the gill append-ages, which are attached to the underside of the abdomen, may be easily perceived. This constant activity always reminds me for some reason of the shuffling of a deck of cards, and at times is rather ludicrous to watch.

On one occasion before the Seaquarium was built, I happened to notice an unusually large Stomatopod swimming along a seawall at Miami Beach. I caught the beast with a dipnet that I happened to be carrying in my car, but having no pail or other suitable container in which to keep him alive I placed him inside an old pith helmet in the trunk of the car overnight, in-tending to preserve him in Formalin the next day. However, on opening the back of the car on the following morning I was quite startled to see him lying on his back in the helmet, dry but still alive, "shuffling his cards" and fixing me with a dismal cross-eyed stare! I hadn't the heart to put an end to him after this, so I carried him to my office where he thrived for some time in a seawater aquarium next to my desk.

In the fresh and brackish water canals of the Miami area lives a giant "shrimp" or, rather, prawn that grows to nearly the size of a lobster. Adult males may reach a total length of more than two feet. Until recently at least, this creature was not at all rare if one knew when and where to look for it, but despite this fact it is comparatively little known in south Florida and specimens were delivered to the Marine Laboratory of the University of Miami from time to time as "new to science" by their excited collectors. Nonetheless, *Macrobrachium carcinus* is well known in various Caribbean rivers and streams, and related species are found in tropical areas of the Old World as well. The fact that it manages to stay hidden most of the time is well attested by the fact that, although I had done considerable fresh and saltwater collecting in and about Miami, I was quite unaware of *Macrobrachium*'s existence until a person who was an authority on this species showed up at the Marine Laboratory where I was then working and asked if I would help him collect some specimens.

I volunteered my assistance with private reservations over the likelihood of our eventual success, but was considerably surprised when my friend informed me that he had caught three the night before and that they were now in his icebox! In fact, he invited me to dine on them that evening before taking me to the place where he had caught them, explaining that these had died because he had not provided a suitable container for keeping them alive, but that he hoped to bring subsequent specimens back to the laboratory for study. My first view of these crustaceans in the refrigerator filled me with astonishment. They had the typical heavy form and slightly humpbacked shape of the little 1-inch-long freshwater prawns with which I was quite familiar, only they were much larger than any saltwater market "shrimp" I had ever seen! They were greenish olive in color with a broken band of cream color along each side, and projecting well beyond the beady black eyes was a flattened curved beak or rostrum armed with small sharp spines. Most surprising of all was the second pair of legs, which were modified into long pincers like those of a lobster, but considerably more slender, and resembling a pair of forceps.

Cooked, they tasted to me like something intermediate between lobster and shrimp, although I must confess I felt somewhat guilty about eating these wondrous creatures, and I kept imagining how we would feel if for some reason we were unable to locate additional specimens. I told myself I should have insisted that those three be deposited intact in the Marine Laboratory museum and that our supper amounted to a sacrilege. What doubts I had were, however, soon to be dispelled for about dusk my companion drove us to the region of a large salinity dam which blocked the rising and ebbing tide of Snapper Creek, a deep drainage canal which enters Biscayne

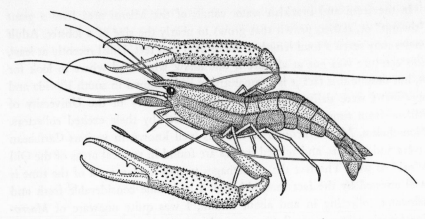

Giant River Shrimp, *Macrobrachium carcinus.*

Bay to the south of the city of Miami. Although I had never seen the giant shrimp I was quite familiar with this spot, as I had previously netted golden shiners, spotted garfish, and foot-long Eleotrid gobies here during the daytime.

We each carried a flashlight and a long-handled dipnet and proceeded along the steep rocky bank as close to the water as possible. Now and then a great blue land crab (*Cardisoma*) would clash his heavy claws together, sploober a mass of wet bubbles at us, and tumble noisily into the canal, while the songs of cone-headed grasshoppers and black crickets began to swell the night air from the palmettos growing along the far shore. All at once from the shallows immediately in front of me my flashlight beam picked out two glowing ruby spots. These were the eyes of a *Macrobrachium* reflecting the light, and they were the most impressive invertebrate eyes I have ever seen. I have observed the green reflection of wolf spider eyes along Florida highways at night and likewise I have seen the bright red glow of the eyes of an approaching sphinx moth in the headlights of my car, but the ruby reflection of the eyes of this fantastic shrimp is a sight that must be seen to be appreciated. I could tell by his greatly enlarged pincers that my specimen was a male, and, disturbed by the light, he was slowly moving out into deeper water. In a moment I had him in my net, from which I dropped him into a pail of water. Within a half hour we had secured a half dozen, several others having eluded our nets in the interim. From this and later collecting trips I observed that *Macrobrachium* were most active along the shore immediately after dusk, appearing to move out into deeper water as darkness progressed, becoming more difficult to secure.

The purpose of my friend's collecting activities was to investigate the feasibility of rearing them in captivity for market purposes, and the last I heard from him he was still attempting to do so, in ponds on Florida's west coast. To my knowledge he has not met with any real success, for although these giant shrimp are highly prolific, they also have decided cannibalistic tendencies, and do not take well to the crowded situation which is unavoidable when attempting to rear them on a commercial scale. I will say, however, that the person who eventually succeeds in mass-rearing *Macrobrachium* should have little difficulty in finding a market for them.

Subsequently I learned of two other large, closely related species in the coastal streams of south Florida. One, *M. acanthurus,* is about the size of the average market shrimp and nearly black in color, while the 3-inch *M. olfersi* possesses, in the case of the male, one pincer considerably larger than the other and furred like a muff in a mat of fine, silky hairs: a most peculiar thing for a shrimp!

In recent years the giant shrimps have appeared to decline in numbers in south Florida canals, perhaps as a result of increasing pollution of inland waters as well as the ever-increasing use of deadly insecticides. We have been able to secure occasional specimens for the freshwater tank section of the Seaquarium, where they never fail to attract considerable attention.

Another noteworthy freshwater crustacean I happened to obtain under fairly unusual circumstances. In the spring of 1957 I was attending an international symposium on sharks and shark-repellents being held in New Orleans. One day, I happened to stroll through a section of the Old French Market there and suddenly my attention was directed to a basket filled with large, live crayfishes which were being sold by the pound. While most crayfishes (which are small relatives of the lobster) are greenish, gray, or tan in color, these were beautiful things, colored various shades of pink and crimson.

They were chimney-building crayfish, *Procambarus clarkii,* a species which is highly esteemed by the natives of New Orleans. They gather in large numbers during the spring and summer, when they swarm and come out of the swamps and creeks, where they normally live, onto higher ground and construct burrows surmounted by tubular "chimneys" of mud close to the water's edge.

I was determined to take some of them back to the Seaquarium with me, but at that moment I had no idea as to how this could be accomplished. I could, of course, have had them shipped in a plastic bag in the same manner as tropical fish, but a simpler method seemed desirable. While looking through a nearby store, I hit upon a likely plan which involved the purchase of a blue cloth traveling bag of the kind that closes with a zipper. I lined its bottom with damp newspapers and carried it to the market, where I informed the vendor that I wished to purchase 50 crayfishes, which I would myself select from the lot. Since the latter varied individually in size and color, I proceeded to pick out the largest and most attractive specimens. I am sure that the crayfish vendor, accustomed to shoveling his wares into sacks en masse with a metal scoop, was more than a little amused by my actions as I picked up and carefully weighed the merits of each crayfish before dropping it into my bag. Having finally obtained and paid for my specimens, I carried the ensatcheled 50 back to my hotel room.

The obvious place for my charges for the time being was the bathtub, and with an inch or so of water to cover them the brightly colored crustaceans added a decorative note to the otherwise drabbish bathroom. Here they remained for two days, being moved to the bag at those times when I required the tub for other purposes. It would have been interesting to know what comments the maids must have made on discovering them, perhaps conjecturing that I was keeping them for the purpose of a midnight snack, since they are eaten alive and raw by some persons.

On the plane trip back to Miami the blue satchel with its restless contents traveled beneath my seat, and I was put in mind of the time several years earlier when I had, under somewhat similar conditions, carried a young boa constrictor in my lap artfully disguised in a cake box. I will never forget my alarm over the possibility of discovery on that trip when, reaching for my coat at the end of the journey, I was disconcerted to see the airline hostess reach for the box in the vacated seat and register obvious surprise at its unnatural weight. "Must be a fruitcake," she said as she handed it to me, and I responded with a nod and managed a weak smile as I hastily took my departure.

At the Seaquarium the red crayfishes shared the tank with the giant river shrimps, where they made a most attractive display. Unlike the saltwater commercial shrimps (*Penaeus*) from the Atlantic and the Gulf of Mexico which release their eggs free in the water and whose young undergo a series of changes before they come to resemble the adults, both the freshwater *Macrobrachium* and the crayfish *Procambarus* carry their eggs attached to special appendages on the underside of the abdomen until they hatch into miniatures of the adult. Both of these latter species were observed to breed freely in the tank, and in the case of the crayfish the young cling to the abdominal swimmerets of the mother for a brief time after hatching.

In the course of our collecting activities about the shallow reefs we frequently found pairs of banded coral shrimp, *Stenopus hispidus,* setting up housekeeping under sponges and in cavities in the coral rock. Strikingly beautiful creatures, these shrimp are found in warm seas throughout the tropics. White in color, the body and pincers of the coral shrimp are crossed by broad bands of crimson and the bases of the pincers themselves are tinged bright purple where they are attached to the body. In addition, the egg masses of the female are a delicate blue-green, and these 4-inch creatures are among the most attractive of all coral reef denizens. Great care must be exercised in capturing them intact, for the pincers as well as the body are densely covered with small, hooked spines which easily become entangled in a net, frequently resulting in one or both of the pincers becoming detached from the body in the process.

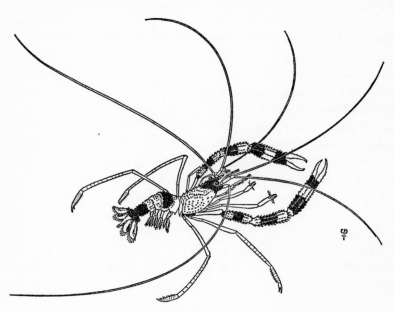

Banded Coral Shrimp, *Stenopus hispidus.*

The coral shrimp shares an interesting habit with the little neon goby mentioned earlier—it is a parasite-picker that enjoys immunity from being eaten by most fish, who allow it to come in contact with their bodies, picking off small parasitic organisms and injured bits of tissue as it does so. As I stated before, one almost invariably finds these shrimp in pairs, and from the frequency with which I have found the females carrying eggs, they are apparently quite prolific.

The yellow-backed coral shrimp, *Stenopus scutellatus,* is a somewhat smaller species, similar in color but with a broad band of clear yellow in the middle of its back. Its habits resemble those of its larger cousin; it also being classed as a "cleaner" species. Although pairs of either species normally live around rocks, coral, and sponges, now and then they are encountered having taken up their abode in discarded beer cans, paint buckets, old tires, and other artifacts of civilization.

Two other colorful shrimps from the Caribbean area are noteworthy for having taken up the habit of living in close association with sea anemones and in some way enjoying complete protection from the stings of the latter in the process. In this singular relationship the shrimps find their parallel in the brightly colored Pacific and Indian Ocean damselfishes of the Genus *Amphiprion* which live for protection in and among the tentacles of large anemones.

Common in Bimini and elsewhere in the Bahamas is the 2-inch, wine-colored pistol shrimp, *Alpheus armatus,* which lives in pairs under the slender anemone *Bartholomea annulata.* These shrimps and their relatives receive their common name from the possession of one enormous claw provided with a plunger-and-socket arrangement by means of which they can emit a loud pop accompanied by a short-range concussion effect for both offensive and defensive purposes.

Another species of like habits is the 1-inch *Paraclimentes yucatanicus,* whose glass-clear body is exquisitely marked with a lacy pattern of lavender spots and white rings, with legs and antennae likewise banded with lavender. This shrimp lives either singly or in small groups on the disk and tentacles of the great sea anemone *Condylactis gigantea* of the Florida Keys and the Bahamas.

On the reefs, fish were caught not only by the use of handlines as described earlier, but also in large wire traps with a funnel in one side. The trapline is normally run once, twice, or three times a day while the boats are in the reef area, and to lift them one of the collecting crew goes overboard with mask and flippers and attaches a hook on the end of a cable to a metal ring in the top of the trap. The traps are then brought aboard the boat by means of a power winch; then a hinged door on their sides is opened, and the specimens dropped into one of the live-wells.

When certain fishes are taken from fairly deep water the gas in their swim bladders will expand so that they have difficulty in maintaining their equilibrium, or even float belly-up in the well. A fish in this condition may die in an hour or so due to the pressure on its internal organs if not relieved in some way, so they are carefully punctured by means of a hollow hypodermic needle and the excess gas allowed to escape. The small wound thus formed quickly heals under normal conditions and the fish appear to suffer little inconvenience as a consequence of this operation.

Smaller specimens on the reefs are captured with hand nets by collectors

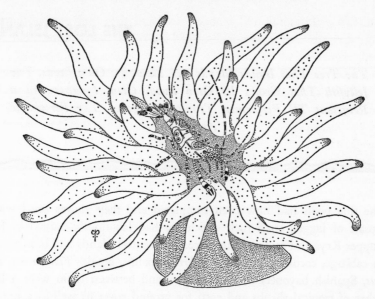

Cleaner Shrimp, *Paraclimentes yucatanicus,* on Sea Anemone,
*Condylactis gigantea.*

wearing aqua-lungs or face masks connected by means of a long rubber
hose to a gasoline powered air compressor. When netted, a fish is transferred
to a large glass jar with a perforated screw-top lid, or in the case of larger
specimens, a perforated metal bucket. For catching small fishes that habitually seek refuge in holes in the coral, Assistant Collector Emil Hanson designed and built an ingenious plunger device that works something like a
Flit-gun in reverse, drawing the specimens from their holes by means of
a powerful suction action. This instrument, which we dubbed a "mazooka,"
has resulted in the capture of many rare and unusual small creatures that
could not be obtained otherwise.

Through the untiring efforts of Gray and Hanson the assortment of specimens in the Seaquarium tanks continued to swell, and as the time for the
public opening approached the latter commenced to take on the colorful
appearance of the undersea reefs themselves. From the time it first started
until the present, collecting has been a full-time operation the year round.
Few persons can realize the amount of time, effort, and expense that go
into this operation as well as the dedication and devotion to their work of
those individuals who undertake this never-ending task.

# CHAPTER 5

# THE LOST ISLANDS

*The Tree That Builds Islands and Plants Its Own Seeds. The Jellyfish That Grows Its Own Food. Giant Iguanas and a Reluctant TV Performer. Tropical Penguins. The Personable Armadillo*

The tide pools had now been completed and their shores lined with a mosaic of jagged coral rock which we had laboriously barged in from the upper Keys and cemented in place. The central islands had been planted with cabbage, coconut, and silver *Thrinax* palms, besides *Ficus* trees, *Pandanus,* Spanish bayonets and sea grapes, and between them were a large number of tropical shrubs and cacti for ground cover as well as a number of limestone boulders from a rock quarry near Homestead, 30 miles to the south. It was our intention to balance the sea life in the surrounding pools with unusual land animals that normally occur on tropical islands or could be easily adapted to the same, and the already junglelike appearance of this area had caused us to name it "The Lost Islands."

At certain areas adjacent to the islands' shoreline we had constructed small tidal mud flats, and on these we planted a number of mangrove trees which normally grow in abundance in such areas. The red or true mangrove, *Rhizophora mangle,* may be found throughout the tropics and subtropics and is often called "the island-building tree." This is due to its peculiar root system which supports the tree, stiltlike, above the mud and like a breakwater this traps large quantities of seaweed and sand brought in by the tide, causing the substrate to rise gradually.

These roots, which are smooth and thick, are of two kinds. The main supporting roots arise from the trunk and lower branches, while from the higher branches arise somewhat thicker, smoother roots called "pneumatophores" which have a respiratory function. In certain places along the Florida coast and elsewhere in the tropics these latter roots will become heavily encrusted with oysters as they grow beneath the water surface. I recall occasions during my boyhood days when I would chop such an oyster-laden root loose with a machete, carry it ashore like a bunch of bananas on a stalk, and pile dry brush on top of it. Burned down to embers, this would provide as delicious an oyster roast as anyone could imagine. Thus along the Florida coast it may literally be said that oysters grow on trees.

Besides standing on stilts, building islands, and growing oysters on its roots, the red mangrove has a singular way of reproducing itself, being known as the tree that plants its own seeds. Actually, the seeds germinate while still attached to the mother tree, and the young plantlets, which resemble dark green cigars, grow to about a foot in length before dropping off into the water. At low tide a falling plantlet may imbed itself in the mud by its pointed lower end and start to grow immediately, but most of them float off in the tide in an upright position and may be borne vast distances in this manner, doubtless one of the reasons why this plant is to be found in all parts of the world where conditions are suitable for its growth. Great numbers of red mangroves line the coastal areas of the Everglades, their distribution being sharply controlled by land elevation as they will seldom survive more than a few inches above mean tide level.

Usually found in association with the red species is the white mangrove, *Laguncularia racemosa,* which is capable of growing on slightly higher ground. Actually quite a different plant, it produces seeds which are small, flattened oval, and ribbed, and it does not have the curved stilt-roots of the red mangrove. Instead, the white mangrove's buried roots produce a great number of small fingerlike pneumatophores that project *up* through the mud in rows, often some distance from the trunk of the tree. A third species, *Avicennia nitida,* is called the black mangrove and characteristically has the surfaces of its leaves covered with tiny crystals of salt. It is less often seen than the other two mangroves and has a heavier build.

Bromeliads or air plants may grow upon the branches of mangroves in sheltered inlets, and in the Florida Keys I have found the Florida butterfly orchid, *Epidendrum tampense,* growing upon the white species. Another orchid, *Epidendrum boothianum,* grows on trees associated with the mangrove community in the upper Keys, and I would not be surprised if it sometimes grows on mangroves as well. Both orchids and bromeliads are "epiphytes," attaching themselves to the bark of trees by their roots, but receiving no direct nourishment from their hosts as do true plant parasites such as dodder and mistletoe.

Despite the fact that they frequently grow in soft mud where the young plants may be dug with virtually their entire root system intact, mangroves are difficult to transplant successfully, and their slow growth makes starting them from seeds or young sprouts impractical. Nonetheless Captain Gray and I managed to secure a large number of mangroves of both species from a nearby mud flat and eventually enough of these survived to give our island shores something approaching a natural appearance. Today these have grown to a considerable height and new seedlings are constantly making their appearance between the original trees.

As was mentioned in the first chapter, the tide pools, which took the form of a shallow 20-foot-wide moat around each island, were connected with Biscayne Bay by means of an underground pipe so that the tidal rise and fall of water in the bay would cause a corresponding natural rise and fall plus a twice-daily water change in the pools. A screen across the pipe inlet prevented the escape of the specimens and a concrete sill or retaining wall held the water at a minimum safe level during the occasional very low spring tides that would otherwise almost completely drain the pools, exposing them to the heat of the sun and endangering the specimens within.

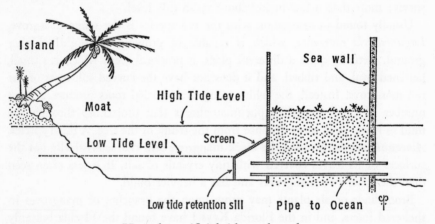

How the artificial tide pool works.

The pools were already populated with parrot fishes, bonefish, small barracudas, mullet, and other shallow-water life including starfishes, spiny lobsters, crabs, sea anemones, and some large, strange jellyfishes of the genus *Cassiopeia*. These jellyfishes, which are common about the clear, sheltered inlets of the Florida Keys, do not drift about in the ocean currents in the adult stage as normal jellyfishes do, but, instead, lie upside down on the sand, contracting their disks slightly from time to time to create a current of water flowing past their gills. Non-stinging, the *Cassiopeia* is provided with a mass of flattened, feathery tentacles in which grow the *zooxanthellae,* or unicellular algal plants which are believed to provide the jellyfish with its food. A similar situation is believed to exist with the 300-pound

*Tridacna* clam of the tropical Pacific, which also carries a "garden" of *zooxanthellae* in its exposed mantle folds.

That *Cassiopeia* is actually dependent on its algal garden is indicated by the repeated observation that if one is deprived of strong light (which in turn causes the algae to grow) it will begin to shrink in size as its body tissues are converted into necessary energy. One specimen, originally the size of a saucer, that an acquaintance of mine kept in a home aquarium under insufficient light, actually "ungrew" progressively until it was not much larger than a dime, although still a perfect jellyfish in all other respects, and this occurred despite large numbers of brine shrimp and other food materials that were constantly offered to it. The *Cassiopeias* in the tide pools eventually disappeared as they were eaten by the spiny lobsters and other creatures that, under normal conditions, would not touch such fare. This is a common phenomenon met with in aquarium situations; animals kept in captivity on an artificial diet often develop strange appetites, perhaps in an attempt to secure some needed food element.

The pools were now teeming with life and the tidal drain was functioning properly after certain necessary mechanical adjustments, and the islands, with their abundance of tropical plant life, were now ready for habitation as well, for a 5-foot wall had been built around the pools to prevent the escape of any venturesome denizens.

Our first specimens were 25 large Mexican iguana lizards (*Iguana iguana*), from 5 to 6 feet in length. These were very similar to the Cuban form, but less green and more orange-brown in color, and had two small pointed scales on the upper side of the snout. We had expected the iguanas to take refuge in the trees and other foliage as soon as they were released from their shipping boxes, but instead nearly all of them promptly dove into the water and insisted on resting motionless on the bottom for long periods of time, coming up only occasionally for air. It was only after several days that the majority of them began to explore the island and to nibble on the bananas, lettuce, tomatoes, and other fresh fruit that we set out in pans for them to eat. Each island was also provided with a large concrete-lined pool through which fresh water was circulated by means of an underground pipe. It was thought that the iguanas would spend considerable time in the pools, but they actually seemed to prefer the salt water of the tide pools to these.

Once the Mexican iguanas had adapted themselves to the island enclosure, we set out to obtain some additional species and were fortunate in securing more than a dozen specimens of the great rhinoceros iguana, *Cyclura cornuta*, from the island of Hispaniola. These lizards receive their name from the presence of a blunt, conical horn on the upper end of the snout, and the

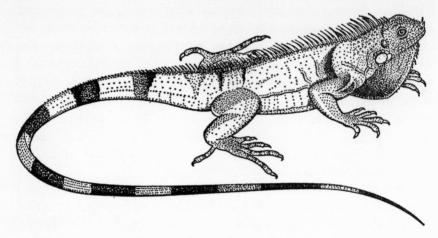

Mexican Iguana, *Iguana iguana.*

body form is especially heavy and bulldog-like in contrast to the slenderness of the Mexican species. I had always wished for an opportunity to observe these majestic beasts in captivity, so it was with considerable anticipation that I drove our new specimens, imprisoned in heavy wooden crates, from a local animal dealer's stockade to the Seaquarium.

After having carried the crates across the moat and set them on the shore of the largest island, an assistant and I pried one of the top boards loose from one of the boxes by means of a crowbar. Immediately a head that might have belonged to a compact-model dinosaur emerged, followed by a ponderous hoisting forth of a rusty-brown bulk of a body with wrinkled skin and ornamented with a continuous fringe of elongated scales extending from the nape of the neck to the end of the tail. The head was positively immense, larger in proportion to the body than in any other iguana, and the powerful jaw muscles formed rounded bulges behind the eyes and angle of the jaws. The eyes themselves might have been said to have a keen and rather calculating expression quite out of keeping with the lizard's alleged low level of intelligence.

As the iguanas began to clamber from the crate one by one I saw that they were heavily infested with large parasitic ticks, some as large as the end of my thumb. While these did not appear to cause much discomfort to their hosts I did not want them to spread to the other specimens, so I hastily replaced the board after four iguanas were already free on the island. Since it would be necessary to de-tick them by hand, I secured a large, heavy-meshed net and approached one of the "rhinos" with it, as I had previously experienced little difficulty in capturing the Mexican iguanas in this manner.

The rhino, however, had other ideas and simply would not be cornered. Instead of running in a straight line until a wall or some other obstruction impeded his progress as I had seen the former species do, he showed considerable dexterity in avoiding obstacles, and on the few occasions when I did get close to him, he gaped his jaws widely at me, disclosing the purplish black interior of his mouth and throat, alternately snapping at the net and aiming powerful sidewise blows with his muscular tail.

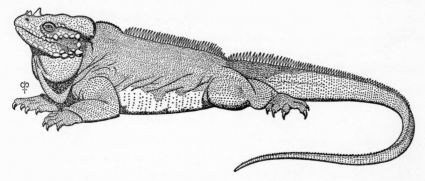

Rhinoceros Iguana, *Cyclura cornuta.*

Despite this disconcerting behavior I at length managed to net him, and, using a procedure employed by professional alligator wrestlers, I worked my hands under the net and held his mouth closed with the fingers of one hand and pressed his hind limbs against his body with the other. Despite his powerful struggles and considerable weight I managed to hold him securely, but I soon discovered that it was quite impossible to keep him immobilized and remove the ticks at the same time, and the various other members of the staff who happened to be present seemed disinclined to offer their immediate assistance. Eventually I received help in the form of my wife Fanny, not, I admit, without a certain amount of persuasion on my part. This was not due to any squeamishness of hers in regard to the iguanas, but rather because she has a decided aversion to ticks, and the latter were in this case of a truly appalling size and appearance.

One by one I netted the rhinos, the latter ones as they emerged from the crate, pinioned their heads and feet as I rolled their great bulks on their side in tactics akin to the bulldozing of a small steer, and while Fanny half held, half sat on a specimen, I went over its body thoroughly, removing the ticks one by one and drowning them in a flask of alcohol. In this manner we eventually de-ticked the whole lot and set them free on the island.

Next morning I discovered most of the rhinos busily occupied in digging large burrows about the base of trees and rocks. By scratching vigorously with their front claws they would fling sand some distance behind them, and as their excavations deepened, mounds of earth grew on various parts of the island. Unlike the Mexican iguanas, the rhinos showed no predilection to enter the water; on the rare occasions when one would cross the moat in order to explore the region next to the wall, he would churn the water to foam with frantic motions of his feet and tail, the energy expended being out of all proportion to the slow progress he was making.

Pieces of melon rind, bananas, tomatoes, and other tidbits tossed to the center of the island from shore were instantly noticed by the rhinos, and they would come rushing from all directions to seize and bolt this food. Swallowing was accomplished in a series of rapid gulps with head held high, followed by a hurried exploration for more. Invariably, competition for food was accompanied by a certain amount of squabbling, and usually ended with one of the iguanas chasing after another with jaws agape; but, after running a short distance, the pursuer would invariably return, the pursued following at his heels, his enthusiasm undampened.

During this initial period all the iguanas were fed large quantities of fresh tomatoes, which came from a quite unexpected source. At this time much grass planting was being carried on about the Seaquarium grounds, and to fertilize the ground truckloads of processed sludge were being brought by truck from the City of Miami Sewage Treatment Plant, which is located on the other side of Virginia Key, across the highway from the Seaquarium. The purpose of a modern sewage treatment plant is to convert raw sewage as it comes from a city to a biologically sanitary product, and in the course of this process the solids are gradually separated from the liquid effluent. This operation requires a number of days in which the concentrated solids undergo a natural breakdown and digestion by contained bacteria; this is accompanied by an internal temperature of more than a hundred degrees brought about by attendant oxidation. It was with considerable surprise therefore that we observed hundreds of young tomato plants sprouting from this purified sludge which had been spread over the lawn. Apparently tomato seeds, most of which had originated in salads consumed by the populace of Miami, have the most fantastic powers of survival.

Although iguanas are commonly thought of as fruit and vegetable eaters, they actually prey to a considerable extent on small animals in the wild. With this fact in mind, I decided to see if the rhinos could be induced to eat cut fish, of which we had a plentiful supply. "Induced" proved to be hardly the word, for they immediately fell upon the fish with the same enthusiasm with which they greeted the tomatoes and bananas, and the larger specimens would gulp down whole blue runners of the same size as those we were feeding to the dolphins. Before long the Mexican iguanas also picked up a taste for fresh fish, and this eventually became the mainstay of their diet. Paradoxically, the large bonefish and parrot fishes that inhabited the moats soon began greedily snapping at stray portions of bananas and tomatoes that fell short of the islands, creating a topsy-turvy situation all around.

The rhinoceros iguanas continued to make their home on and in the ground, neither (excepting to a most limited extent) swimming nor climbing the trees as did the Mexican species. Although occasional biting and tail-slapping battles would occur between two males of either species (which appeared to inflict little if any damage on either contestant), the two quite different iguana species got along well together on the island, each spending the greater part of their time ignoring the other.

Soon we added two more species of large tropical lizards to the island fauna, the Central American spiny-tailed iguana, *Ctenosaura similis,* and the tegu, *Tupinambis nigropunctatus,* both of which reach a total length of about 4 feet. The spiny-tailed iguanas showed habits intermediate between the arboreal Mexican iguanas and the burrowing rhinos, and they also swam well, but spent less time in the water than the first-named species.

The tegus were quite different from the iguanas in all respects. These lizards lack enlarged fringe scales or any other adornments on their bodies, and their black and white hides shine and feel like soft, polished leather; in fact, as my wife says, one would almost expect to find upholstery tacks fastened here and there in their skins. Tegus are active prowlers, constantly moving about and exploring every nook and cranny with their slender, forked, snakelike tongues. They are also capable of considerable speed, and are completely carnivorous in feeding habits. Like the rhinos, they took at once to a diet of fresh fish and would even plunge into the water to snatch morsels away from the aquatic inhabitants. One tegu was actually trained by a feeding attendant to jump in the air for his food, and during this performance he once lacerated the feeder's fingers rather severely with his sharp teeth.

About this time I was doing a series of television appearances on a local station, during which I displayed various forms of sea life and other creatures, live, before the cameras, outlining the more interesting facts of their lives and habits. On one of these programs I decided to use the largest of our rhinoceros iguanas, taking him to the studio and returning him in my car. There were two very large males, about equal in size, to choose from, but one of them had recently lost several inches from the tip of his tail in an unfortunate accident involving a power mower used to cut the grass on the island. The iguana, unnoticed by the man operating the mower, was lying concealed beneath a large bush, and as the machine passed the iguana aimed a powerful tail swat at it, as iguanas are wont to do when anything out of the ordinary disturbs them. The abbreviated tip would eventually grow back, though not quite to its original length. The other iguana was eventually netted and placed in a heavy burlap sack, and I then drove it to the TV studio after having arranged for one of my assistants to meet me there and help me handle the beast before the cameras. Since reptiles, being cold-blooded, regulate their activity according to the temperature of the surrounding air, I had dampened the sack as an additional measure, hoping that the resultant evaporation would slow down the animal's excitable disposition to some extent.

My assistant was late in arriving, and as the minute hand of the studio clock rapidly approached the GO signal, I became progressively more ill at ease. With only two minutes remaining I was handed an extension phone and my fears were confirmed as I listened to the hurried voice of my assistant explaining that he had suffered a flat tire en route and since it was too late to catch a taxi, I would have to go ahead without him. This I proceeded to do, and since I had by now had a fair measure of experience in handling the rhinos, I anticipated no special difficulties with this one.

First, I displayed several unusual small lizards from my own home collection, including a foot-long tokay gecko that gave a squawk reminiscent of a rubber-bulb bicycle horn whenever he was interfered with, and a giant Australian blue-tongued skink that was fond of eating almost anything including fruitcake and strawberry jam, a most unlizardlike trait. Following these I produced a tegu who waddled about on the tabletop with his long tongue flicking this way and that, followed by one of the highly photogenic but relatively inactive Mexican iguanas. And for the grand finale I picked up the sack containing the massive rhino and unwound the cord with which it was bound.

The rhino's emergence was most impressive, and by stealing a sidewise glance at the small monitor TV set in the studio, I could see that his head now filled the screen. He seemed quite docile after nearly an hour in the dark, cool sack, and I had no difficulty in guiding him about the table by prodding him gently with a short stick. My time was nearly up now, so taking a portion of the sack between my teeth and spreading it with my hands I formed a triangular opening which I spread invitingly in front of the moving iguana. Instead of entering, however, he simply raised his head and opened his mouth. The hot studio lights were rapidly warming him up and I could see that the more unpleasant side of his nature would rapidly manifest itself if I did not succeed in getting him inside the sack in a hurry. I was on the point of attempting to flip it over his head when my host Jim Dooley suddenly placed his hand on the rhino's tail in an effort to make him move forward. Instead of this happening, the rhino sent one of the lizard cages clattering to the floor with a heavy smack of his tail, and at the same time lunged at me.

I grabbed him about the neck with both hands at once as he all but left the table, and as his tail continued to rearrange all objects with which it came into contact I was mainly aware of a cavernous expanse of black iguana maw uncomfortably close to my face. His jaws snapped shut just short of my nose, and before I realized it, both rhino and I were struggling on the floor. Jim stepped forward helpfully and received a tail swat across the shin. Finally, I wedged the beast firmly between my knees, held his mouth shut with one hand, and worked the sack over him with the other just as the program went off the air. I looked up in time to see both cameramen beaming broadly and giving enthusiastic OK signs with their fingers. They had recorded the entire sequence in detail and agreed that it was one of the best animal shows they had shot to date!

Nearly a year following our acquisition of the rhinos, two young appeared on the island, newly hatched from some concealed underground clutch of eggs. They were, to my knowledge, the first of this species ever successfully bred in captivity and were quite different from the adults in appearance, being slender and grayish with numerous alternating narrow dark and light bands crossing the back and sides.

The Lost Islands were for a time also the home of several Humboldt penguins (*Spheniscus humboldti*) from Peru. In the mind of the general public, penguins are always associated with the frigid Antarctic region, and it comes as a surprise to many persons that there are penguins that thrive in warm or even tropical regions, one species, *Spheniscus mendiculus,* living in the Galapagos Islands directly on the equator.

Where most swimming and diving birds use their webbed or lobed feet as oars and propellers, the penguins use their wings, which are modified into narrow but powerful flippers. With these they glide through the water in a most unbirdlike way, using their webbed feet merely as a rudder. Since the latter are located at the very rear of the body, the penguin, in order to balance himself when out of water, usually stands straight as if at "attention" (the "at ease" position is assumed by falling forward on his belly, which a penguin does whenever he wishes to rest). The usual bracing posture, together with the armlike flippers and black and white coloration of most species, is what gives penguins the appearance of stiff-backed little diplomats and endears them so much to cartoonists.

When I opened the crate containing our first pair of Humboldt penguins

I noticed that they appeared quite thin; nonetheless they showed no inclination to eat the choice pieces of fresh fish we offered to them. Puzzled, I put through a phone call to Bob Mattlin, who was then director of the Crandon Park Zoo in Miami. Bob informed me that penguins are curiously stubborn creatures and that considerable persuasion must often be used in order to induce them to feed voluntarily but that they would have to be fed at once, otherwise they would die. This meant force-feeding, not a simple process since the average penguin strenuously objects to this indignity.

In order to show me how this was done, Bob helpfully arrived on the scene carrying a bucket of fresh smelts, a medicine dropper, and a bottle of vitamin concentrate. After we had captured each bird by hand and had run the gamut of their strong darting beaks and still stronger flippers which could deliver a most painful slap, we proceeded to stuff several whole smelts down their protesting gullets, following this with a squirt of the vitamin concentrate to stimulate their dormant appetites. After several days of feedings administered in this manner the penguins commenced to feed on their own and from that time on we had no trouble with them.

Humboldt Penguins, *Spheniscus humboldti.*

"Humboldt" and "Lolita," our first two penguins, promptly made themselves at home on the islands. They would make underwater circuits of the moats with astonishing rapidity, chasing and occasionally catching the smaller fishes, briefly bobbing up for a breath of air from time to time. On other occasions they would row themselves leisurely on the surface, walk about on the islands with a toddling gait, or sometimes simply stand at attention for periods with a stoicism that would put the Coldstream Guards to shame. I was concerned at first lest they might be attacked by the iguanas or vice versa, but they all got along well together from the first. The iguanas simply ignored the penguins, but the latter seemed to take a certain interest in the iguanas' activities and would spend long periods of time observing them with inscrutable concentration. Whether the iguanas ever felt that their privacy was invaded by these ever-present "watchbirds" will never be known.

A most interesting addition to the Lost Islands community came in the form of several nine-banded armadillos, *Dasypus novemcinctus*. Originally confined to the American southwest as well as Mexico, Central, and South America, these unusual mammals made their appearance in central Florida about twenty years ago and are now well established in the state. How they first arrived is not known with certainty, but it is commonly believed that the Florida population are all common descendants of several pairs that originally escaped or were released by a traveling animal show, or else by somebody who no longer desired them as pets or novelties. Armadillos belong to a strange and biologically distinct group of mammals which also includes the tropical American anteaters and the sloths.

I have always found armadillos to be most intriguing creatures, and in captivity they show interesting traits that could easily be overlooked by casual observers. Although encased in a tough, horny, jointed shell, they are warm, supple, and much less turtlelike to the touch than their appearance would indicate. They are also very cleanly animals and, oddly enough, the 9-banded species at least shares one singular habit with cats—that of digging and covering whenever it goes to the bathroom. The armadillo in this case is more methodical, since it always digs with the hind feet and covers with the front. Also, armadillos in a sense are naturally housebroken animals, since two I happened to observe in captivity for some time would never soil their cage so long as they were taken out and placed on the ground at least once a day. These are indeed remarkable traits for animals of fairly low intelligence.

Fanny and I kept the latter two armadillos, which were captured while young at Vero Beach, Florida (and which we named "Flotsam" and "Jetsam") between us in two wooden peach baskets while we were students at the University of Miami. Occasionally I would allow them the run of my apartment, although they had to be constantly watched as their curiosity led them to poke about in all available nooks and crannies, as the following incident will show.

On this occasion I had let both armadillos out in the living room, and followed one of them as he trotted into the kitchen with his small, sharp claws making brisk clicking sounds characteristic of these animals on a hard surface. He promptly disappeared beneath the stove and almost immediately a large spoon, which had been missing for some weeks, came flying out as he kicked it behind him. This was soon followed by a sound much like someone beginning to take a crate apart with a wrecking bar. Dropping to the floor and peering under the stove I saw him prying away the molding strip that connected the wall and floor. Before he succeeded in accomplishing this with his powerful front claws I dragged him out by the tail and carried him into the living room, where suspicious grating sounds were emanating from behind the sofa. Pulling this away from the wall, I was horrified to see the other armadillo busily engaged in rooting his way into an electrical outlet, alternately wrenching at it with his claws and then exploring it with his long, pointed tongue. I got him out of the way before damage was done to either armadillo or the wiring system, and returned them both to their baskets for the time being.

One thing our armadillos especially loved was to take baths. I would run an inch or so of water into the tub, and they would flop alternately on one side and the other, wallowing about like enthusiastic little pigs until, tiring of this, they would scuttle about and attempt to jump out of the tub until removed.

Their main diet was canned dog food, but they were fond of being taken out and placed at the base of a tree or any convenient rubbish heap where they would sniff and root about with gusto, uncovering all sorts of roaches, crickets, ants, sowbugs, and large millipedes that reeked with an iodine odor when disturbed. All of these would immediately be caught and eaten with little discrimination, as armadillos are omnivorous almost beyond belief.

One of the armadillos eventually escaped and several days later was discovered, asleep and unharmed, inside a Bendix washing machine in a nearby building which it had entered during the night. The machine was one of the vertically oriented type that rotate in the manner of a squirrel cage. Whether the armadillo had used it in this manner before finally going to sleep was an interesting point on which to ponder.

The Seaquarium's armadillos, which were likewise captured in Florida, immediately disappeared inside the iguanas' burrows, and here they spent most of the daylight hours. Since they were usually in evidence only during the early morning and late afternoon hours or briefly following a rainstorm they were not particularly good exhibit animals. However, those of us who worked at the Seaquarium were able to observe some interesting activity on their part from time to time.

Now and then they would cross the moats, and we could see that they were rapid swimmers, though they usually sank very low in the water with just their heads above the surface. I had read in books that they are supposed to cross small streams by holding their breath and walking along the bottom, but we never observed them to do anything like this, although it may possibly be true of other species. Although they liked to splash about briefly in shallow water, when actually swimming they would make for the opposite shore as fast as they possibly could with their feet moving with great rapidity.

Like the iguanas, they soon took to a diet of fish, although they had to rip these apart first with their claws in order to obtain morsels of swallowing size. How they coexisted with the iguanas while underground we were unable to observe, but on the surface they would frequently compete for food. More than once we saw an armadillo receive a thumping tail swat from a rhino iguana, only to attempt to leap on the latter's back and claw-spike him a moment later. Owing to the mutual antagonists being well protected by nature, little or no damage was done in either case and, for the most part, they seemed to display a mutual aloofness.

As time progressed additional lizards, land crabs, and a pair of tropical king vultures were added to the Lost Islands fauna, and five great alligator garfishes, *Lepisosteus spatula,* which normally are seldom found in salt water, have been successfully adapted to the tide pools. This particular exhibit, unique among aquarium displays, continues to be one of the most popular at the Miami Seaquarium.

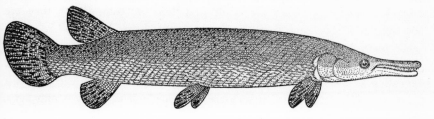

Alligator Garfish, *Lepisosteus spatula.*

# CHAPTER 6

# DOLPHINS — INTELLIGENTSIA OF THE SEA

*"Carolina Snowball"—First White Dolphin. The Dolphin's Remarkable Intelligence and Social Behavior. Maternal Care. Dolphin "Talk" and Animal Sonar. Episode of the Tiger Shark. Catching Dolphins. Unusual Species. The Incredible Boutu—A Link with the Past*

Early in 1961, reports began to reach the Seaquarium that a white bottlenosed dolphin with pink eyes had been seen a number of times by fishing boats plying out of Beaufort, South Carolina. Nothing of this sort had previously been heard of locally, and the first reports had the ring of wild rumor. Nonetheless, the possibility of its being true was worthy of investigation, so a member of the collecting staff who happened to be vacationing in South Carolina at the time went to Beaufort to check on the story.

Arriving there, he took a boat trip along the coast, and shortly thereafter phoned the Seaquarium that it was entirely true; an albino bottlenosed dolphin did exist in Beaufort's coastal waters, he had seen it with his own eyes, and furthermore, she was a mother accompanied by a half-grown, normally colored youngster.

A white dolphin! Never before had a potential exhibit specimen captured the imagination as this one did, and plans for its collection were made immediately by Gray and Hanson. Albino animals, besides occurring only rarely in nature, have their probability of survival reduced by two main factors. First, because they are white and therefore conspicuous, they are "sitting ducks" for large sharks and other natural predators; and secondly, other hereditary traits which normally are carried along with albinism are a weakened resistance to disease and a less aggressive drive in other respects, including that of self-preservation. Finally, the lack of normal eye pigments interferes with their vision as they are abnormally sensitive to strong light.

By good fortune, this particular specimen had already survived long enough to mother at least one offspring, and it is possible that the remarkably high intelligence plus the protective herd instinct that characterizes dolphins had contributed in some measure to this fact. If collected alive and unharmed the mother and her offspring (which itself would be likely to carry recessive genes for albinism) could be protected and cared for; and besides the albino's becoming a valuable exhibit animal, it could also become an object for scientific study under controlled conditions. Finally, it would furnish an opportunity for later attempts to breed a race of white dolphins in captivity, since a number of normally colored specimens have been conceived and born to date under captive conditions.

As soon as the *Sea Horse* and its collecting gear had been readied, the crew headed northward through the eastern Intercoastal Waterway to the region of Beaufort, and the adventure was on. But almost at once a stroke of ill luck occurred, one that came very close to ruining forever the chances of catching the prized dolphin. Soon after she was located with her young by her side, swimming as usual in the company of a number of others with her nearly milk-white body standing out sharply against the dark waters whenever she surfaced for air, the school was quickly surrounded with a long net. By careful maneuvering, the crew herded mother and young into the far end of the net away from the remainder of the school, which was allowed to escape. Closer and closer the pocket of the net was drawn until scarcely any swimming room remained, and the boat's crew leaned forward in breathless anticipation of the moment when both would finally entangle themselves in the mesh. At this moment both would panic, and they must be hauled from the water carefully and immediately before there was any danger that they might drown.

With a final, desperate rush, mother and youngster hit the net in a splash of foam and simultaneously strong hands grasped the bagged-up net and proceeded to take it aboard the boat. But at this critical moment a few weak strands in the net gave way and the dolphins managed to thrash themselves free. To the crew of the *Sea Horse* this was most disheartening, as they knew that following this experience the dolphin's natural intelligence and wariness would make her more difficult to capture.

Captain Ahab in his obsession to follow the White Whale had nothing on Gray and Hanson as they continued to watch for the albino dolphin in the waters of Beaufort County. Again and again they saw her shimmering form cut the water as she and her companions chased fish about the inlets. Repeatedly she managed to evade their net, which was now repaired and in readiness at all times. Their assumption had proved correct—she was now too wary to be taken easily, and all that could be done was to follow her constantly in the hope that she might eventually relax her vigilance and allow herself to be cornered and surrounded by the net. This battle of wits continued until the fall weather made further collecting activities in the area impractical, so the chase was abandoned until the following spring. It was hoped that in the interim "Carolina Snowball," as she was now called, would become less wary.

At this point, however, human nature began to rear its inevitable head.

The local residents of the Beaufort area who had previously regarded the white dolphin (or "porpoise" as they are known on the Atlantic and Gulf coasts) as little more than a curiosity, now began to have second thoughts about the possibility that "Snowball" would soon be taken to an aquarium in a different state where she would have considerable value as a commercial attraction. Legislative pressure was accordingly brought to bear with the result that a law was passed prohibiting the capture of any "porpoise" by any means whatever in the waters of Beaufort County, and further efforts by the Seaquarium to obtain permission to collect within its territorial limits were fruitless, as the lawmakers were unrelenting.

Fortunately, the law did not apply to the waters of adjacent counties, and the Seaquarium's only hope was to net "Snowball" when she ventured outside of Beaufort's territorial waters, which on occasion she did. Meanwhile, the white dolphin remained as elusive as ever. Once she and her baby were again completely enclosed by the net—and so were about a dozen others with whom she was traveling. To attempt to catch them all at once would be mass slaughter, as the net could not be worked quickly enough to free the others before they drowned, and "Snowball" herself might be dragged to her death in the melee. Accordingly, a portion of the net was opened in hopes that most of the others, having better eyesight and stamina, would leave before 'Snowball," but as fate would have it, she was the first one to rush out of the net.

The hunt continued, and by now it was becoming a nerve-racking experience for the crew who maintained their watch at the county line. A total of 16 attempts had been made to net "Snowball," who it seemed was un-catchable, but eventually the day arrived when a run was made around the elusive dolphin and she and her young were once again completely cut off from the rest of the school. "This is it!" exclaimed Gray and Hanson simultaneously, and tension mounted almost to the breaking point as the circle of net narrowed, enclosing the two animals in an ever-decreasing space. For moments it looked as if she might attempt a jump—and if she once learned this trick as some dolphins do, she would become forever un-nettable as there would then be no way to hold her. But she did not jump, and once again as they had done a year earlier, both dolphins became entangled in the net.

This time it held. "Snowball" and her offspring, which turned out to be a nearly sexually mature male, were taken aboard the *Sea Horse* and placed in an inflated rubber swimming pool on deck where she could be kept under constant surveillance until the boat returned to Miami.

True to the general nature of albinos, "Snowball" proved uncommonly docile from the first, eating fish from Emil's hand in the swimming pool within a few hours after capture. The boat's arrival at the Seaquarium was wildly hailed by photographers and newsmen, and the dolphins were carefully carried beneath wet blankets on canvas stretchers to a large pool maintained by the Seaquarium's Animal Trainer, Adolf Frohn. This was to become their home for the time being, and as "Snowball" and "Sonny Boy" swam about accustoming themselves to their new quarters all persons, the crew of the *Sea Horse* in particular, heaved a great sigh of relief.

"SNOWBALL" and "SONNY BOY"

I saw "Carolina Snowball" in person about a week after her capture, and during this time she had become tame enough to come to the side of her tank and permit herself to be touched, although "Sonny Boy" still remained aloof. Although she appeared to be pure white while under several inches of water, her skin was actually a very pale pink due to the myriads of tiny blood capillaries in this region. In the immediate region of her blowhole, as well as around her eyes, the color was deep pink, although her eyes themselves were actually pale blue in hue. The top rear portion of her dorsal fin was missing, probably having been bitten off by a shark at some time in her life, and "Sonny Boy" showed a prominent scar on his side, apparently from this same cause. Otherwise, both dolphins appeared to be in excellent physical shape.

"Snowball," whose age is estimated roughly at 10 years (dolphins may live to be about 40), offers a possible source for genetic studies on albinism. Since her offspring in keeping with Mendelian law should carry recessive genes for albinism there is likely a fifty-fifty chance of a white offspring should it ultimately be possible to back-cross him with his mother. The creation of a strain of captive albino bottlenosed dolphins is an intriguing possibility, especially since they breed quite readily in captivity.

"What is the difference between a porpoise and a dolphin?" This is a question I am frequently asked due to the popular confusion that exists over the two names which refer to two related but distinctly different families of marine mammals, of the whale order, or *Cetacea*.

First, let us dispose altogether of a certain large fish, *Coryphaena hippurus,* which is called the "dolphin" by some fishermen, but should be more correctly termed "dolphinfish." This creature is of course in no way related to the marine mammals, but because of its name and the fact that it is well known to tropical marine sport fishermen, it tends to add confusion to the issue, at least in the popular mind.

The differences between porpoises and dolphins are mainly technical ones, but they can be distinguished by the following characters: The porpoises (Family *Phocaenidae*), which are relatively few in species, have blunt snouts and their teeth are slightly concave and flattened, much like human incisors. The dolphins (Family *Delphinidae*) are more numerous species-wise and tend to have elongated, beaklike snouts and teeth which are round in cross-section and pointed, like those of a dog.

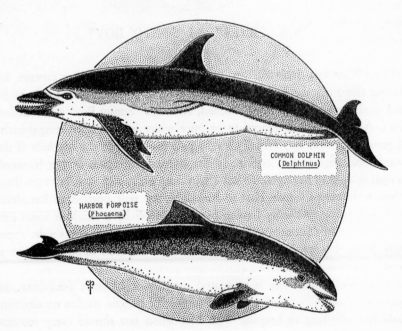

COMMON DOLPHIN
(Delphinus)

HARBOR PORPOISE
(Phocaena)

Dolphin and Porpoise compared.

Unfortunately, popular usage has placed these names into a great muddle. Ever since the bottlenosed dolphin, *Tursiops truncatus,* was first tamed and trained at Marineland, Florida, in 1937 (it has now become a featured attraction at a number of large aquariums) under the name of "porpoise," this designation, though absolutely incorrect, has been almost a household word and "porpoise" it will doubtlessly remain in the future. However, at the risk of appearing pedantic to my colleagues in the aquarium field, I shall for the sake of accuracy call dolphins "dolphins" and porpoises "porpoises" throughout the remainder of this book.

Much has been written of late concerning the intelligence of captive dolphins. They are beyond doubt among the most intelligent of living animals, certainly ranking close to the highest primates and the elephants in this regard. This is all the more remarkable considering the great limitations the creatures' environment and body form place upon them in expressing said intelligence. Remember, an animal such as the dog can easily enter a man's world; he can shake hands, run and fetch objects, wag his tail and bark on command, and do many other things which are natural and easily understood signs of intelligence. But a dolphin is chained to an aquatic existence and its simple and fishlike form to begin with places a considerable handicap on any rapport with human beings. The fact that, despite this, the dolphin *does* communicate its intelligence to human observers in some startling ways reveals it to be a creature of considerable mental capacity and personality as well.

A second factor—and this can be misleading—in judging the intelligence of a given animal is the matter of whether or not it tends to cooperate with its trainer. Some animals (the dog again) seem to be naturally cooperative and to have a desire to please, while others such as the pig can be decidedly uncooperative, though actually very intelligent. The raccoon is more intelligent than the dog, and while it responds to humans to a considerable extent, it definitely has a mind of its own, and if one plays games with a pet raccoon, it is most advisable to let the raccoon win.

Fanny and I have kept several raccoons as pets, and as they grow older they seem to spend most of their time thinking up ways to outwit us, and at the same time showing considerable resentment at our efforts to outwit them. Once Fanny was testing the ability of one of them to remove grapes from a long plastic tube, making the process progressively more difficult by placing a stopper first in one and finally in both ends of the tube. The raccoon solved the problems for a time in good humor until she was finally presented with a grape in a long tube that was firmly stoppered at both ends. After reflecting on the situation briefly, she decided that enough was enough.

Dropping the tube, she walked over to Fanny and bit her on the hand, thus adjourning school for the day!

Cetaceans (whales, dolphins, and porpoises collectively) are descendants of animals who once roamed the land, and their fossil record gives only a hint of what their ancestors were like. The modern scientific consensus is that they have a common ancestry with the odd-toed ungulates, so the dolphin counts among his living relatives such diverse creatures as the horse, tapir, and rhinoceros! Obviously, the relationship is but a distant one, so fish-like in form have the Cetaceans become in the long course of their evolution.

Dolphins, porpoises, and all the other toothed whales (as opposed to the ones that strain their food through great brushes of baleen, or "whalebone") are most peculiar in having skulls that are slightly lopsided. The bones of the two sides do not quite "match up," the left half of the brain case is slightly larger than the right, and the beak or snout of most of them is slightly skewed to the right as a result. While not readily apparent in the living animal, this deformation of the skull makes them unique among mammals, and as yet there is no known reason for this, though various theories have been proposed.

Save for internal vestiges of the pelvic bones, the hind limbs have completely disappeared as in the manatee, and a pair of boneless, though stiffened, flukes on the end of the tail serve the same purpose as the caudal fin of a fish. A recurved dorsal fin grows from the back of most species as well, and the forelimbs are modified into stiffened flippers, though they enclose well-developed hand and finger bones. The body hair is reduced to a few scattered bristles on the snout of a few primitive species, and the skin is exceedingly smooth and rubbery, feeling, in the living animal, "like a hard-boiled egg with the shell off," as a friend of mine once described it.

Dolphins and porpoises are highly social animals for the most part, usually traveling in schools or family groups, and they appear to show a certain degree of protective instinct for one another. I once saw a most remarkable instance of behavior in a color film made by the staff of Marineland of the Pacific. In it a pilot whale was shot off the California coast for scientific study preparatory to the attempted capture of specimens for exhibitory purposes, and no sooner had the "whale" (actually a large member of the dolphin family) been dispatched by means of a high-powered rifle, than another member of the school swam over the carcass and pushed it down out of sight, so that it was never seen again. This performance was repeated on another occasion, although the desired study animal was eventually obtained.

In the same film was shown an example of the extreme degree of maternal care sometimes indulged in by Cetaceans, where the dead and badly decomposed body of a baby pilot whale was being repeatedly pushed to the surface by a large one, presumably the mother, who was described as squeaking pathetically by forcing air through her blowhole the entire time.

The birth of a dolphin is a most interesting process, and I had the good fortune to witness this for the first time in the main Seaquarium tank on September 24, 1955, which by remarkable coincidence was the first day the Seaquarium was opened to the public.

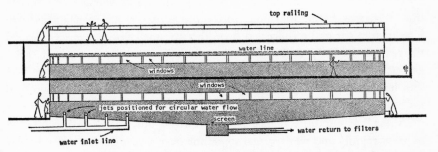

Diagram of the 80-ft. Main Seaquarium tank.

The first inkling we had of what was taking place was when we suddenly saw the baby's tail protruding from the mother's genital opening. Reversing the normal mammalian procedure, dolphins are born tail-first, perhaps because the baby would be in danger of drowning should the head be first to appear. The birth process in this instance took about 20 minutes from the time our observation started. The actual moment of birth came quite suddenly as the baby was expelled and at the same time the mother twisted away from it, severing the very short umbilical cord. She then immediately pushed the baby to the surface. We could see that the tiny dorsal fin was soft at first and folded to the side, and the baby's tail flukes were slightly rolled up as well.

I had been watching through an underwater window, and as I rushed up to the top deck I saw that another female had joined the mother, with the baby between them. The baby was making rapid swimming movements on the surface, though not too effectively at first, as its tiny flukes were still quite limp, and they flopped up and down in the water like a wet rag. Guided by the mother, the baby rose again and again for air, and these first few moments of life must be indeed a critical time in a dolphin's existence.

The thing that perhaps struck me as most remarkable was the role of midwife adopted by the other dolphin. She continued in this capacity for a number of weeks, and during this time the two females swam constantly with the baby between them as closely as planes in formation. I might add here that this same form of cooperation between mother and another female in protecting the young has been observed at other aquariums as well.

Within hours after birth the baby's dorsal fin and flukes had unfolded and stiffened, so that it swam more easily and less floppily. At the same time small creases or wrinkles appeared behind its head and at the base of its tail from its initial muscular activity, although these disappeared within a day or so.

Since dolphins are mammals, they must nurse their young, and they do this by means of an ingenious sort of underwater fuel-injection system. The mother's teats lie concealed beneath two small horizontal slits toward the rear of the body, and as the baby places its snout against one of these, powerful muscles surrounding the milk glands squirt the nourishing fluid into its stomach. This process apparently takes only a few seconds, and no milk is wasted.

"Alpha," as our little female bottlenosed dolphin was named, continued to grow rapidly and was weaned sometime over a year later, about the time that "Beta," our second arrival, also a female, was born to another dolphin in the tank. As soon as they were old enough to leave the mother for a time, both young quickly learned to approach the side of the tank to make friends with the visitors. "Alpha" loved to "run and fetch" a small inflatable rubber ring tossed into the tank, spear it with her nose, and with a sudden nod of her head, send it sailing back to the person who threw it. She also was fond of retrieving coins, which she would catch in her mouth as they sank in the

"ALPHA" and her mother.

tank, then return them with the same quick nod of her head, but this time the coin would be accompanied by a small stream of water. When doing this, "Alpha" always reminded me of one of the ornamental stone dolphins used as a water jet in a park fountain.

Much publicity has been given of late to the "speech" of dolphins—the remarkable and varied assortment of sounds they are capable of making both beneath and above the surface of the water. I have no doubt from my own observations made over a number of years in close association with these creatures that they do communicate with one another thus, but whether or not man can ever eventually "crack their code" or learn to join in conversation with them is highly problematical.

Most of the sounds are made by forcing air through the tightly closed blowhole, as they do not have vocal cords. By this means a delightful approximation of a full-bodied and juicy Bronx cheer is often emitted when the head is above water, or this may be modified into a rasping and repeated

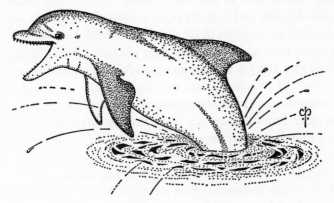

Bottlenosed Dolphin in an exuberant mood.

"keek-keek-keek." At other times the sound strongly resembles that of Donald Duck or the wailing of a child. But the most characteristic and constant of the sounds produced by dolphins is an intermittent twittering which reminds some persons of a small bird but which I liken to the note of a bosun's pipe in the Navy.

This latter type of sound is not only audible; it is visible as well, for as the dolphin swims through the water a sort of Morse code is left behind it, in the form of small strings of bubbles. All the above-mentioned sounds are clearly produced by streams of air, but there are others the source of which is less obvious. By pressing one's ear against the glass as a dolphin swims past a window, one can occasionally hear a noise that is somewhere between a creaking door and that produced when one scratches his fingers along the surface of a wet balloon. Also, a dolphin will sometimes produce a sharp sound, almost a bark, a number of times in succession. Although no air bubbles are produced in either of the latter cases, the surface of the skin immediately behind the blowhole will be seen to quiver slightly when the barking sound is made.

Since the receiving flume between the two main Seaquarium tanks forms the roof of the laboratory and because underwater sounds carry well, I have frequently listened by the hour to newly captured dolphins "conversing" among themselves, and have in some cases been able to tell when they were being fed by the increase in sharpness and tempo of their twitterings.

A prevalent popular idea in regard to dolphins is that they are the sworn enemies of sharks. This is to my knowledge quite untrue since I have seen them living in captivity with certain species of sharks (including those known to attack humans) in perfect harmony. Doubtless certain of the larger and swifter sharks such as the white shark, *Carcharodon,* would offer a threat to the dolphin, and it seems equally likely that the noisy activity of a herd of dolphins or porpoises in the vicinity of a public bathing beach would certainly cause most sharks to keep their distance (from the dolphins, at least). Otherwise, there is little or no natural ecological or biological competition between the two. Sharks are scavengers by and large, and when they prey on living food this mainly consists of fair-sized things such as skates, rays, and other fishes that are set upon and devoured in a series of bites. Dolphins and porpoises, on the other hand, chase the smaller, swifter schooling fishes and squid which they must swallow whole, as their teeth are adapted only for holding, not for biting things in pieces.

Except for certain species, dolphins are much swifter and more maneuverable than sharks. They can and do swim rings around the latter, in captivity at least; and, well aware of this, they seem to take mischievous delight in nipping sharks' fins and tails, often getting a free ride in the process.

On only one occasion have I seen dolphins show what appeared to be fear in the presence of a shark, and this was when for the first time we placed a large tiger shark, *Galeocerdo,* in the tank with our dolphins. The shark, a 12-foot female, had been caught on a set line that day, and toward evening we hoisted her into the flume and a short time later opened the gate and let her swim in to join the dolphins, turtles, small sharks, and other large fish that were already there.

The dolphins' reaction was instantaneous. All five (the number we had on hand at that time) rushed to the far side of the tank and continued to keep as much distance between them and the shark as possible until it became too dark for further observation. I was not worried for fear that they might wander too close to the shark for safety during the night, for dolphins always have a keen awareness of what is going on in the tank at any moment, and, as is now known, the echoes produced by the sounds they make provide them with a highly efficient form of navigational animal sonar. (I first became aware of this possibility when we placed our first newly captured dolphins in the recently constructed and then uninhabited shark channel for temporary holding. It happened to be a moonless night when they were brought in by the collecting crew and the channel was full of mud and silt besides. By listening carefully, I could determine that the dolphins were racing about the channel at full speed, seeking a way out, and yet never coming into contact with the concrete walls as they did so.)

To return to our dolphins and the tiger shark: next morning I noticed that the former had regained considerable composure, yet they continued to give the shark a wide berth at all times. Then, as I watched the shark making its characteristic leisurely circuit of the tank, I suddenly witnessed a startling incident. Unwittingly swimming toward one another, the shark and our largest loggerhead turtle (the one I had brought from St. Petersburg in the back of a jeep) abruptly came face to face. In a moment the shark took the great turtle's entire head in its mouth, and for a few seconds I feared that this was the end of our turtle.

However, the shark, after shaking its head sideways once or twice, suddenly released the turtle, which did a barrel roll as the shark passed and clamped its jaws firmly on the latter's tail! The shark, all belligerence gone, took off at great speed, scattering the dolphins as it did so. A few seconds later it broke free of the turtle, and from that point on I never witnessed another encounter between the two. Except for a slightly lacerated neck which healed quickly, the loggerhead appeared none the worse for its encounter, but the shark bore a permanent V near the tip of its tail where the turtle's horny beak had closed down. During most of that day the dolphins refused to participate in the feeding shows, but the day following they were back on schedule. From that time on they casually regarded the tiger as a permanent fixture and even nudged its tail and fins occasionally, but never allowed themselves to get directly in front of it for any length of time.

An interesting trait of bottlenosed dolphins, and probably other species as well, is the fact that they become quite excited on the approach of a thunderstorm. I have observed this repeatedly at the Seaquarium and at Marine Studios. Invariably, just before the storm hits, the dolphins will commence to race wildly about the tank, apparently in a state of considerable exuberance. At such times the water surface will be roiled into choppy waves by their action.

Certain fishes and reptiles show this same characteristic. I once had a pet python that would never feed except immediately before a storm, when he would appear very restless, moving back and forth about his cage. It may be that many animals react in a similar way to this phenomenon; whether it is due to atmospheric conditions such as falling barometric pressure, or the visual effects of a darkening sky, distant thunder, or a combination of these, I cannot say, but I must confess that I myself find the sudden approach of a thunderstorm highly stimulating, especially when driving in a car.

Dolphins are exceedingly wary of attempts made to catch them in the wild (as we experienced in capturing "Snowball"), but despite this we have successfully used several methods of doing so. One way is to stretch a net across an inlet or estuary at high tide, trapping the animals when the water recedes. Another is to use a hinged device known as a tail-grabber, which snaps a loop of rope around the base of the tail, when they can be quite easily hauled alongside a boat. This can be done when dolphins run forward beneath the bow of a boat as they will often do for considerable distances at sea. When doing this they are actually "hitching a ride" on the bow compression wave, much as a human surfboard expert rides the breakers to shore, although dolphins do this completely submerged.

The most common means of capture, however, is the one that was developed by Captain Gray during his years of experience with these animals. This is to encircle a milling school rapidly with a net by running around them with a boat, and since the bottlenosed species can swim at approximately 35 miles an hour (at least for short distances), this must be done with all possible speed. The first portion of this net is called the "bluff net," since it serves merely to frighten the dolphins into the center of the circle, where they may then be surrounded with the final, heavy-mesh net as it is laid down by the boat in an inwardly decreasing spiral. As was explained at the beginning of the chapter, the dolphins usually become entangled in the net at the last moment, although some, the big males in particular, will often jump over it and escape. To remove them from the net requires all possible alertness and speed on the part of the crew, for the dolphins are in immediate danger of drowning as the net shifts position.

After being taken aboard the collecting boat (and to haul in and free from the net without injury a dolphin weighing several hundred pounds is a considerable task), the specimens are then either placed in a live-well or carefully laid on their sides on a mattress and covered by a wet blanket. If placed belly-down on a solid surface they experience much more difficulty in breathing, owing to their great body weight and comparatively light and flexible rib cage.

Recently, attempts have been made to capture dolphins by shooting them with hypodermic projectiles containing a nicotine sulfate solution, a means now frequently employed to secure large land animals in an uninjured condition in the wild. Although this method works well with most other animals, dolphins are invariably killed in the process since their breathing stops whenever they lose consciousness.

Besides the bottlenosed dolphins, there are other species that have been kept in captivity with varying degrees of success. The long-snouted dolphin, *Stenella plagiodon,* is an offshore species that is smaller, slenderer, and swifter than the bottlenose. The adults are nearly black, covered with irregular white spots like snowflakes. Although they do well when kept by themselves, they do not mix well with the bottlenose, as they tend to be bullied by the latter.

Along the U.S. Pacific coast is found the rather small and attractive *Lagenorhynchus obliquidens* or skunk dolphin, so named from the broad pale stripes running along its dark sides. In captivity this species makes up in personality and enthusiasm for what it lacks in size, and at Marineland of the Pacific, specimens take particular delight in snatching squid from the jaws of the ponderous pilot whales during feeding time. I first became acquainted with the skunk dolphin during World War II aboard the transport U.S.S. *Audubon* as schools of them would race along beneath our bow while we were on training maneuvers off the California coast, and ever since the first day I saw these strikingly marked creatures I have had a particularly soft spot in my heart for them.

Although, up to the time of writing, the small black harbor porpoise, *Phocaena phocaena,* has not been exhibited in aquariums in this country, it should make a very worth-while addition because of its small size (about 5 feet) which would make it easy to keep in a small tank. Also, these porpoises are known to ascend rivers for hundreds of miles, so it may be possible to adapt them permanently to fresh water. Two very similar forms are known from the Atlantic and Pacific coasts of North America respectively, and they prefer cooler water than the foregoing species. Fishermen often call the harbor porpoise "herring hog" or "puffing pig," terms that I consider particularly delightful.

One of the most remarkable of all the true porpoises is Dall's porpoise, *Phocaenoides dalli,* which is an offshore species particularly designed for speed. Like the tuna, swordfish, mako shark, and other speedy fishes, this bullet-shaped porpoise has its tail base developed into a wide flange or keel for stabilization, only this keel is vertical, since the tail flukes are horizontal, the reverse of fishes. Coloration in this species is striking, being jet black with a large oval area of pure white on each side.

(upper) White-Sided or Skunk Dolphin, *Lagenorhynchus obliquidens.*
(lower) Dall Porpoise, *Phocaenoides dalli.*

Kenneth Norris, formerly curator of Marineland of the Pacific, tells me that as the Dall's porpoise rushes along just beneath the surface of the sea it does not seem to break the surface to breathe in the ordinary manner of Cetaceans, but instead appears to draw the air down to it in a sort of vortex created by the "bow wave" above its head. The few specimens captured by Marineland's collecting crew to date have unfortunately died, apparently of shock, soon after they were taken aboard the collecting boat.

The dolphins and porpoises previously mentioned make their home in the sea, but what is perhaps the oddest group of living Cetaceans is a small family consisting of four distinct genera but only four species in all, living in widely separated parts of the world and known collectively as the Platanistids, that live in freshwater rivers and lakes. They are remarkable in being exceedingly primitive, at least one retaining vestiges of the body hair that once clothed their terrestrial ancestors. Their flippers show the outline of separate fingers beneath the skin; their tail flukes are relatively soft and flabby; their dorsal fins are poorly developed; and their neck bones are so mobile that they can turn their heads upward, downward, or to the side with ease—something no true dolphin, porpoise, or whale can do.

One Platanistid called the susu lives in the Ganges River in India, and another inhabits the Tung Ting Lake in China. A third lives in the La Plata River in Argentina and is said to venture out to sea occasionally. The fourth kind inhabits the upper reaches of the Amazon River system, in northern South America. Called the boutu (*Inia geoffroyensis*), this strictly freshwater Platanistid is perhaps the most interesting of all its group, as it is pink in color, has a peculiar head with a long, bristly snout, and its dorsal fin is replaced by a low ridge along the back.

The boutu shares its habitat with a small freshwater manatee (*Trichechus inunguis*) as well as several true dolphins of the genus *Sotalia* which also make their home in the rivers of South America. (Being true Delphinids, these latter animals are quite unlike the boutu, but resemble their marine relatives in form.) Two of them, a light- and a dark-colored species respectively, are known as Buffeo Blanco and Buffeo Negro by the local natives.

Ever since I first read Ivan T. Sanderson's vivid account of a first-hand encounter with the boutu in *Follow the Whale*, I had been highly intrigued over the existence of these creatures. What remarkable aquarium specimens they would make! My excitement was therefore unbounded when I read in the papers a short time later that an expedition was being set up for the purpose of capturing some boutus at Leticia, Peru, in the upper reaches of the Amazon River. Leticia is located at the point where the borders of Peru, Colombia, and Brazil come together on the map, and the area is noted for having some especially interesting forms of tropical fauna.

When I subsequently learned that the expedition had captured three boutus which were being flown to Silver Springs, Florida, I resolved to have a look at them if possible on their arrival. Through the grapevine I heard that the plane was to make a refueling stop at St. Petersburg; and, on arriving there, I was generously allowed on board to see and photograph the boutus in their canvas traveling slings.

It is no exaggeration to say that my first sight of a boutu in the flesh was one of the high points of my life. They were even more remarkable than I had imagined. There was a young one, about 5 feet in total length and two adults, each about 7 feet long. The youngster was a dark slaty blue-gray in hue above and slightly lighter underneath, while the adults were what I would call a bathroom-tile pink. They had quite small eyes which were probably of only limited use in the muddy water in which they lived, and their snouts were exceedingly narrow, long, and ever so slightly curved downward, reminding me of an anteater.

But the most surprising thing of all about them was the scattered tufts of short, stiff hairs along the snout like toothbrush bristles. Although some whales possess a few hairs on the snout at birth, none of them could possibly vie with the boutu in this respect. Not only are they the hairiest of the Cetaceans, but they look positively prehistoric in other ways as well. Their flippers, though clawless, looked like flattened rubber gloves with the fingers grown together much like the movie monster in "Creature from the Black Lagoon." The tail flukes, like the flippers, had none of the flowing grace of the Delphinids, being broader and more flexible to the touch.

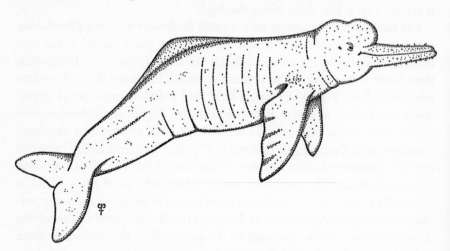

The Boutu, *Inia geoffroyensis.*

Exhausted from their long trip, the boutus lay nearly motionless in their rubber-lined canvas slings, twitching a flipper or tail now and then and periodically expelling the breath and inhaling quickly in a labored, shuddering sigh. I was moved with pity for the poor creatures, as they must have felt most uncomfortable, and I was subsequently much relieved to learn that they had reached Silver Springs safely and had been placed in a pen built out into the main spring that forms the river there.

It was not until several more had been captured and most had died that I was able to visit Silver Springs and observe them swimming about in their enclosure. This time I was even more intrigued, especially when I saw the way they would swim about on their backs with their snouts pointing up in the air, or surface and turn their heads sideways, glancing at me over their shoulders, so it seemed. They were without doubt among the most amazing animals ever captured, and these were the first ever to leave their native haunts.

During the year of 1955 and the year following, perhaps a dozen boutus were captured and brought to Florida where they were kept alive for a time in ponds and springs, but, sad to say, not one of them ever found its way into an aquarium. One by one they all eventually expired, either because of the outside winter temperature which was too cold for them or more probably because, as I later learned, they were fed primarily on mullet, grunts, and other easily obtained "rough" fish, a diet which had been tried experimentally but had failed adequately to maintain even the first dolphins that were exhibited at Marine Studios. I cannot go so far as to say that they perished from deliberate neglect, but it seemed to me that, once the fanfare of publicity attending their capture had died down, the boutus were apparently considered to have served their purpose.

Their bodies were in some cases dissected and studied by the scientific staff at the University of Florida, and no doubt much of value was subsequently learned concerning their anatomical structure, but it seems to me that in not making every effort to provide them with proper care while they were living, much was lost to science. The assistance and advice of experts on the maintenance and rearing of captive Cetaceans was obviously required, and such persons were available for consultation, but to my knowledge their assistance was never sought in this matter.

Perhaps because of the unfortunate history of these first few boutu specimens imported, there arose a general supposition among zoo and aquarium people that the species was not hardy and thus unsuited for captivity so, for the year or so following, the quest for additional examples of *Inia geoffroyensis* was abandoned. But finally, during the summer of 1962, I learned that a pair of boutus, captured at Leticia by Mike Tsalickis of the Tarpon Zoo in Florida, had been successfully transported to the Ft. Worth Zoo and Aquarium in Texas, where they were placed in a large freshwater tank that was especially constructed for them. Thanks to the special care lavished on them by zoo director Lawrence Curtis and his staff, the specimens are thriving at the time of writing, and early in 1963 I had an opportunity to see them in person.

Despite their very small eyes and presumably poor vision, the specimens appeared very alert, poking here and there about their tank with their long snouts, and although I could hear none of the characteristic whistling or twittering sounds that one associates with their marine cousins, they seemed to experience little difficulty in navigating. Although these had not been trained to jump for their food when I saw them, they showed definite signs of playfulness, deliberately splashing water in the direction of visitors with their tail flukes and playing with a block of cork placed in the tank for this purpose. The extreme mobility of *Inia's* flippers was demonstrated by the holding of the cork block against the chest while underwater, a feat which the higher dolphins are unable to perform.

Mr. Tsalickis informs me that he has twice observed the birth of baby *Inias* at Leticia, and in both cases twins were born. From this it would appear that either twin births are the rule, or else quite common with the species. It is to be hoped that with the successful maintenance of these Platanistids at Ft. Worth, other aquariums may follow suit and enrich our knowledge of the life and habits of these extraordinary creatures.

# CHAPTER 7

# THE MYSTERY OF THE PILOT WHALES

*Whales Run Aground at St. Augustine. "Herman," First Captive Atlantic Pilot Whale. Training Pacific Pilot Whales. Ambergris, the Mystery Substance. Spitting White Whales. Orca, Renegade of the Whale Clan. A Night Spent on the Back of a Whale. Possible Solution to the Pilot Whale Mystery*

In the winter of 1948, a school of more than 40 pilot whales swam ashore at Crescent Beach, south of St. Augustine, Florida, to die in the surf. This is an incident that is repeated every few years, and sometimes more than once a year, at some point along the Florida coast, and it also occurs in many other parts of the world.

Just why pilot whales do this is one of the many unsolved mysteries of the behavior of Cetaceans; and there is evidence that certain other species of these mammals may also occasionally kill themselves in this same manner. This behavior gives the impression that it is a form of deliberate suicide for, if a line is attached to a grounded whale and he is towed into deeper water, he will promptly swim ashore again the moment he is released.

Various theories have been advanced to attempt to explain this unseemly behavior. One is that the school blunders into shallow water while following a leader in the group, but this may be rejected as all the evidence shows that each animal is acting on his own and not following any hypothetical leader, since the stranded whales may actually be strung out over a considerable area of beach and they frequently do not arrive all at one time. That the stranding is deliberate and not accidental is indicated by the behavior previously mentioned. Another prevalent theory is that they have been frightened out of their wits by some predator such as killer whales or white sharks and are trying to escape. However, nothing of the sort has been seen to follow them and they hardly ever show fresh scars or other signs of battle; and, most important of all, they nearly always come ashore slowly and listlessly.

In fact, any sort of "accidental" beaching can probably be ruled out since pilot whales in common with other members of the dolphin family (of which they are members) navigate very efficiently by means of animal sonar, and under normal conditions will never venture into water that is too shallow for them. On the other hand all such beaching animals are quite obviously sick, and in fact appear to be suffering from a severe gastrointestinal ailment. Grounded specimens will often belch up quantities of a bilious-looking fluid, and the stomachs of these whales that I have later autopsied, or witnessed being dissected, were always empty of all solid material.

Despite their sick condition, occasional specimens can be saved. Of the 1948 stranding four of the smaller ones were, with some difficulty, loaded aboard a 4-wheel-drive truck that went out into the surf to receive them, and then driven to the oceanarium at Marineland, about a half hour away. They were then lifted in slings by means of the electric hoist into the receiving flume, and finally allowed to swim through the drop gate into the circular oceanarium tank to join the bottlenosed dolphins and other specimens there.

I made a special trip to Marineland to see them, as the only previous living ones I had seen were at some distance from the deck of a ship in the Pacific. Although called whales which they technically are, these creatures, *Globicephalus melas,* are actually a type of overgrown dolphin. They differ in appearance from ordinary dolphins mainly in the lumpy, rounded form of their heads and their totally black color which earns them the most particularly appropriate name of "pothead" in some areas, as well as "blackfish" in others. In size they are among the very largest of the dolphins, reaching a length of close to 20 feet in the male, and somewhat less in the female.

The recurved dorsal fin is situated quite far forward, and the flippers are especially long and pointed. While slower and more deliberate in their actions, they are otherwise quite typical dolphins in all respects. At sea they usually travel in large groups or pods, and because of their dark coloring they can be seen from some distance away as they surface to breathe.

When I first glimpsed them at Marine Studios, the four pilot whales were milling slowly about in the center of the tank. They varied in size between 9 and 12 feet, and I was impressed at once by their heavy blunt heads and the great length of their flippers, which, together with their size and dark coloration set them sharply apart from the bottlenosed dolphins which shared the tank. Still weary and exhausted from their ordeal, their movements appeared labored and ponderous, while the dolphins, filled with great curiosity, gathered about them twittering shrilly as interrupted strings of small bubbles emerged in Morse-code fashion from their blowholes.

From above, these blackfish looked like black submarines, or rather, torpedoes, a resemblance that was heightened by their rounded potheads with little or no beak showing beneath. Two of them were quite badly sunburned as a result of being partially beached as the tide receded, and these, I learned, died a few days later, followed shortly thereafter by a third.

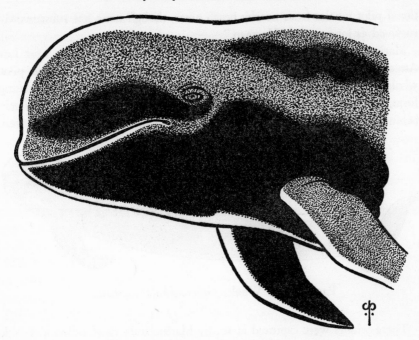

Atlantic Pilot Whale, *Globicephalus melas.*

The one remaining pilot whale, the comparatively small 9-footer, eventually recovered from his illness, began to eat squid, and thrived for a number of months. "Herman," as he was named (for it was a male) nearly always fed at night when the dolphins were dozing on the surface, during which time he would consume about 40 pounds of fresh squid dumped to him from a bucket. After that he would join the dolphins in the quiet sculling about on the surface that passes for Cetacean slumber. (Whether or not these animals really "sleep" in the true sense of the word has not as yet been decided, as they scarcely ever have been seen to cease swimming at night. However, their movements are generally slower at this time and they have been seen to close their eyes for brief periods, although they will continue to rise for air while doing this.)

When "Herman" eventually died, an autopsy revealed partially healed broken ribs and other internal injuries. It was thought at the time that he may have received his injuries through being rammed at night by a jealous bull dolphin (the latter always seem to resent the intrusion of other species, and sometimes even their own kind), but it is equally likely that some of them may have resulted from his original stranding or moving to the oceanarium tank. Since that time Marine Studios has rescued several additional pilot whales from nearby beach areas, though none has subsequently survived as long as did "Herman."

Marineland of the Pacific, situated on Palos Verdes peninsula near Los Angeles, California, has had considerable success with the Pacific pilot whale, *Globicephala scammoni*. This species is very similar to the Atlantic form, but is somewhat slenderer and has a large grayish patch immediately behind the dorsal fin and a prominent whitish patch on the chest as well.

Pacific Pilot Whale, *Globicephala scammoni*.

These whales were captured at sea by Marineland's chief collector, Frank Broccato, who snared them with a large net from the bow of the collecting boat. A number of them have lived in the giant 90-foot oval tank at Marineland from time to time, and recently several were successfully transported by air in large rubberized tanks to Marine Studios in Florida.

When I saw them during a trip to California, I was impressed by the lazy good-naturedness of these huge beasts (the largest was about 15 feet long) as they swam about the tank. Like the small striped skunk dolphins who shared their tank, the pilot whales had learned to leap for their food from the feeder, who stood on a raised platform with squid held in his extended hand. Sometimes these great black leviathans would rise almost completely from the water and sink back gracefully with hardly a splash, but at other times, perhaps for the pure devilment of it, they would land sideways or do a bellywhopper that would send a curtain of water and foam flying in all directions. If one were standing looking through a viewing window in the uppermost corridor just beneath the water surface he could easily feel the concussion reverberate through the tank wall as the whale crashed back into the water.

In addition to the food they received during the course of the jumping show, the whales were also fed quantities of squid which were brought to them in large metal buckets. At such times the pilot's great mouth would open as if the head were suddenly split in half, and the feeding attendant would then empty the squid into the waiting jaws. This procedure was something akin to the dumping of a garbage pail into an incinerator, and the whale would consume all the squid in one mighty gulp.

At this time the little skunk dolphins (*Lagenorhynchus*) would make a game of snatching as many squid as possible out of a pilot's mouth before it could close its jaws. I observed this happen repeatedly in the case of the large male pothead until, thoroughly teed off, he made a great rolling lunge at the nearest dolphin, his jaws clapping noisily at his tormentor. The result was much like a blimp attempting to overtake a fighter plane. After bumbling this way and that for a time and having rings run around him by the exuberant dolphin, the poor whale resignedly came back for the remainder of his dinner.

Squid, incidentally, forms the bulk of the food consumed by all toothed whales. Encounters between the sperm whale (*Physeter*) and the giant squid *Architeuthis* are legendary, though it must be pointed out here that in this case the "battle" is usually very one-sided, as the whale attacks and eats the squid, though it frequently gets its hide scarred by the horny-ringed suckers of the latter in the process.

Since the horny beaks of the squids are indigestible, these often remain in the whale's stomach for some time, sometimes forming clumps somewhat in the manner of a hairball in the stomach of a cow. It happens that these beak remnants become imbedded in a waxy secretion from the lining of the whale's digestive tract, which helps to rid them of these scratchy and irritating "leftovers." This hard, waxy substance, which sometimes washes up on beaches, is the ambergris of commerce. As it ages, natural bacteria which originate in the stomach of the whale give it a strong aromatic odor and, although its main practical use is as a fixative for scents in the perfume industry, it has been credited with various medical and mystical powers down through the centuries. Ambergris may be irregular in shape, mottled on the outside, and marbled in cross section, and it has somewhat the feel of a very hard cake of soap or a lump of wax. In fact, when lumps of carnauba wax were lost overboard by a freighter along the Florida coast a few years ago, it created a short-lived "ambergris rush" to the local beaches and considerable publicity in the tabloids.

Since the average layman has little knowledge of what ambergris really is or what it looks like beyond the mistaken notion that it is a highly repulsive substance when fresh, persons have scooped up dead seaweed, rotting sponges, lumps of tar and soap, and even portions of long-dead fish and still less delectable items from along beaches and, with visions of newly acquired wealth dancing in their heads, have brought or sent these to various marine laboratories for identification. In fact, for a time the Marine Laboratory of the University of Miami was so beleaguered with "ambergris" specimens that they finally found it necessary to charge a fee for identification.

For those who are interested, there is a fairly simple test which will at once eliminate nearly all of the non-ambergris substances. This is called the "hot-wire test" and it is conducted as follows: Take a short piece of stiff wire (a straightened-out paper clip will do) and heat the end of it with a match. Jab the hot wire tip into the substance, and, if it bubbles slightly instead of simply melting, forms a tacky thread when the wire is drawn away, and if a tiny bit on the tip of the wire burns with a bluish flame, then the substance *may* be ambergris.

I say "may" because I was once myself deceived by a small lump of something that was found by a man along a Miami beach and subsequently brought to me for identification. Superficially at least, it did look very much like a piece of genuine ambergris, and when it passed the hot-wire test as ambergris should, I rushed over to the Marine Laboratory for additional tests. Removing a small portion, the chemist placed it in a small flask with a special solvent and together we watched it slowly dissolve over the heat of a Bunsen flame, the liquid turning a brownish color. He then poured out a portion into a watch glass, but as the solvent evaporated, only a greasy sludge remained instead of the small crystals that would have formed in the case of genuine ambergris. We were never able to learn the true nature of this particular find, but it appeared most likely to be some kind of heavy grease or pitch in which sand and marl had become incorporated.

I should say here that the value of ambergris has sharply declined in recent years. Today it is worth about $8 an ounce, while the same amount once fetched $400, the reason being mainly that its use in the perfume industry has been largely replaced by synthetics. Still, the name "ambergris" has a magic ring to it and it continues to be used in the most expensive perfumes.

Although confirmed squid eaters, pilot whales are not known to produce anything comparable to ambergris as a result, possibly because the relatively small beaks of the squid on which they feed are easily passed on through their digestive tracts. I have often wondered how these big potheads are able to catch squid in the ocean, since most squid are exceedingly swift and capable of rapid turns, while the whales appear to be so cumbersome in their movements, in captivity, at least. Evidently in their native element they are swifter than they seem in captivity.

While in California I learned that a pair of belugas or white whales had recently been captured in Alaskan waters and flown alive to the aquarium at Pacific Ocean Park, some distance north of Marineland. Never having seen this species before, I was most interested to see how well they had adapted themselves from a life among the ice floes (at least in wintertime) to the mild climate of southern California.

The belugas were confined in an 80-foot tank at the Park, where they had already adapted themselves well to captivity. One of them had an injured flipper which had subsequently healed, and otherwise they appeared to be in excellent shape. What impressed me at once was how much they differed from the other Cetaceans I had seen in the flesh. For one thing, they were an immaculate lead-white all over, being in the process of transition from the dark color of the young to the pure glistening white of the adult animal. (It must be mentioned here that the true White Whale, *Delphinapterus*

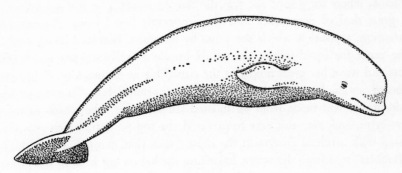

White Whale, *Delphinapterus leucas.*

*leucas,* has nothing to do with the fictional "white whale," Moby Dick, which was an albino sperm whale.) The true White Whales are found only in Arctic and subarctic waters, and, along with the narwhal, *Monodon monoceras,* comprise the only known members of the family *Delphinapteridae.* These two whales are highly primitive in many respects, such as in lacking dorsal fins and in having movable necks, though not nearly so flexible as in the freshwater Platanistids mentioned in the preceding chapter.

One thing about the belugas I found most remarkable. This is that they are capable of moving their lips slightly, thus changing their expressions! I know of no other whale that can do this, and it was most surprising to see. Most whales, dolphins, and porpoises wear perpetual "smiles," as the corners of their mouths are ever so slightly turned up and they have small creases above and below their eyes as well, which is appropriately in keeping with the amiable dispositions of the captive species. It was most surprising, then, to see the belugas making faces at me in addition.

Their movable lips are useful in another fashion, and I learned of this the hard way. While I was standing with my back next to the tank engaged in conversation with the whales' trainer, a considerable volume of cold and very wet water suddenly hit me between my shoulder blades. Spinning around in consternation, I saw one of the whales facing me with his head and foreparts out of the water and wearing a particularly diabolical smile. A moment later he sent a second stream from his mouth, and this would have caught me full in the face had I not been adept at dodging. When I had first arrived at their tank I wondered at the reason for a large plastic windshield that was mounted between the tank railing and the benches, but now it seemed a practical idea indeed.

The most engaging tame whale I have encountered to date was a large female pilot whale named "Bubbles," who resided at Marineland of the Pacific, where for a time she was the star attraction. She was a whale with a great deal of personality and she apparently loved being the center of attention, a position which she came by naturally. Besides leaping clear of the water for squid tidbits, she would hurdle a horizontal bar like a track star and wave her great flipper at the crowd for an encore. One of her most absurd antics, however, was to wear an enormous hat. This whale-sized adornment was made from an inflated rubber inner tube which served as the brim, and over this was constructed the top portion, which was decorated with artificial flowers in the most flamboyant manner. When mighty "Bubbles" rose from the water, balancing the hat on her head in the process, she presented a most spectacular appearance, her natural coy smile giving her the perfect air of twittery foolishness of a Helen Hokinson clubwoman about to address a meeting.

On one occasion "Bubbles" caused great consternation and anxiety among her keepers by actually swallowing one of the inflated inner tubes. For some days they feared for her life, but finally a large dose of mineral oil, forcibly administered, coated the tube and at length she managed to belch it up, intact and still inflated. From that time on, all loose tubes of swallowable size were kept strictly away from the whales.

In talking with Frank Broccato about the whales he had caught offshore from Marineland along the California coast, I once asked him if there was any species that he had not captured so far, but eventually hoped to obtain. His eyes lit up at once and his face became animated as he told me of his ultimate hope—to catch the fabulous killer whale, *Orcinus orca!*

A killer whale would come as close as anything to being the "ultimate" aquarium specimen, though it would in all probability be a tremendous job to care for one. These giant members of the dolphin family reach a length (in the case of males) of 30 feet, and they have a most striking appearance besides, being mainly black like the pilot whale, but marked with large irregular patches of white on the sides and belly, including a strange spectacle-like spot behind the eye. The flippers are broadly rounded and the dorsal fin grows straight upward in a narrow, high triangle with the tip, in the case of an old male, actually lopping over like the ear of a spaniel.

I have seen the killer only once—and this was a long-dead specimen washed ashore in the Florida Keys in 1946. I thought the thing was a defunct hulk of some old barge at first; then I caught sight of the distinctive fins and the mouth full of great peg-shaped, daggerlike teeth. As may be surmised from this, the killer occurs in all parts of the world though it congregates mainly in the cooler oceans where it feeds on dolphins, porpoises, and even seals which it bumps and topples off the ice floes from beneath. Also, it is well known from its habit of attacking the larger whales in marauding packs, tearing large chunks of flesh from the unfortunate creatures' lips and tongues in the process.

A captive specimen would not only require considerable room and a considerable flow of water in order to keep its enclosure clean, while the amount of fresh meat a large one would consume in a day might equal that used by the average lion house in a zoo. In this respect it would undoubtedly be the most expensive of all individual animals to maintain. And if its intelligence measures up to that of the average dolphin—and it almost certainly does—it might be a highly dangerous one as well. However, the keeping of heretofore untried animals is frequently fraught with surprises, and when one is eventually obtained, it may even surprise aquarists by becoming docile as a lamb provided it is given an adequate food supply!

In his observations of the killer at sea, Frank related the following incident. Following a pack of orcas, the crew of the collecting boat overtook a young specimen which lagged behind the group. None of them had ever seen a baby of the species before, and they were surprised to note that it was beautifully colored, with all the parts that are normally white in the adult replaced in this case by a bright lemon yellow!

The youngster appeared so attractive and its small size made it look so innocuous that the collecting crew for a time seriously considered attempting to net it as it raced alongside the bow of the boat. However, closer scrutiny revealed an immense, shadowy object in the clear depths beneath the baby. This was the mother swimming along on her side, with one great eye staring fixedly and purposefully upward at the crew of the boat. Needless to say, the project of whale-catching was quickly abandoned for the time being.

At the Miami Seaquarium we made several attempts to rescue and "reclaim" stranded Atlantic pilot whales, but up to the time of writing without

Killer Whale, *Orcinus orca.*

any lasting success, mainly because of the distance it was necessary to transport them. In the winter of 1957, a large herd of them came ashore in the
lower Florida Keys, but both the two specimens we attempted to carry back
individually by truck expired during the final leg of the Miamiward journey.
One especially memorable incident occurred a short time later following a
telephoned report to the Seaquarium that a whale of some kind had just
washed ashore near Boca Raton Inlet, some 40 miles north of Miami.

Several of us jumped into a car and raced ahead to investigate, and after
being briefly detained along the highway by a motorcycle policeman who
might be described as decidedly un-whale conscious, the spot was eventually
reached and the whale identified as a 15-foot pilot, the largest we had seen
to date. Also present was a bulldozer busily occupied in digging the poor
creature's grave, although it was still very much alive, and, insofar as we
could determine, in a pretty fair state of health at the time. Accompanying
the bulldozer was a group of local citizens whose thoughts were mainly
concerned with the tidiness of the beach and whose sole objective at the
time was to remove the unfortunate corpse-to-be from the realm of sight,
sound, and smell forever.

There promptly ensued a verbal tug-of-war between ourselves and the
good citizenry, with the great whooshing and sighing pothead as the prize.

We won only after signing a paper in which we assumed full responsibility thenceforth for the whale. Since there were already a number of workmen on the spot armed with shovels, we promptly set them to work excavating and deepening the water edge depression in which the whale lay, as we wanted it to be as comfortable as possible until we had arranged means for its transportation.

First, we summoned the Seaquarium truck to come immediately with a 20-foot oval inflatable life raft and, secondly, we chartered a boat for the purpose of towing it to Miami through the Intracoastal Waterway which runs along the entire eastern Florida coastline a short distance from the sea. When the raft arrived, we unrolled it and managed to work it under the whale with some difficulty, as the tide had already begun to fall. This was done by wedging it under and slowly inflating it with a portable air compressor at the same time. As the raft began to bulge, the whale eventually rolled into its center. As soon as it was totally inflated, a line was made fast and our "full-responsibility" was towed past the breakers, in through the Boca Raton Inlet, and southward through the Waterway toward Miami.

The whale was lying partly on its side, and although well and evenly supported by the rubberized raft, it was having some difficulty in breathing as whales always do under such conditions. I elected to ride in the raft with the whale so I could keep him under constant surveillance and later, as it proved necessary to do, occasionally bail out the splash water that collected in the bottom of the raft.

Although it was a cool night and dark had already settled, there was no gust of wind stirring and the sky was clear and bright with stars. Aside from the labored sighing of the whale, the muffled puttering of the boat's motor up ahead, and the slap-slap of the waves against the sides of the raft, all was calm and peaceful. My feet, clad only in wet canvas shoes, were slightly chilled, so I slid the shoes off and reclined in a comfortable position, half on the inflated rim of the raft and half on the whale, placing my feet on the smooth side of his head just behind his blowhole. His warm hide and breath soon took the chill out of my feet and for a long time I lay thus, puffing on my pipe and contemplating the stars overhead. Eventually I drifted off to sleep.

When I awoke it was midnight and the boat was tying up at a dock at Ft. Lauderdale, where I joined the crew at an all-night refreshment stand for hamburgers and coffee. On leaving, we announced to the proprietor that we had to get back to our whale. I'm sure he took it as a joke, and a lame one at that, for he showed no sign of surprise at this remark.

From midnight until just before dawn I was spelled by another member of the crew, taking my place with the whale just as the Waterway widened to form the upper reaches of Biscayne Bay. The raft was taking more water aboard now, the whale had shifted position slightly so that it was more on its side than before, and its blowhole was so close to the floor of the raft that it was necessary to bail every few minutes in order that the creature have ample space to breathe. Between bailings I splashed water over his side as an additional measure to keep his skin damp and cool.

The sun rose just as we passed under the Rickenbacker Causeway drawbridge, and as we came through on our final run for the Seaquarium docks, we were joined by a helicopter full of news photographers, so I could see that our public relations department had already spread the word of our coming. Like a great roc with swishing wings the helicopter followed us overhead until we came alongside the docks, when a portable crane that had been previously summoned lifted raft, whale, and all from the boat slip and deposited it carefully on the ground next to the circular shark channel.

During the day our pilot whale was removed to one of the dolphin training tanks where we set up a round-the-clock watch over it to see how it would fare. It proved to measure just a little over 15 feet, and in the tank I was able to determine positively that it was a male. While a local veterinarian gave it vitamin shots in hopes of soon stimulating its appetite, as well as penicillin and combiotic in an effort to counteract any bacteriological infection that might be in its system, I took the opportunity to hold a stethoscope against the whale's chest. The thumping of its heart came through loud and clear, and while I recorded its pulse (88), and rectal temperature (98), this information was virtually useless to us, as we knew nothing in regard to what might be normal for the species.

We soon saw that the present pool, which was 8 feet deep and 20 feet in diameter, was quite inadequate for the specimen, as he had no room to swim and looked as if he might turn over from exhaustion at any minute. While a makeshift harness was devised in order to hold him upright, the crane was again summoned, and this time he was moved in a stretcher to animal trainer Adolf Frohn's large Sea Show Arena, where the performance of sea lions and dolphins was temporarily suspended pending the eventual outcome of the transfer.

For two days the whale swam slowly about the pool and we were entertaining high hopes for his recovery, but sometime during the early morning of the third day he began to have periodic tremors and convulsions. I was routed out of bed by a phone call from the night watch, and arrived on the scene the same time as the veterinarian. The two men assigned to watch him had entered the pool and were supporting the now nearly life-less whale between them with considerable difficulty.

Suddenly the whale exploded into a frenzy of violent convulsive thrashings that drenched the area with water and knocked down both his handlers, though fortunately not injuring them in the process. For half a minute the thrashing continued, then tapered off into a shuddering tremor, followed by a gradual cessation of all motion. Swiftly the veterinarian thrust a hypodermic loaded with adrenalin into its side, but to no avail. Our whale was dead.

The autopsy was performed by Dr. Charles E. Lane, physiologist of the University of Miami Marine Laboratory. His findings were the same as those noted in previous cases: a nearly empty digestive tract with considerable bilious fluid in the stomach and a blood-congested appearance of the lining of the latter. The whale's spine showed several minor fractures and there was a broken rib or two, apparently suffered either during the initial stranding or the subsequent handling, but not enough in themselves to have caused the animal's death, to the best of our knowledge.

From the foregoing it may be reasonably concluded, as mentioned earlier in the chapter, that these pilot whales that come ashore in schools are sick whales. It might also seem logical at first to assume that they drift ashore through sheer physical exhaustion and gradually decreasing ability to maintain themselves against wind and tides at sea, but I am convinced that this is not the case. As previously conjectured, their coming ashore is a deliberate act and once they have grounded themselves, they apparently refuse to return to deeper water, but remain stranded to die of exposure and the abrasive action of sand and waves. The next question is, obviously, are they deliberately committing suicide?

Again, though I admit this to be conjecture, I must answer in the negative. Whales, like all other wild creatures, have strong survival instincts and will go to extraordinary lengths in order to preserve their own lives in a crisis. In fact, this is what I believe they are trying to do when they run aground, even though death almost invariably results.

Although whales, through evolving a fishlike shape, have adapted themselves more perfectly to the sea than any other living mammals, they must rise to the surface to breathe every few minutes of their lives, else they will die. Because of this necessity it can be seen that, aside from those that may be killed outright, such as by a harpoon gun or through being slaughtered by sharks and killer whales, the *immediate* cause of any whale's death, whatever may be the predisposing cause, is drowning.

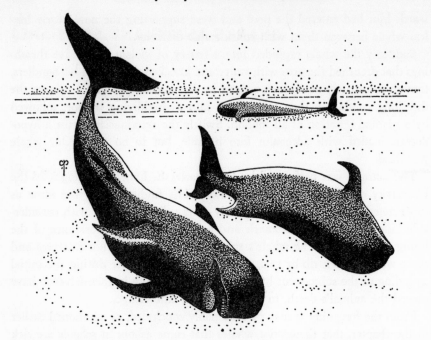

Atlantic Pilot Whales stranded on St. Augustine beach.

It may be that some whales, weakened by the ravages of some disease, injury, or old age, can prolong their existence during their final hours through floating upright in a calm sea, but for most of them death must come suddenly and frighteningly at the moment when they no longer have the strength to hold their heads above the surface. To drown suddenly in an element that has sustained it all its life must be a terrifying experience for a whale, and being an animal of high intelligence and sensitivity, it may have an intuitive as well as an instinctive fear of this eventual fate. To run aground, then, may be its sole means of prolonging its existence, if only for a short while.

As a matter of fact, most known species of whales are regularly observed to strand; and, though evidence is not as yet sufficient to show whether this, as in the case of the pilot whale, is deliberate, I strongly suspect that it is in some cases. The main difference is that the latter usually strand themselves, not individually, but *en masse,* and the most likely explanation for this seems to be that the herd has been feeding on something that later poisons them, or else that they are suffering from some as yet unknown communicable sickness that produces severe gastrointestinal symptoms.

# CHAPTER 8

# SHARKS AND GIANT SAWFISHES

*A Purse-Snatching Shark. The Circular Shark Channel. An
Odd Case of Shark Attack. Catching Nurse Sharks by the Tail.
The Strange Hammerhead and Sharkommensals. How to Carry
a 13-foot Sawfish in a 10-foot Tank*

"One of your sharks just ate my pocketbook!" "Our shark just did *what?*"

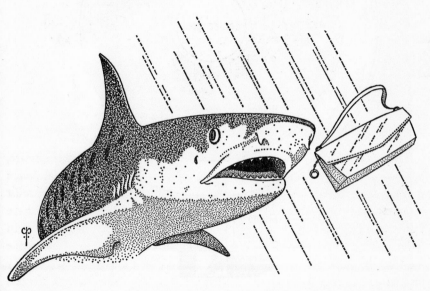

Tiger Shark, *Galeocerdo cuvieri.*

This exchange of excited conversation took place one afternoon before
the information desk in the main lobby of the Seaquarium. On being ques-
tioned further, the distraught woman explained that, as she was leaning over
the rail engrossed in the shark-feeding show taking place in the circular
Shark Channel, she happened to let her white plastic purse slip from her
grasp into the water, where it was promptly swallowed by a large shark.
This sort of thing is just what might be expected of a shark, for they will
devour almost anything in sight when excited over the presence of food.
Fortunately, the purse contained no valuables and only a small amount of

change, and another one was given to her free of charge by the Seaquarium gift shop.

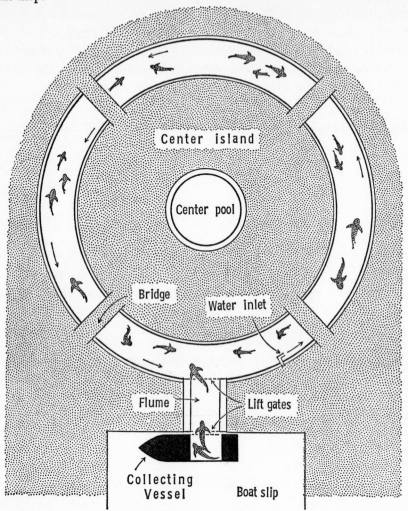

Diagram of Seaquarium Shark Channel.

The previously referred to circular viewing channel soon after construction proved to be particularly well suited to the keeping of large sharks, so that early in 1957 it was officially designated the Shark Channel, and since that time it has been devoted almost exclusively to the display of these creatures. Doughnut-shaped, the concrete-lined channel measures 750 feet in outer circumference and 24 feet in width, and has a water depth of about 7 feet when the channel is full.

Water entering the channel is jetted from a nozzle in such a way as to provide a slow but steady clockwise current to put into practical use the universal tendency of fishes to maintain themselves against a stream, and, because of the shape of the channel, large sharks can swim endlessly around the great circle without encountering any abrupt walls as may occur in a tank of conventional design, no matter how large. In the case of sharks this is especially important as they are incapable of making abrupt stops and their turning radius is generally greater than that of ordinary fishes. In the true bony fishes, the two forwardly located pectoral fins can be moved freely, serving as both brakes and steering organs, but a shark is built more like an airplane, the stiffly projecting and horizontally set pectorals being analogous in function to wings.

Although perhaps a dozen species of sharks, plus sawfishes, large rays, and a few bony fishes, such as mullet, large sea basses and jewfish, etc., have been maintained successfully in the channel from time to time, in practice, because of their hardiness and availability, the display has been confined principally to four species: the bull shark, *Carcharinus leucas,* the lemon shark, *Negaprion brevirostris,* the nurse shark, *Ginglymostoma cirratum,* and the tiger shark, *Galeocerdo cuvieri.* The average length of the captive sharks is about 8 feet, though an occasional tiger shark of 12 feet or over has survived for a time.

The habits and "liveability" of the four species mentioned vary somewhat when they are kept together. The best species for exhibition, in my opinion, is the bull shark. Given the proper conditions, it lives and feeds well in captivity, and if there is any such thing as a "typical" shark, this is it. Large, active, and aggressive, the bull is a proved attacker of man on occasion. Ranging throughout the tropical Atlantic, this species is one of the few sharks known to enter freshwater rivers, and in Lake Nicaragua in Central America it has given rise to the variety *nicaraguensis,* which is somewhat more colorful than the typical form. By way of coincidence, the lake is also the home of a large sawfish, *Pristis perotteti,* which also occurs in the Atlantic Ocean, having made its way into Lake Nicaragua by way of the San Juan River.

The lemon shark is quite similar to the bull in appearance, but may be distinguished easily by the fact that its two dorsal fins are the same size, while the first dorsal in the bull is much larger than the second. The lemon shark also has the habit—rare among the big sharks—of occasionally resting motionless on the floor of the tank, and is a fairly hardy species in captivity. The common name of this shark comes from the yellowish appearance of newly captured specimens, but after a time in the channel this color for some reason darkens to a brownish tan.

An odd fact about sharks, and one regarding which I have never read,

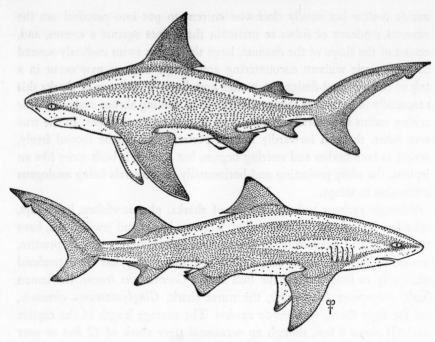

(upper) Bull Shark, *Carcharhinus leucas.*
(lower) Lemon Shark, *Negaprion brevirostris.*

is that they appear to acquire tans from excessive sunlight when kept in shallow pools. Whether this increase in bodily pigmentation is due to the same factors as in the case of humans, I do not know. I have also seen this phenomenon in the case of stingrays (*Dasyatis*) and the spotted eagle ray (*Aetobatus*). Ross Allen and Wilfred T. Neill of the Florida Reptile Institute at Silver Springs mention that this occurs in alligators as well.

The nurse shark reaches a length of about 8 feet, but a goodly portion of this consists of tail. It is strictly a bottom- and reef-dwelling species, poking about in fissures in the rocks for crustaceans, which appear to be the nurse's favorite food. There is some dispute over the reason for this shark's common name, possibly being derived from the fact that the eggs are retained in the body until they hatch, when the empty egg cases are expelled along with the living young.

The nurse shark is far and away the hardiest of all the local sharks; it is practically indestructible. I know of cases where specimens have been caught, tossed onto a burlap sack in the back of a truck, and then driven several miles to an aquarium, where they show no ill effects from handling when liberated into the water. As aquarium specimens nurse sharks are disappointing to the public, for not only do they spend a considerable part of their time resting motionless on the bottom, but their heads are quite unsharklike with the small, forward-located mouths with short, fleshy barbels on either side. The eyes are very tiny, silvery, and lack a nictitating membrane, or false eyelid (the fact that most sharks can blink their eyes makes them unique among the fishlike vertebrates).

Most popular books describe the nurse as "innocuous," or "harmless to man," but recent evidence has proved them quite otherwise. A number of skindivers have been bitten by them, fortunately without serious consequence to date, but it would be quite possible for a person to be drowned by a nurse shark. Having small teeth, the nurse lacks the shearing bite of the average predatory shark, but instead clamps down on objects with great tenacity, and even small ones can be pried loose only with considerable difficulty.

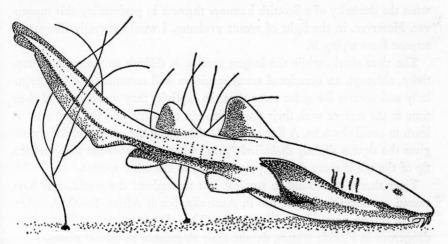

Nurse Shark, *Ginglymostoma cirratum.*

In our book *Sea Pests,* Winfield H. Brady and I described the following incident, which gives a fair indication of the boldness of occasional small specimens:

A rather unusual instance of attack on a student at the Marine Laboratory of the University of Miami by a small unidentified * species of shark occurred at Rock Harbor in the Florida Keys in July 1950, and was witnessed by several persons. The student, Mr. Warren Rathjen, was goggle-diving for seaweeds in

* In view of the nature of the circumstances, we now feel certain that a nurse shark was involved.

three feet of water about 50 yards offshore. He was bending over in the rather muddy water when he suddenly felt something clamp itself firmly to the extreme upper portion of the back of his right thigh, immediately below his swimming trunks. He surfaced at once and removed the object, which proved to be a 2½-foot shark, by grasping its tail and twisting. In the excitement the shark was thrown some distance away and escaped before it could be identified. Only a small amount of bleeding occurred, and recovery was rapid.

Since nurse sharks frequently rest about coral reefs with their heads concealed and their tails projecting, the latter may be considered an "attractive nuisance" to waders and skindivers, as the temptation to grab one, especially if it is fairly small, can be hard to resist. I have on occasion jumped out of a boat in shallow water, seized a sleeping nurse shark's tail, and tossed the surprised and flailing shark into the boat, all in one continuous motion. And over the years I have acquired a certain measure of finesse and somewhat the dexterity of a Scottish hammer thrower in performing this maneuver. However, in the light of recent evidence, I would strongly discourage anyone from trying it.

The tiger shark, while the largest species, is difficult to maintain in captivity, although an occasional small specimen will commence to feed regularly and survive for quite some time. In captivity they spend most of their time at the surface with their dorsal fins out of water, and they are slow to learn to avoid obstacles. A line or fold of skin about the corners of the mouth gives the tiger a slightly diabolical "grin" when seen from the side, and the tip of the tail is more sharply pointed than in the other species.

Tiger sharks are found in tropical seas throughout the world, and have caused considerable loss of life in Australia, South Africa, South America, and in certain parts of the West Indies. They do not appear to be nearly so dangerous in Florida waters, despite their abundance in certain places.

The explanation for this, in some cases at least, seems to lie in conditioning. In many of the places where sharks are a constant problem, the disposal of offal, garbage, and raw sewage consists of its simply being dumped into the sea, and since sharks are among the most indiscriminate feeders in nature, they flock about seaside slaughterhouses, whaling stations, and open sewers, and in these areas may become quite fearless where humans are concerned.

The list of happenstance objects taken from sharks' stomachs is quite surprising: bricks, ballast rocks, a sack of coal, chunks of coral rock, pieces of wood, tin cans full or empty, pieces of fabric, etc., although a certain number of these tidbits must have been ingested when the sharks were seeking other food, as when chasing small fishes about some floating object. Furthermore, what cannot be digested, and this applies only to totally inedible objects, is usually regurgitated in time or passed on through the digestive tract.

Most of the Seaquarium's sharks were captured in from 30 to 40 feet of water at a point about 3 miles offshore from Bear Cut between Virginia Key and Key Biscayne at Miami, in the following manner. Captain Gray and the collecting crew would set out a long line anchored to buoys and bearing hooks on individual chains at 20-foot intervals with whole fresh fish, usually blue runners. The line is left lying along the ocean floor and tended once daily during the shark-fishing periods.

The collecting barge was fitted with a sliding underwater door opening into the 12-foot live-well which held the captured sharks. As the line is being run, whenever a shark is discovered on a hook, the chain is unsnapped from the main line and clipped onto a special line running from the live-well through the open door, through which the shark is then hauled by the concentrated efforts of the crew without removing it from the water. Sometimes considerable effort was required to bring a thrashing shark aboard, but often they offered little resistance, being worn out through fighting the line for a number of hours previously. Occasionally large sharks, and almost invariably hammerheads, would be dead, as these are particularly delicate despite their size. Often these would be half-eaten, and often just the severed head of a hammerhead would be recovered, the neck completely bitten through by some large shark.

As the sharks in the live-well increased in number they were arranged so that all their heads pointed in one direction, as it was discovered that for some reason if arranged this way they would tend to lie quietly without fighting one another while the boat was under way. The procedure was continued until all sharks were removed from the set line and all hooks replaced and rebaited, when the barge and towing boat would return to the docks. The boat was then maneuvered against the receiving flume of the close-by shark channel, and the sharks released out the door one by one through the two lock gates leading into the channel. This handling of sharks without ever removing them from the water insured their arriving unharmed in most cases.

However, due to the exhausted condition of many of them, they had to be prodded with long poles in order to start them swimming into the current so that they could catch their breath. Sharks generally depend on their forward momentum through the water to obtain sufficient passage of oxygen over their gills. At Marineland and at the Seaquarium newly caught sharks are occasionally "walked" by divers in order to start them swimming, and sometimes hours may elapse before this is accomplished.

For a time we had only partial success with our specimens in the channel, and they seemed indifferent over feeding. Finally, many grew quite thin and some were released as a result, and we eventually began to wonder whether our idea of using the channel exclusively for sharks was a good one after all. We took some oxygen readings on the channel water about this time and discovered it to carry only 3 to 4 parts per million by weight of dissolved oxygen, compared to a normal of 6.4 parts per million for ocean water. This deficiency was soon corrected and raised to a remarkable high of 7 parts per million by reducing the diameter of the pipe containing the incoming water and jetting it into the channel from just above the surface. This also increased the rate of the circular flow slightly, which proved advantageous in the long run.

Almost immediately a change appeared in the sharks. Their activity increased and they showed an alertness where before they had been definitely lethargic, and before long all of them were feeding actively. At first we gave them whole blue runners, but soon it became apparent that they would accept virtually anything in the way of food, so we began to include in their diet fish heads, backbones, viscera, and other materials that formerly had to be discarded in the course of food preparation for the other specimens. On one occasion we were left with several boxes of blue runners that had become offensively "high" due to a temporary breakdown in our freezing system, and the sharks accepted these as readily as if they had been perfectly fresh.

In order to make our shark-feeding show as spectacular as possible, we constructed an overhead walkway much like a ship's bridge spanning the top of the channel, and to the rail of this was attached a block and tackle device so that large chunks of meat could be lowered into the water at the end of a rope. Through an arrangement we made with the City of Miami fishing docks, we obtained the remains of tuna carcasses, as well as portions of other large fish that were normally unusable, for shark food.

The feeding show was an instantaneous success and gained great popularity with the public. As the feeding attendant would lower a tuna carcass by the tail, the sharks would gather around, thrashing the surface to a foam and rolling over one another to get at the meat. Tough hide, flesh, and bone would be bitten off in clean chunks by the razor-sharp teeth of the frenzied sharks until there was nothing left but the end of the rope, several inches of which would usually be severed by the shark that took the last bite. The activity at times would be so great and the tugging on the rope so violent that pieces of meat would now and then be flung completely out of the channel onto the adjacent sidewalks.

Often visitors would ask me why the sharks, ravenous as they were, never attacked one another in the course of their feeding. My answer is that they behaved like any well-fed animals in captivity; all of them lived in close proximity and were used to the others' presence, and their feeding activity would be triggered off only by the sudden presence of some unfamiliar object in their midst. However, once in a while one of them would be attacked by the others, possibly because it had been more or less accidentally bitten at first in some vulnerable area that would cause it to bleed. This usually occurred at night, and in the morning very little, if any, of the unfortunate creature remained. Once a newly captured bull shark was suddenly set upon and completely devoured in a matter of minutes (this being witnessed by several persons), but such incidents were relatively infrequent and, generally speaking, the specimens got along fairly well with one another, although most of the specimens bore scars here and there from superficial bites.

The hammerhead sharks, which comprise the family *Sphyrnidae,* are among the most remarkable and specialized of all sharks, as well as one of the most difficult to maintain in captivity. We had only partial success with them, although one species, called the bonnet shark (*Sphyrna tiburo*), seems to thrive for a time under favorable conditions. By and large they are active, nervous, and panicky creatures, fighting to exhaustion when hooked, and it is seldom that we have recovered live specimens taken in this manner. Almost invariably they will be found dead, tangled, and partially eaten on the set lines, and their heads are often all we ever recover of them.

The peculiar head shape sets the hammerheads apart from all other sharks, although what function the "hammer" may serve is a point in question among ichthyologists. Because their eyes are so widely spaced they may have a wide visual range, and their nostrils bear a leading groove which is thought by some to serve the purpose of increasing the olfactory acuity of these predacious creatures. Among the various species one may find a gradual successive modification in the width of the head which ranges in appearance from a half-disk in the previously mentioned bonnet shark to the fantastic development of the small *Eusphyrna blochii* of the Indian Ocean, which reminds one of the handlebars of a bicycle.

Soon after the Seaquarium opened to the public we were fortunate in catching a 7-foot hammerhead alive and virtually unharmed, and this specimen swam actively about the channel for several days before finally panicking and killing itself by repeatedly bumping into the side walls. With the bonnets we have been somewhat more fortunate, as they may often be caught on a hook close to the seawall surrounding the Seaquarium grounds and immediately conveyed to the tide pools, where they seem to adapt themselves quite well to the shallow-water environment. Some have also been kept from

Great Hammerhead, *Sphyrna mokarran.*

time to time in the channel, but they seem to compete poorly with the larger sharks and do not last for long under these conditions. In the large tanks they have never lasted more than a day, owing to their apparent high sensitivity to the copper sulfate algicide. I still entertain the hope that aquarists may eventually solve the problem of keeping the larger hammerheads in captivity successfully, as much remains to be learned concerning their behavior, and continued observation of them under controlled conditions might ultimately furnish some clues in regard to the function, if any, of their strangely modified heads.

In the course of our shark-collecting activities we have frequently obtained various fishes that accompany sharks wherever they go. Most characteristic of this category are the well-known remoras or sharksuckers, but these are but one of the several kinds of fishes that have adopted this commensal relationship under the apparent philosophy, "If you can't lick 'em, join 'em." These sharkommensals, as I term them collectively, all apparently enjoy complete freedom from molestation by the shark, who is evidently used to their constant presence, and they in turn presumably help themselves to the smaller tidbits whenever the shark makes a meal; at least, this is what happens in the aquarium.

The common remora, *Remora remora,* is usually found on the larger sharks, the tiger in particular, sliding freely over the shark's body while at the same time maintaining a firm hold in the manner of two pieces of wet glass that may be slid freely back and forth over one another, but cannot be pulled apart. When a shark is hooked or lifted from the water the remora often slides through one of the shark's gill slits and remains in its branchial chamber until the shark is placed into the channel, when it will make a cautious reappearance. This performance is somewhat comical, and I always form a mental picture of the shark going into a fit of coughing as a result.

Less timid is the much larger and slenderer whitestriped sharksucker, *Echeneis naucrates,* who frequently swims along with the shark several inches from its body, attaching itself to the skin only when the shark puts on a sudden burst of speed. While swimming, I have sometimes seen young specimens of the whitestriped sharksucker attached to my legs and body, their presence unfelt, as the suction can be perceived only if something should pull against it. This probably accounts for the fact that sharks pay no mind to the contact of the oval, fluted sucking-disk (actually a modification of the dorsal fin) on the top of the sharksucker's head.

The whitestriped sharksucker is the commonest and most frequently observed of the sharkommensals, but almost equally common in the tropics is the pilotfish, *Naucrates ductor.* This species belongs to the jack family, and its torpedo-shaped body is boldly banded in black and white. Instead of fastening itself to the shark, the pilotfish usually swims slightly to the side or slightly below its head, often directly in front of its mouth. It is a singular sight to see one of these fishes, as it moves in exact unison with the shark, as though it were attached to it by invisible wires. I have seen photographs of a tiny, inch-long pilotfish swimming along with its tail almost touching the tip of a shark's nose, and it may be that in this position the fish is assisted in its progress by a compression wave, much as dolphins are able to "hitch a ride" on the bow wave of a passing ship.

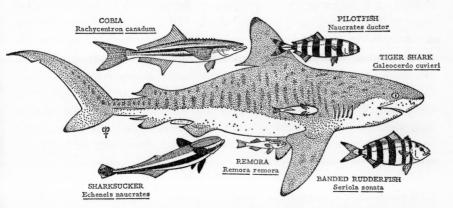

A Shark and his commensals.

A relative of the pilotfish is the banded rudderfish, *Seriola zonata,* which receives its name from its habit of occasionally swimming beneath boats when no sharks are available, and when very young this species will often lie close to surface-swimming jellyfishes for protection.

The final and in ways the most unlikely of the sharkommensal entourage is the cobia, *Rachycentron canadum*. This fish grows to about 5 feet in length and is well known for its sporting properties, but when young it bears a remarkable resemblance to the whitestriped sharksucker, even to the point of having a rounded tail fin, while that of the adult is strongly lunate (crescent-shaped). Cobias up to 3 feet in length will frequently swim along with sharks and large rays, often adopting at this particular time a whitestriped pattern like the sharksucker, so that only the absence of a sucking disk on its head betrays its true nature. Ichthyologists have for some time debated as to whether this fish might actually be related to the sharksuckers, but this may be just another of nature's remarkable instances of parallelism in form and habit.

Sharks are wondrous creatures in form and design as they propel their streamlined bodies through the water, and I have never ceased to be struck by their primeval beauty and perfection in adapting themselves to their environment. As I say this, I realize that my feelings are shared by few others, especially those who may at one time or another have been attacked by them. For myself, I feel sorry for those persons who permit popular prejudice against certain living creatures to blind them to the enjoyment of admiring them.

Almost all things in nature are beautiful, though I will confess to a certain degree of aversion in my own case when it comes to the appearance of hamadryas baboons, be they advancing or retreating. Vultures, bats, octopuses, gaboon vipers, tarantulas, and sharks—all these are creatures of wondrous form, design, and beauty if only we have the eyes to perceive it. To do so we must divorce ourselves from our early acquired prejudices which are almost invariably associated with something unpleasant connected with the habits of the creature under observation. For instance, we cringe at the sight of the venomous scorpion, but are enthralled at the harmless dragonfly, both variations on the same architectural theme. If their habits in regard to man were reversed, so would be our opinions concerning their physical appearance.

In the course of their evolution and resultant specialization, the sharks have given rise to the rays. Rays themselves are nothing more than flattened sharks, most of which have adopted a semi-sedentary life upon the ocean floor. They differ, however, from the true sharks in several respects. For one thing, their enlarged pectoral fins (the "wings" of a skate or ray) originate at the sides of the head, and their gill slits are entirely on the underside of the body. Since the mouth is also nearly always on the underside (the great manta ray with its terminal mouth is the one exception), water for breathing purposes is normally drawn in through a pair of auxiliary respiratory openings, called spiracles. These are equipped with fleshy valves and are located on the upper side of the body, immediately behind the eyes. Water drawn in through the spiracles is thus expelled through the true gill slits on the bottom, and in this manner the ray can breathe without ever opening its mouth.

There are several interesting borderline cases of raylike sharks on the one hand and sharklike rays on the other, although by the position of the gill slits and for other reasons all can be assigned to one side or the other of the great divide. The most striking example of this is in the case of the sawsharks on the one hand, and the sawfishes, which are true rays, on the other. In each case a peculiar, bladelike extension of the snout has developed quite independently, armed with sharp teeth along the sides for the purpose of securing food. The sawsharks (Family *Pristiophoridae*) are small, usually deepwater forms, while the sawfishes (Family *Pristidae*) are large in size and live in shallow areas, sometimes entering freshwater rivers and lakes in the tropics. The smalltooth sawfish (*Pristis pectinatus*) of the Atlantic coast is fairly common about the Florida shores, where it reaches a length of 16 feet, and possibly larger. Specimens have been taken in the St. Johns River as far inland as Jacksonville, and they even appear to bear their young at times in fresh water.

To avoid injury to the mother while they are still in the oviducts, the "saws" of the babies are lined with a rubbery material which strips off soon after birth, exposing the teeth. (In the sawsharks the teeth lie flat before birth.)

Until very recently it was thought that the sawsharks were confined entirely to the Indo-Pacific region, but in 1957 a new species, *Pristiophorus schroederi*, was discovered in deep water in the region of the Bahamas. This species, in common with other members of its family, has one feature lacking in the true sawfishes—the possession of a pair of long, trailing sensory barbels attached to the sides of the "saw."

Whereas the Atlantic sawshark has not been exhibited alive to date, the smalltooth sawfish is extremely hardy in captivity, and specimens will thrive for years. In this respect they are almost unique among Elasmobranchs, sharing this trait with the hardy nurse shark.

The "bill" or "saw" of the sawfish is used in securing its natural food, which consists of invertebrates including crustaceans, as well as small fishes. The sawfish will swim into a school of fish and disable or snag them on

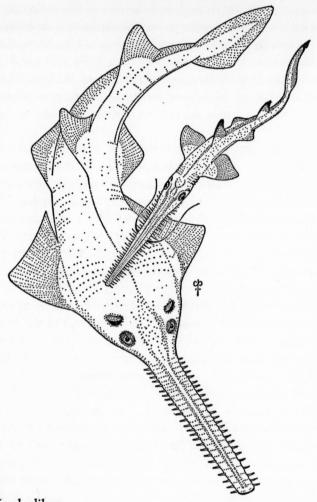

**Look-alikes:**

(upper) Atlantic Sawshark, *Pristiophorus schroederi.*
(lower) Smalltooth Sawfish, *Pristis pectinatus.*

the teeth of its saw by rapidly vibrating the head from side to side. Then it will scrape the impaled hors d'oeuvres thus secured against the bottom, swim forward, and devour them. It is also believed that the sawfish uses the saw to stir up the bottom mud in its search for buried prey. Well known as the sawfish is, many persons tend to confuse it by name with the sword-fish (*Xiphias gladius*), which, of course, is an entirely different fish related to the sailfish and marlin, and whose bill is smooth and toothless.

The spiky snout of the sawfish is often its undoing, for specimens frequently become hopelessly entangled in the nets of fishermen, thereby inciting the wrath of the latter, as the net invariably becomes severely damaged and must be cut apart to free the unfortunate ray. Some of the finest specimens we have obtained were secured in this manner. On one occasion we received a long-distance phone call from a fisherman at Marco Island on the Florida west coast, approximately 125 miles from Miami. He had trapped two very large sawfishes in one of his nets during the night, and offered to sell them to us.

We accepted his offer and loaded our largest wooden tank on the Seaquarium truck, along with a compressed oxygen tank of the sort used by welders, and which is part of our standard equipment on such trips. On arriving at the Marco Island fishing dock, there was no sign of fishermen or sawfishes. At first we wondered whether we had inadvertently come to the wrong place, or whether the whole thing was a joke, but soon we spied two men waving from a small launch that was rapidly approaching the dock. On coming alongside, the gentlemen shouted that the sawfishes were still very much alive, and still tangled in the net, which was set on a shallow flat about a mile away. We got into the boat and rushed to the spot where a single bobbing buoy marked the location of the net. One of the men caught hold of the buoy with a boathook and made the net fast to the stern of the launch. Then, shoving the throttle forward, he started up the launch and towed net and fish back to the dock.

Cutting the sawfishes loose was a considerable task as they were each wound up in a vast cocoon of netting, which would soon have suffocated anything but a sawfish. When we finally had freed them, we wrapped the saw of each carefully in burlap and then bound this with heavy twine. This is standard procedure when handling these beasts, as it gives complete protection from the slashing saw, and also the bound saws make convenient handles by which to move them.

At this point we ran into an unforeseen problem. The sawfishes were larger than we had expected, being 11 and 13 feet in total length respectively, and our tank was only 10 feet long! There was nothing to do but fit them into the tank as best we could and hope that their traditional tenacity would keep them alive during the two and a half hour trip.

We bent the smaller fish into an S-shape and placed him in the tank corner-wise, and the larger one we arranged with his head in the opposite corner and his tail dangling over the side of the box. I knew that the wind would dry out his fins en route, a thing that would be fatal to an ordinary fish, but since the fins of sawfishes and sharks are stiff and lack the soft folding membranes found in ordinary bony fishes, I felt that our specimen was in no special danger. Then, recalling my days as a Navy hospital corpsman in World War II, I took an additional measure. We had covered the fish with only enough water to support their weight in the box, as more would have allowed them to thrash around and perhaps injure themselves during the trip, and I knew that by the time we reached Miami this water would be thick with slime from their gills and low in oxygen content.

To offset this, I attached two long plastic tubes to the valve of the oxygen tank, and to the end of each I affixed a porous airstone of the type used in home aquaria to break up the oxygen stream into tiny bubbles. Dropping each airstone through a spiracle directly into the gill chamber of each sawfish, I secured them in place with strips of friction tape which held underwater owing to the roughened skin of the fish. Following this, I opened the valve of the tank slightly so that a fine stream of bubbles appeared from the airstones. We then cushioned the tail of the larger specimen by placing a folded mattress between it and the top of the box, and in this manner we successfully transported them to Miami.

At the Seaquarium we hoisted box and sawfishes into the receiving flume by means of the electric winch, and next day we opened the gate leading into the 80-foot tank and allowed them to swim in to join the dolphins, sea turtles, and giant jewfish.

After a week had passed the sawfishes still had not fed voluntarily, so I decided to attempt to get them to do so before too much time had elapsed. In order to do this, I selected a long pole, at the end of which was a two-pronged spear with the barbs filed off. Selecting several large blue runners from our freezer and placing them in a wire basket, I instructed one of our divers to approach the sawfishes and poke the fish down their throats with the spear, hoping they would swallow them once they got a taste. After several tries with each sawfish, the diver succeeded in getting them to take the blue runners and I was elated, knowing that from then on they would take food on their own accord.

Having watched them feed, I myself felt hungry, and since it was time for lunch I thought of the barbecued half chicken I had bought that morning and placed in a paper bag in the laboratory refrigerator alongside a large filefish that had died in one of our corridor tanks the night before. Opening the refrigerator, I was dismayed to find it empty. Just then my assistant Ed Nichols walked into the lab with a peculiar look on his face. "Craig," he said slowly, "was that your chicken?" "Yes!" I snapped. "What the devil did you do with it?" "Well, you're not going to like this," answered Ed, "but I thought it was a dead specimen at first, so I dumped it into the Shark Channel!"

# CHAPTER 9

# THE MIGHTY MOLA

Mola, *the Millstone of the Sea. The* Plectognaths—*Individualists and Nonconformers. Poisonous Puffers. "Clancy" and "Lancy." Hand-Feeding an Ocean Sunfish. A* Mola's *Garden of Parasites*

Seated at my laboratory desk, I heard the sudden hum of the public address speaker outside, followed by the announcement that our collecting boat was just arriving at the dock with a newly captured giant ocean sunfish. I jumped up in a state of excitement; this was a fish about which I had heard a great deal, but had never as yet seen in the flesh. I hurried to the landing and shouldered my way past the crowd at the dockside, just as Captain Gray brought the *Sea Horse* to berth. In the large live-well, lying on its side, was a most immense and unbelievable object.

This was a *Mola mola,* a name which means "millstone" and is most apt, for the creature is flattened and nearly circular in shape, and has a sand-

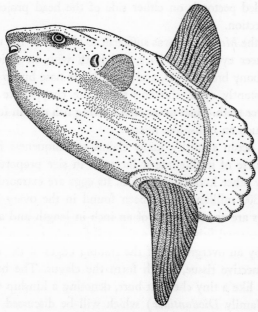

Ocean Sunfish, *Mola mola.*

paper-like skin the color of granite. This specimen stared at us with an eye the size of a teacup and sent noisy spurts of water in our direction through a mouth that appeared to be a circular hole beneath a bumplike nose on the front of its head. In fact, the great ocean sunfish appears to be *all* head, as it loses its true tail in early infancy and its place is taken by a stiff hinged structure called the clavus, which is used for steering but not for swimming. Swimming is instead accomplished by the two great vertical fins, the dorsal and the anal, which are shaped like the blades of an airplane propeller. Since the body is so compacted some strange rearranging has taken place internally, and its kidneys are located close behind and above the rear of the skull. The brain, incidentally, is smaller than either kidney.

Transported by truck to the main 80-foot tank and placed therein, our *Mola* commenced to swim at once, and I rushed down to view him through the first subsurface row of windows to see in what manner this was accomplished. Beneath the surface I could see the two high vertical fins (which were stiff, but hinged at the base) both bend to the same side of the fish at the same time, then swing to the opposite side, rotating slightly on their bases as they did so. This action was highly mechanical in appearance, like the sculling of a boat or the churning of a propeller, and the *Mola* swam much more like a machine than a fish. The rudder or clavus with its evenly scalloped trailing edge swung from side to side like the rudder of a plane, and the rounded pectorals on either side of the head projected stiffly in a horizontal direction.

The face of the *Mola* alone was sufficient to place it in the unworldly class. The great saucer eyes moved back and forth with an eerie stare beneath their curving bony brow ridges, and beneath the nose bump the tiny mouth remained constantly open, showing the white chopperlike beak of fused upper and lower teeth. I had never seen a living fish that in form and actions had adopted such an unfishlike mien.

One of the ocean sunfish's many claims to uniqueness is the fact that during the course of its lifetime it increases in size proportionally perhaps more than any other known living fish. Its eggs are extraordinarily minute, an estimated 300 million having been found in the ovary of one female! The hatchlings are about a tenth of an inch in length and are a reasonable facsimile of a normal fish, having a tiny tail fin which, however, is soon lost and replaced by an overgrowth of the trailing edges of the dorsal and anal fins, plus connective tissue, which form the clavus. The body for a time becomes spiny like a tiny chestnut burr, denoting a kinship with the porcupine fishes (Family *Diodontidae*) which will be discussed later on in the chapter. While still under a half-inch in length, the baby *Mola* "turns in its fish papers," so to speak, and decides to try to become something else. Its body abruptly becomes much higher than long and skewed so that it appears to be forever going downhill, and from then on its appearance becomes progressively more outrageous until the final adult form, 6 to 8 feet long and with a weight of over a ton, is achieved.

The adult *Mola* feeds largely on plankton, or free-floating and drifting organisms, including jellyfishes and other Coelenterates, swimming mollusks, fish larvae, and whatever small fishes it can catch, and has itself the distinction of being the largest form of plankton, according to Dr. Hilary B. Moore, Planktologist of the Marine Laboratory of the University of Miami, owing to its usually aimless manner of drifting about in the sea and often being accidentally rammed by boats in the process.

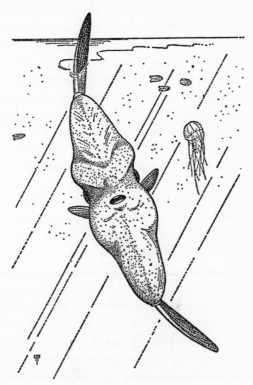

Ocean Sunfish feeding.

The name "sunfish" comes from its habit of lying basking on one side or the other at the surface of the sea for long periods, and it should not be confused with the well-known family of freshwater basses (Family *Centrarchidae*) which bear the same common name.

Our specimen had been discovered, incidentally, by a party boat engaged in trolling in the Gulf Stream off Miami. When the fish was spotted on the surface ahead of them, one of the fishermen easily snagged it with his line; it was then brought to gaff and tied with rope against the side of the boat, as the swimming efforts of these leviathans are really very feeble. As Captain Gray would say, "One man can catch one, but a dozen men can't lift it into the boat." The party boat then radioed the Seaquarium via ship-to-shore, and the *Sea Horse* went out to meet them.

Before the transfer had occurred, however, the fish had received somewhat of a battering where his left side had rubbed the boat, and I knew that in a few days he might be in bad shape, although the injuries didn't show very much at first. As I watched him swimming, or rather, sculling about the tank, he seemed to become orientated very quickly, despite his little pea-sized brain. He kept a measured distance away from the circular wall of the tank and never bumped into any of the numerous rocks and other obstacles. In this way he was behaving typically for the singular group of fishes to which he belonged—the order *Plectognathi.*

The Plectognaths are in many ways the most interesting and unusual of all living fishes, because, while sharply set off as a unit and consisting of several families of fishes obviously closely related to one another, each family has gone off on its own particular tangent. In doing this the Plectognaths (the name referring to the compact nipping jaws of these fishes) have evolved some of the most far-out body shapes and improbable means of defense in fishdom. They are truly an offbeat group and most of them make wonderful aquarium exhibits as well. As a group they show evidence of having evolved from flattened, small-jawed fishes similar to the marine angelfishes, butterflyfishes, and spadefishes. Their closest living relatives are believed to be the Acanthurids or surgeonfishes, a group so named because of a pair of forward-directed sharp movable spines which are used for defense and are carried on the fleshy portion of the tail base.

One single feature that nearly all Plectognaths have in common is the almost total absence of pelvic fins (the paired fins located under the chest or belly according to species). In most freely swimming fishes these fins act as stabilizers, and the effect the lack of pelvics has upon swimming may readily be seen in the harvestfish (*Peprilus*) and the butterfish (*Poronotus*), two typically shaped fishes that are pelvic-less. As these fishes swim through the water they "jog" up and down to the rhythmic beats of the pectorals, and their bobbing and bouncy gait always reminds me of Mr. Hulot, that delightful comic character of the French screen.

In the Plectognath fishes, however, swimming is typically accomplished largely by a fluttering or stroking action of the vertical fins, which work

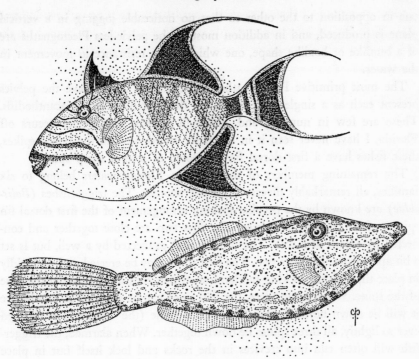

(upper) Queen Triggerfish, *Balistes vetula*.
(lower) Scrawled Filefish, *Alutera scripta*.

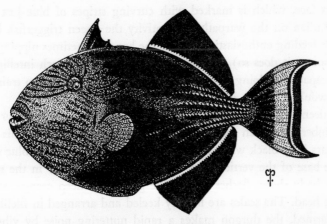

Black Durgon, *Melichthys radula*.

one in opposition to the other so that no noticeable jogging in a vertical plane is produced, and in addition most of the pelvic-less Plectognaths are of a bunlike or boxlike shape, one which offers resistance to movement in the water.

The most primitive Plectognaths, and the ones which have the pelvics present each as a single stout spine, are the spikefishes or Triacanthodids. These are few in number, and, although at least one species occurs off Florida, I have never seen it in the flesh. In addition to the pelvic spikes, these fishes have a first dorsal fin composed of several sharp spines.

The remaining members of the order in Florida waters belong to six families, all remarkably diverse from one another. The triggerfishes (*Balistidae*) are known by the peculiar locking arrangement of the first dorsal fin spines, of which there are three. The first two are close together and connected by means of a web. The third is also connected by a web, but is set a bit apart from the other two. The first spine may be erected and set rigidly in place through the locking mechanism, which consists of bones at the base of the spine. When set in place, the first spine can be snapped in two before it will lie down normally, but if the third spine (the "trigger") is touched ever so lightly, all three spines lie down together. When alarmed, the triggerfish will often run into crevices in the rocks and lock itself fast in place until danger ceases.

Two strikingly beautiful triggerfishes occur in Caribbean waters. The first of these is the queen triggerfish, *Balistes vetula,* which is a deep blue with flushes of rose pink, green, and yellow on the head and body. Most remarkable is its face, which is marked with curving stripes of blue just like an Apache Indian on the warpath. In captivity the queen triggerfish becomes very tame, feeding enthusiastically from the hand (sometimes nipping fingers to the bone as it does so), and showing just about as much intelligence as a fish is capable of doing. If anyone should wish to attempt to train a fish, this one would make an ideal subject.

The queen's opposite number is the black durgon, *Melichthys radula,* large numbers of which are found about the reefs at Bimini. This triggerfish appears inky black when in the water, with a line of livid blue running along the base of the vertical fins. When seen out of water in the sunlight, the black body shows flashes of metallic green and deep orange, especially about the head. The scales are heavily keeled and arranged in filelike rows. When alarmed, the durgon makes a rapid puttering noise by vibrating a membrane adjacent to the gill flaps in front of the pectoral fins. These two species of triggerfishes make a particularly beautiful display when kept in the same tank together as they are often found thus on the open reef.

Once I had twelve black durgons together in one tank, and passing the tank one morning, I noticed one of them wearing a peculiar expression, as if he were about to spit. Now, fishes have immensely varied countenances and look like many different things, but these expressions are always constant and not subject to change. However, this particular one looked strange, and I didn't know quite what to make of it.

Because of its bizarre form and coloration, *Rhinecanthus aculeatus* from Hawaii has been dubbed the "Picasso Triggerfish."

Next day there were three durgons all with the same spitting expression. Something was definitely ruining their looks, but I couldn't imagine what. Normally these fish have a tiny, somewhat coquettish mouth, but the affected specimens had their lips rolled under in an odd way and their teeth showed in an unpleasant manner. The mystery was solved the next day when the lights were turned on in the morning. I happened to be standing close to the tank at the time, and no sooner did the bright fluorescent tubes flash on than all the durgons started racing frantically around the tank. Apparently they were all unduly sensitive to what we call photoshock, which can actually kill some fish. As I watched I saw one large specimen race the whole 7-foot length of the tank, hit the far wall with a heavy thud, and then slowly turn in my direction. His face had likewise been changed. We solved the problem by moving the durgons to a tank near a small night light, and subsequently they showed no further photoshock when the morning lights came on.

One other triggerfish deserves special mention. This is the large gray ocean triggerfish, *Canthidermis sufflamen,* which swims along with majestic sideways flaps of its unusually high dorsal and anal fins in imitation of the ocean sunfish, though it is of course considerably smaller in size.

The Family *Monocanthidae* contains the filefishes, which are actually modified triggerfishes and included in the same family with them by some biologists. Instead of a "trigger" arrangement, the first dorsal in these fish usually consists of a single rough spine. This can likewise be locked into an upright position when the fish wishes to do so. The bodies of filefishes are considerably compressed (flattened in the vertical plane).

The planehead filefish, *Monacanthus hispidus,* is the commonest species, is plain brown in color and, while most fishermen call it a "trash" fish, I consider it to be one of the best eating of all marine fish (and I am something of a seafood addict), as well as one of the easiest to clean. The rough skin can be peeled from the flesh with thumb and forefinger, and the pure white boneless fillets can be removed from the backbone much more easily than in the average fish. Since they are not large, however, they will probably never be in any great demand.

One trait of the planehead filefish that is apparently not shared by other members of its family is its nasty habit of attacking the eyes of other aquarium fishes, so for display purposes we keep them in a tank to themselves.

The fringed filefish, *Monocanthus ciliatus,* has a long pelvic bone that is jointed at the base, and the males of this species can literally open up like a Japanese fan by swinging this bone forward. It is likely that in doing this, they make themselves difficult to swallow by potential predators, although the main purpose of this device appears to be sexual display.

What I consider to be one of the most interesting of this group is also one of my favorite aquarium fishes, the scrawled filefish, *Alutera scripta.* This species reaches a length of over 2 feet and has a long front profile reminiscent of a Russian wolfhound, tipped with a tiny mouth with sharp teeth well designed for nipping things, which they seem to be constantly engaged in doing. The tail fin is very large, fanlike, and oval, and the skin is plain gray or yellowish gray, marked with spots and broken lines of bright blue, hence the common name.

The next family are the *Ostraciidae,* or trunkfishes. They have a compact build and most of them have the body encased in a solid box consisting of a mosaic of smooth, hexagonal plates, with the eyes, jaws, gills, fins, and tail free to move. Most of them are quite flat on the underside, and as a result are pathetically helpless when set upright on a flat surface out of water. Under such conditions the poor creatures will vainly flap the fins and tail, smack their lips, and roll their eyes, but be completely unable to move from their position.

The most common Ostraciid in Florida waters is the cowfish, *Lactophrys quadricornis,* which has a pair of forward-directed, bony spines projecting from the forehead. The color is a very pale sea-green overlaid with bright blue dots and curved lines, and like many other Plectognaths it is able to vary the intensity of its coloration at will.

Along with the triggerfishes, I place the cowfish and its relatives high on the fish intelligence scale. Once I caught a cowfish in shallow water (they are fairly easy to catch by hand) and placed him in a tide pool which had only a narrow connection to the sea—too small and shallow for him to swim through, but the rising tide was breaking through in small waves. After appearing to make an unhurried search of the entire pool, my fish finally poised himself in front of the exit, rising and falling with each incoming wave. When one of sufficient magnitude to raise the depth of the sill by an inch or so arrived, the fish swam over the barrier against the current and, once free, headed for deep water and safety as fast as he could.

Sharing the shallow-water grassy flats with the cowfish is the green trunkfish, *L. trigonus.* When viewed head-on, this fish shows a silhouette that is almost a perfect equilateral triangle, as the back rises in a sharp keel. Grass-green to gray-green or blackish green in color, this fish is a much more powerful swimmer than the cowfish. Young of both species are nearly spherical in shape and are frequently observed hovering beneath floating pieces of seaweed. Sometimes called "dingleberries" by aquarium collectors with a flair for naming things, these little fish with their babyish faces, soulful eyes, and tiny, petulant mouths remind one of Betty Boop on close inspection.

My favorite trunkfish is a Caribbean species that could aptly be called the "whistling teakettle fish," since it has a smoothly rounded shape and its mouth is prolonged into a sort of spout by means of which it blows jets of water into the sand and bottom debris for the purpose of uncovering morsels of food on the coral reefs where it lives. Actually called the smooth trunkfish, *L. triqueter,* this species is marbled like black, gray, and white calico, and its eyes and mouth are jet black. Along with the large spotted trunkfish, *L. bicaudalis,* which also shares the reef habitat, the smooth trunkfish has a mysterious habit—in some fashion it can put out a poison which will quickly asphyxiate other fishes kept in the same container with it.

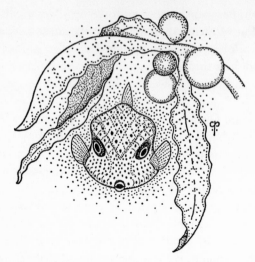

Young trunkfish under floating Sargassum weed.

In the course of our collecting activities, Gray and I now and then would encounter a baffling phenomenon. Suddenly an entire tub or live-well full of fishes would start thrashing and rushing about, gulping air at the surface, and within two minutes would stiffen and die with their colors intensified and darkened—an obvious indication of severe oxygen deficiency. No amount of water changing did any good. Once the symptoms appeared, the fish were doomed, and the symptoms themselves were almost identical to those produced by rotenone, a chemical extract of the derris root.

The only fishes that seemed quite immune were the trunkfishes, large groupers, and moray eels, and for a long time we thought that the latter were entirely responsible. When morays are removed from a trap, they often show a form of behavior that would certainly meet the disapproval of Emily Post. Starting with a knot in the end of the tail, the moray works this rapidly up the body and over the head, literally wringing out its stomach contents as it does so, and since no moray has a "weak" stomach, the remains of its last meal make their appearance with considerable force. Since we eventually learned through experience that the powerful acids in the stomach would quickly kill most fishes if they mixed with the water, we always handled the morays in a separate compartment. Later, we did the same with the sea basses, as some of them also had a tendency to regurgitate when newly caught.

Still, we kept losing groups of fish from this mysterious cause, although the presence of the trunkfishes and their subsequent survival would cer-

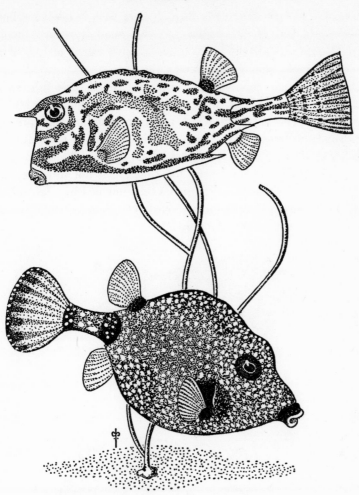

(upper) Cowfish, *Lactophrys quadricornis.*
(lower) Smooth Trunkfish, *Lactophrys triqueter.*

tainly have tipped us off in due time, had these occurrences been frequent enough. It was Dr. Earl S. Herald, Curator of the Steinhart Aquarium in San Francisco, who cleared up this mystery for us when he reported the poisoning of water by certain Ostraciids in the Pacific.

The Family *Tetraodontidae* comprises the puffers or swellfishes, which are unique in several respects. All have a false stomach or bladder which they can rapidly inflate by swallowing water or air until the fish becomes a living balloon, making them impossible for the average predator to swallow. Secondly, certain puffers have developed in their livers, gonads (reproductive organs), and in some cases their flesh as well, a substance known as tetraodontoxin, one of the deadliest poisons found in nature. Finally, this group contains a few species which live in fresh water, making it unique, so far as is known, among the Plectognaths.

Tetraodon means "four-toothed," and the teeth of these fish are actually fused into a turtlelike beak, which is split in the middle. The body is covered with a tough, elastic skin which may or may not be quite prickly when the fish inflates. Inflation is accomplished by a series of rapid gulps accompanied, if in air, by a characteristic "uk-uk-uk-uk-uk-uk" sound as the throat valve leading to the air sac opens and closes. It is not surprising that this remarkably effective form of defense has been imitated by a few other fishes, including at least two filefishes, a shark (*Cephaloscyllium*), and certain angler fishes of the Family *Antennariidae*.

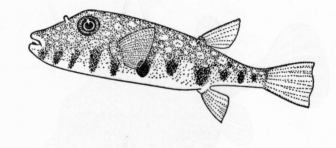

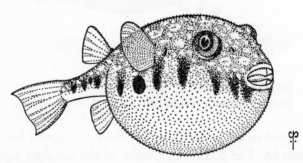

Northern Puffer, *Sphaeroides maculatus,* swimming and inflated.

The famous poison puffer of the Pacific, *Tetraodon hispidus,* is legendary for the deadly qualities of its flesh. The gall of this fish has been reported to be used by Polynesian natives for the purpose of poisoning their spears, and they call it "maki-maki" or "deadly death," an alarmingly redundant phrase. I have seen the maki-maki in Honolulu, and it is an attractive and colorful fish, despite its poisonous properties. Quite recently I visited a famous Polynesian restaurant at Ft. Lauderdale, Florida, and was somewhat nonplused to see maki-maki included on the menu. Ominous as it sounded at first, on inquiring about and trying it, I discovered that this is also the name for a superb Polynesian dish composed of chopped chicken livers, bacon, and water chestnuts!

A smaller relative of the poison puffer is the freshwater river puffer, *Tetraodon fluvialatus* of India, which is sold alive in tropical fish stores. Nothing is known of any poisonous qualities this species might have.

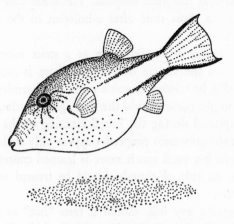

Sharpnose Puffer, *Canthigaster rostrata.*

In the United States, the flesh of some of the common puffers, particularly that of the northern puffer, *Sphaeroides maculatus,* is eaten, as it is nearly bone-free and very delicious. However, their livers and gonads can be highly dangerous, and these should never be eaten under any circumstances. During the past ten years I have been called in as a consultant in two separate fatalities resulting from the eating of livers from puffers caught at Miami. In one case I examined the remains of the fish involved, but unfortunately it was skinned, so I could not identify it positively as to species, though in all probability both specimens were the checkered puffer, *Sphaeroides testudineus,* which is the commonest local species. This form abounds in the tidal inlets and estuaries of the south Florida area, and twice I have observed it in fresh water above the reach of the tide.

The poison, tetraodontoxin, is an alkaloid very similar to muscarin, which is found in the truly deadly mushrooms of the genus *Amanita,* and the symptoms produced by both are similar. Once the onset of the symptoms begins, little hope remains for the unfortunate victim. In the one case where

I viewed the fish remains following the death of the victim, I got the following story from the attending physician: a woman tourist, new to the Miami area, was told by a friend that fresh fish liver was a health-giving tonic. Unfortunately believing this nonsense, she set about to procure the first fish available, which ironically turned out to be a *Sphaeroides.* Shortly after having cooked and eaten the liver, she was afflicted with a curious tingling, and later, numbing, of the tongue, lips, fingers, and toes. She rushed next door to the house of a neighbor where she told her story and collapsed. The neighbor summoned an ambulance at once, but the woman was dead on arrival at the local hospital. The other case involved a man who lived for only a short time after admission to the Miami Veterans Hospital.

These ominous examples should serve as a strict warning to anybody who customarily eats the viscera of puffers. There is some evidence that the flesh itself might be tainted in some cases and harmless in others, and artificial tainting might occur should the liver, gall, ovaries, or other viscera be accidentally ruptured during the initial cleaning of the fish. Indications exist likewise that the poisonous properties appear only at the onset of sexual maturity of the fish, but until much more is learned concerning the subject of tetraodontoxin, no rule of thumb should be trusted and extreme care exercised in all cases.

In fact, when eating *any* fish, should it taste "hot" as if seasoned with red pepper, or especially if the lips and tongue should begin to tingle, discard the portion at once (or better yet, save it for subsequent laboratory analysis) and take an emetic so as to rid the stomach of all possible poison.

Another mysterious type of fish poisoning, called Ciguatera, is confined mainly to the tropics. Its cause is unknown to date, but it appears that on certain reefs and in certain atolls, etc., many fishes carry the poisons (themselves little known), while at other places only a short distance away, they are completely free from them. Elsewhere, Ciguatera may be produced at random by certain fishes including barracuda, sea basses, snappers, and related forms. The initial symptoms of Ciguatera are somewhat similar to those produced by tetraodontoxin, though less severe, although they often have fatal results.

Related to the puffers are the porcupinefishes (Family *Diodontidae*) which differ from the former in having the fused beak consisting, as in the *Molas,* of a solid upper and lower plate, and in having the head and body in most species covered with long, thornlike spines which give them a truly formidable means of protection.

In the local genus *Chilomycterus* these spines are somewhat recurved and

set solidly in the skin, while in *Diodon* they lie flat, springing into an upright position only when the fish inflates. In this latter condition the porcupinefish, *Diodon hystrix,* is as large as a basketball, and the close-set thorns,
each over an inch in length, give it a fantastic appearance. To attempt to
pick one up in a dipnet is the quickest way to ruin the latter, for the fish will
almost invariably inflate, and the more tightly it becomes enmeshed, the
more stubbornly it continues to work its pumping system, and the body
remains inflated even after death in some cases.

I have a remedy for this, however, which is to run a heavy plastic or
metal tube down the fish's throat, meanwhile keeping fingers away from the
chopping jaws, as the porcupine can deliver a formidable bite. With the
tube in place his inflating sac can be readily collapsed and the fish worked
free from the net.

Porcupinefish, *Diodon hystrix.*

Since the head and eyes of the porcupinefish are so immense and the face
relatively flat in front, they bear a certain resemblance to teddy bears when
seen head-on. In swimming, the fish flutters its large pectoral fins constantly,
while the paddle-shaped vertical fins (which lie immediately above and
below the tail) are both flipped to one side while the tail is flipped to the

other. This action alternates rapidly, and the effect is rather similar to that of a propeller when the fish is viewed from the rear.

A much smaller Diodont is the lesser porcupinefish or balloonfish, *Diodon holacanthus.* This is a hardy and attractive aquarium fish, and the surface of its eyeballs reflects a beautiful blue-green opalescence when seen from the side.

The full flowering of the Plectognath branch is met with at last in the ocean sunfishes of the Family *Molidae,* of which there are three main kinds, each on close scrutiny seeming more inexcusable than the other two. Besides the giant *Mola* already mentioned, there is the sharptail mola, which is sometimes placed in a separate genus, *Masturus.* Of similar size, this one has a slightly more elongated and a smoother body form, the vertical fins are positively immense, and the clavus terminates in its central portion in a ridiculous little nubbin. And as if this creature weren't enough of a spectacle already, the posterior part of the body is adorned with white polka dots.

Finally, there is the slender *Mola,* an armored creature only a yard in length. Found in the Pacific, this sunfish (*Ranzania*) has the rear part of the body chopped off so abruptly that it looks like only half of whatever it is supposed to be. The vertical fins of this species are quite small and feeble and the clavus is very narrow and bandlike.

Returning to our own *Mola* in the Seaquarium tank, I was delighted when I realized that, despite his great size, he had adjusted himself to swimming around a limited space. This is unfortunately not true of all large creatures of the open sea, as, having no barriers to their progress in nature, they cannot adapt themselves to any sort of enclosure, but collide repeatedly with the restraining walls, eventually injuring themselves with fatal results.

While swimming, "Clancy" (as we came to call him) would occasionally rest on his side at the surface, basking in the sun. This was the activity for which the species is famous, and his ponderous bulk would cast a dark shadow through the water as he did so. While viewing him thus, with his rounded pectoral fin slapping the water surface with a motion like the ears of an elephant, I was impressed by the great symmetry of his form. Without noting the exact placement of his eye, gill slit, and pectoral, it was difficult to see whether he was lying on his right side or his left. After having "sunned" one side for a while, "Clancy" would do a slow barrel roll with the waves lapping at his sides, the great dorsal fin would slowly rise from the water and settle once more as his other side would come uppermost. After a time he would scull leisurely around the tank again, and an hour or so later again pause to "sun."

Meanwhile, the effects of the beating he took against the side of the launch

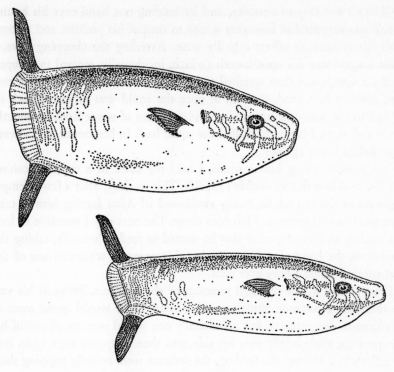

Two forms of the Slender Mola, *Ranzania laevis*.

vere beginning to show. There were rope-burns on his side, and, as I had anticipated, a considerable amount of skin on the one side began to slough off. I prayed that the dissolved copper in the water would ward off infection (I knew it would kill off any body or gill-parasites, which are always plentiful on ocean sunfishes) and, should he begin to feed on his own, there seemed to be at least an even chance of his eventual recovery.

In response to a phone call, Dr. Eugenie Clark of the Cape Haze Marine Laboratory at Punta Gorda, Florida, kindly mailed me some literature on the feeding habits of ocean sunfishes, which I perused. Since it appeared that they take in such solid food as occasional small fishes along with their usual jellyfish fare, it seemed that fresh squid might be worth a try, being available and somewhere between the two extremes, consistency-wise.

I instructed a diver to offer "Clancy" some whole squid on the end of a pole, but this did no good, despite repeated attempts. After the second day of failure, I decided to try to feed him by hand myself, so I put several squid in a cloth sack, and, donning swim fins and a face mask, entered the tank with the neck of the sack thrust through the belt of my swimming trunks.

"Clancy" was easy to overtake, and by holding one hand over his button nose, I was surprised at how easy it was to control his position and at how feeble his swimming efforts actually were. Avoiding the chopping jaws, I thrust a squid into his open mouth (which, incidentally, seemed to be open all of the time), and then watched to see if he would swallow it. For a moment nothing happened, then all at once the squid was projected back in my face to the accompaniment of a sudden stream of water from his mouth. Again and again I patiently stuffed the squid back in his mouth, and always he propelled it out again.

Finally, after giving him a squid, I held my hand in a cupped position over his mouth so that he couldn't expel it. This worked; after a few attempts to get rid of the morsel, he finally swallowed it! After forcing him to take three more in this manner, I left him alone. The next day I was able to feed him twelve, and the day after that he started to feed voluntarily, taking the squid from the hand of a diver. During this process I witnessed one of the most comical sights I have ever seen.

"Clancy" had a pair of small remoras, or sharksuckers, living in his vast gill chamber, a common situation with *Molas*. These would spend most of their time in concealment, but occasionally one would pop out of one of his gill openings, glide briefly over his side, and then disappear once again into the gill shelter. During the feeding, the remoras were actually popping their heads out of "Clancy's" open mouth, nipping at the squid that was being offered by the diver. The entire effect was that of some kind of insane cuckoo clock. That the remoras were so patiently tolerated by "Clancy" was almost as pathetic as it was ludicrous.

That was the last time "Clancy" fed. His injuries had proved too extensive, and he died three days later. After his death I opened his stomach cavity and found all of the squid undigested. Perhaps they were really too solid a food for him, but, more likely, his weakened condition had prevented digestion and the sudden appearance of food in his stomach may, in this case, have actually hastened his death.

"Clancy's" passing was attended by another coincidental event. Several days earlier, a worker at the University of Miami Marine Laboratory on Virginia Key noticed a great dark shadow drifting under the nearby Bear Cut Bridge, and, on rowing out to investigate, discovered another sunfish! He gaffed it without difficulty and maneuvered it back to the dock, where we were summoned by phone.

On arriving at the dock, I was surprised to see that this was a different species, *Mola lanceolatus*, commonly called the sharptail mola and, like "Clancy," the first one of his kind I had seen. Moreover, so far as I could tell, this one was in perfect shape. We towed him slowly around the end of the Key to our receiving docks and transported him to the big tank to join our first specimen. Once in the tank, it was easy to see that there was a considerable difference between the two fishes, though they were of similar size.

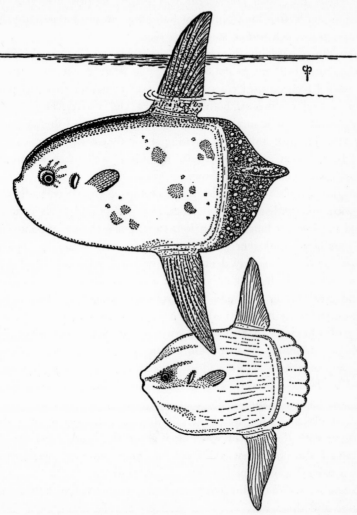

Sharptail Mola, *Mola lanceolatus,* with *Mola mola*
swimming in background.

"Lancy," our new mola, swam much faster than "Clancy" since his vertical fins were proportionately larger and longer and his body more streamlined. He lacked the bony brow ridges that gave "Clancy" his personality, and his nose was more evenly rounded, looking in profile like the front end of a dirigible. The white spots on his rear section darkened soon after he was placed in the tank, since their colors appear to be, as in many other fishes, partly under bodily control. Although appearing to be in excellent condition when caught, our *Mola lanceolatus* was unable to orient himself to the confines of the 80-foot tank and kept bumping the walls repeatedly. Three days later, and much to our sorrow, he died.

One of the remarkable things about the ocean sunfishes is the fact that they are almost without exception a veritable floating garden of parasites. Never have I seen any sea creatures that seem to harbor so many parasitic and commensal organisms, both in number and variety, as a matter of course. Doubtless the leisurely existence led by these giant fishes at the ocean surface and the great amount of inviting shade they cast, welcomes "colonization" by parasites and commensals and this is well taken advantage of, as the following instance will show.

A very large mola was brought in one evening a year later, badly injured by an encounter with a boat's propeller, and it appeared fairly certain that it would not live for long, but, anxious to give it a chance, we moved it at once to the larger tank where we could observe it through the underwater windows. As the fish slowly drifted past the windows I wondered if I was seeing things, for the fish not only had the absurdly human face of its species, with the great saucer eyes and small round mouth, but this one bore a definite resemblance to Tolouse-Lautrec, for it unquestionably wore a Vandyke beard! On closer examination I saw the "mustache" and "goatee" to be individually composed of vast numbers of parasitic Copepod crustaceans, each about an inch in length and of a greenish color. The Copepods were attached to the skin by their heads, and their trailing flattened bodies and forked tails flapped about in the water currents, looking for all the world like a mat of hair. They had evidently arranged themselves in a pattern conforming with the lines of water flow about the head, hence the "Vandyke," and I also noted that additional Copepods above the eyes had given the fish a pair of well-defined "eyebrows" as well!

My attention was soon directed to another peculiarity. On the sides of the body here and there were scattered perfectly circular transparent disks up to an inch in diameter, and each of these in turn bore two slightly opaque spots situated opposite one another at the edges of the disk. These also appeared to be parasites of some kind, but just exactly what they were I was unable to decide at the time.

Two days later, the fish died after we had made several unsuccessful attempts to feed it. As we lifted its tremendous bulk from the water by means of a cable and hoist (it measured just under 9 feet between the tips of the vertical fins), a pair of small remoras dropped from its gills. As mentioned in the preceding chapter, they are not true parasites but commensals, sharing a relationship with their host that is neither harmful nor perhaps beneficial to the latter.

I had never before dissected an ocean sunfish, and since they are so peculiarly constructed I was anxious to have a firsthand look at the internal anatomy of this one. Despite its great size and bulk, I had little difficulty in cutting it apart with an ordinary butcher knife, as its bones were degenerated into a gristly condition (normal for the species) and offered about as much resistance to the knife as cheese. The hardest structure was the roughened, metallic-looking skin, and beneath this, the 2 inches of white collagenous material that encases the fish much like the peel of an orange.

From within, as from the outside, the sunfish appears to be mainly head, with a massive soft skull followed by a rod of immovable backbone! The heart, liver, digestive tract, and other viscera are largely crowded into what might be mistaken for the "chin" and "throat" of the fish viewed in its entirety, and the great vertical fins and clavus are manipulated by rows of bandlike tendons originating from the well-developed muscle tissue in the rear portion of the body.

Inside the gill chamber, where remoras had set up housekeeping, I saw that these fishes had not been the sole tenants. Immense, 2-inch Copepods related to the ones that formed its "beard" were clinging to the gill filaments, and many of them bore egg strings attached to their posteriors. There were so many of these Copepods that in places the gills were greatly scarred and in some of the individual filaments had shriveled to the point of uselessness as a result.

The strange transparent disks I had seen were easily removed with a knife blade and proved to be an unusual type of flatworm (Platyhelminth), the two opaque spots I had noted earlier being suckers for attachment to their host. The short, saclike digestive tract of the fish showed odd lumps and nodules where smaller parasites had imbedded themselves in the walls, but most amazing of all was the condition of the liver. This was literally laced with whitish roundworms of considerable length, and so filled with these was the entire organ that it reminded me strongly of chunks of wood I have seen riddled by shipworms.

It seemed remarkable that sunfishes can live in any semblance of health when thus parasitized, but apparently this is a fairly normal condition, since all I have heard of being examined were in similar shape. It must be borne in mind that some of the most efficient and successful of all biological para-

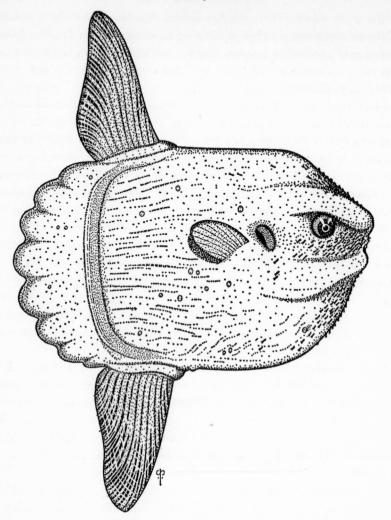

A Mola and his problems. (Ocean Sunfish wearing a "beard" of parasitic copepods and with flatworms clinging to his sides.)

sites, such as certain tapeworms and roundworms, are those which cause their hosts very little harm or damage, thus assuring their continuation. Whether the sunfish parasites fall into this category, I cannot say for sure.

Since our initial experience with these two different ocean sunfishes, additional specimens of each have behaved consistently in opposite ways. Invariably, the sharptails have lived only for a short while, being unable to adapt themselves to confinement, while the molas oriented themselves well from the beginning. An interesting parallel to this situation may be seen in the trunk turtle (*Dermochelys*) on the one hand, and the loggerhead (*Caretta*) on the other. Though both are of similar size and habits, the former cannot survive for long in a tank, while the latter almost invariably thrives.

Through an almost ironical coincidence, all sharptails we have obtained were in excellent shape to begin with, while the rarer molas had always been roughly handled and injured by their original captors and have eventually died (to all appearances) because of their initial condition which had placed them beyond recovery. Twice again we succeeded in getting a mola to feed for a short time, and for this purpose my wife Fanny has developed a "squidball mix" consisting of ground squid and Pablum which shows possibilities as a permanent diet for these enormous plankton-feeders.

Whenever I am asked, "What is your favorite aquarium fish?" my answer remains the same—it is the great ocean sunfish, the millstone of the sea, the weirdest, most perplexing, and most delightful fish of all, the mighty *Mola mola.*

# CHAPTER 10

# THE RED-EYED BOA OF BIMINI

*The Sargassum "Jungle." Fish That Soar and Fish That Fly.*
*Episode of the Haunted Sleeping Bag. The Capture of a Manta*
*Ray and Hanson's Secret Weapon. The Octopus and the Beer*
*Bottle. "Spooking" Spiny Lobsters. A Boa Hunt on South Bimini*

As the *Sea Horse* headed eastward across the Florida Straits toward Bimini, the Gulf Stream showed the deep, glowing indigo blue that can be appreciated only by one who has seen it firsthand. It is not the green-blue or the blackish blue of the more temperate seas, but a color associated with great depth plus the great clarity of tropical waters. Here and there windrows of the yellow-brown weed *Sargassum fluitans* buoyed by its many tiny gas-filled "berries" drifted on the surface, offering shelter to various young oceanic fishes, crustaceans, and soft-bodied invertebrates, many of which are colored so as to blend with the drifting seaweed.

While certain of these little *Sargassum* "jungles" offer shelter and concealment to small fishes, others may lure them to their doom, for clinging and crouching among the weedy fronds may be found examples of the goblin-like little sargassumfish, *Histrio histrio*. With a satchel mouth and baggy stomach that can encompass fish larger than half its own size, *Histrio* has fleshy, limblike, paired fins that are provided with wrist joints so that it can hold onto the weed. Its body is covered with small leafy tabs, and when it drifts from one patch of *Sargassum* to another it looks very much like a detached portion of the weed itself, especially since it has a habit of moving forward without moving a fin, but progressing through the power of twin water jets produced by the backward-directed, porelike gill openings.

I was engaged in dipping up portions of *Sargassum* with a long-handled dipnet and shaking them over a bucket. Besides a few *Histrios,* I was finding young triggerfishes, filefishes, Bermuda chubs, and young dolphinfishes. The latter, which ranged down to a length of less than an inch, were reddish brown with blackish vertical bars in contrast to the silver, brassy, green, and glowing blue of the majestic adults which, like the flyingfishes, spend all their lives at the surface of the sea and seldom venture downward more than a few feet.

Young flyingfishes were plentiful, and these would skim across the surface

152

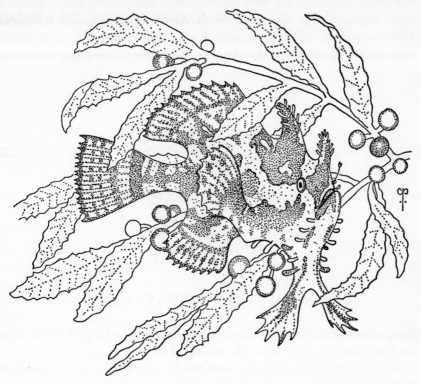

Sargassumfish, *Histrio histrio.*

Young Flyingfish, *Cypselurus sp.*

like small dragonflies for brief distances with tiny, tablike wings spread at right angles. Unlike the small South American freshwater hatchetfishes (*Gasteropelicus*), which have pectoral wing muscles attached to the breastbone in the manner of a bird and possess the power of true flight, the oceanic

Freshwater Flying Hatchetfishes, *Carnegiella sp.*

flyingfishes are merely exceedingly skillful gliders, and can skim for hundreds of yards at a time across the surface of the sea.

Occasionally one of the larger ones would scoot out in front of our bow and glide above the waves until it began to lose altitude and/or air speed, when it would allow the elongated lower lobe of its forked tail to dip beneath the surface. Then the fish, still airborne, would, by sculling rapidly with its vibrating tail, once again attain sufficient speed for another sustained glide. The process would often be repeated again and again until the flyingfish was a considerable distance away from the boat, or he might re-enter the water after only a short flight. Re-entry is not gradual, but appears to take place fairly abruptly, the fish suddenly "braking" his fins in the air and diving into the water at an angle. I believe that this is done to avoid injury to the delicate fin membranes which might occur should the fish attempt to plunge into the water at high speed.

When there is a strong wind, flyingfishes will often rise into it and be borne several feet above the sea surface, sometimes being inadvertently blown aboard a boat. I once witnessed an amusing incident of this type that occurred on an oceanographic trip I was making aboard one of the University of Miami Marine Laboratory vessels.

It was growing dark. The Gulf Stream was fairly rough, and flyingfish were coming aboard every few minutes. These were promptly collected and

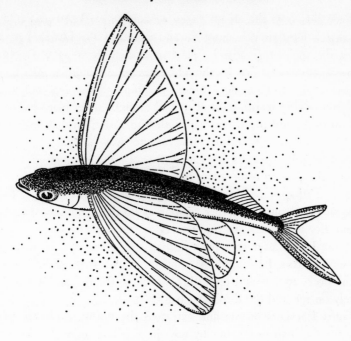

Clearwing Flyingfish, *Cypselurus comatus*.

preserved, as they appeared, by the ichthyologist in charge. Our craft was of a type that tended to bump and pound over the top of the waves rather than cutting through them, and perhaps through happenstance or diabolical intent on the part of the builder, the galley was located far forward below decks, where the rise and fall of the vessel could be most fully perceived. We were being served supper in groups of four, and I was trying to manage a full coffee cup which alternately became weightless and then was nearly wrested from my grip by strong gravity as the bow performed its endless ups and downs. The evening meal was a distinctly unrelaxed one and, although I am somewhat more than averagely resistant to the effects of motion at sea, the galley heat, combined with the aroma of cooking grease mixed with diesel fumes, made me feel that it was inadvisable to press my luck too far.

Securing two slices of bread, I quickly made a sandwich of the meat portion on my plate and left the galley, accompanied by one of the other crewmen, who, it turned out, was making one of these trips for the first time. He had just barely managed to gulp down his coffee before giving up supper as a lost cause, and, as we settled on the afterdeck which was the most stable part of the boat, I noticed that my companion looked rather listless. Thinking he might still be hungry, I offered him a portion of my sandwich, but he declined this with the air of a man refusing a weekend pass to a leper colony. For a long time he just sat and stared at the horizon, no doubt admiring the interesting abstract patterns caused by wind on the waves, then finally announced that he thought everything would be all right if he could just manage to go to sleep. Since the cabin and sleeping compartments were uncomfortably warm, most of us had brought along blankets for sleeping out on deck, and my friend had with him a sleeping bag inside which he slowly settled himself, and in a few minutes was asleep.

It was now quite dark, so I began to spread out a blanket on a mattress next to my slumbering companion, but, as I did so, a flyingfish sailed across the deck and disappeared inside his sleeping bag. A muffled wet flopping sound emanated from the nether regions of the bag, and my friend's eyes flew open. For a moment his face was frozen in an expression of the most abject terror I have ever seen on a human countenance, then with a wild flailing of his arms, he fought his way out of the sleeping bag, stumbled across the deck, and wound up with his back to the rail and his eyes fixed alternately on me and the throbbing bag.

Helpfully, I reached inside and extracted the unfortunate fish, which I held up for the man to see, but by now he was bent over the rail and the sounds I heard told me beyond a doubt that he was in no condition to be entertained by a discussion of flyingfishes and their lore. The fish ultimately joined the others in the Formalin can and my companion, I'm afraid, spent a somewhat sleepless night.

I made no effort to catch the young flyingfishes that I saw on this trip, simply because they are so delicate that they normally survive only a few hours, at most, in captivity. Placed in a bucket, live-well, or jar, they repeatedly bump their snouts against the restraining side and flutter their tails futilely until they die from exhaustion. Some day I hope to design a wide, shallow pool where these and other surface-living fishes may be kept and observed, and the movements of the soaring species studied by means of high-speed photography.

The purpose of the present trip was to collect a large number of specimens from the coral reefs adjacent to Bimini for the corridor and reef tanks of the Seaquarium. For this we were using the collecting boat *Sea Horse* with the floating live-barge *Sea Cow* in tow, both having recently been remodeled for collecting purposes by Captain Gray and his assistant, Emil Hanson.

Although I had accompanied the collecting crew many times on their trips to the upper Keys, this was the first time I had gone along with them to Bimini, and I was looking forward to my first view of the islands and reefs fringing the vast area of shallow and crystal-clear water known as the

Grand Bahama Bank. The distance from the Florida mainland is about 40 miles, and since the Gulf Stream flows northward through the Florida Straits at a speed averaging 4 knots, our starting-off point had been Angelfish Creek, between Elliot Key and Old Rhodes Key about 30 miles south of Miami. On our due-eastward trip we would be carried northward by the Stream and reach the Bank, according to calculations, just south of Bimini Island.

As we moved eastward into the prevailing wind, we encountered occasional small groups of redstarts and other warblers on their annual migration from the Bahamas to the mainland, and now and then one of these small birds would rest briefly in the rigging or on the deck of one of the boats before resuming its flight toward Florida. Often they reach the shore in a state of near exhaustion, and this sustained flight across the Straits seems a hazardous one for such small creatures to undertake. As I watched the warblers flitting across the glowing indigo sea with its yellow windrows of *Sargassum,* I suddenly noticed something unusual about the distant cumulus clouds that appeared to ring the horizon.

Like most clouds seen at sea, these were perfectly flat on their bottoms as if they floated on an invisible liquid, though their tops rose in billowing peaks and spires. To the north, west, and south these billows were white, but far toward the eastern horizon they were suffused with a pale blue color. This blue, which was the first indication that we were close to Bimini, is caused by reflection of the shallow waters of the Grand Bahama Bank. Long before our first landfall, the area of blue clouds continued to increase until they covered most of the eastern half of the sky.

The first point of land we saw proved to be Gun Cay, and we proceeded northward offshore past Cat Cay and other small islands and points of land until we reached the island of Bimini, which Gray and Hanson made their base for collecting. Director Michael Lerner of the Lerner Marine Laboratory kindly permitted us to keep our boats at the Laboratory dock, next to the penned enclosures where various sharks, rays, dolphins, and fish are kept for scientific study.

Hardly had the *Sea Horse* and the *Sea Cow* been made fast to the dock than we heard shouts of excitement close at hand. From another nearby dock we saw several native Bimini Negroes waving their arms in the air and pointing out into the channel that runs past the docks, where a great dark shadow was progressing upstream against the tide. As the shadow came nearer we saw a pointed fin on either side slowly break the water surface. This was a *Manta birostris,* one of the giant rays that live in tropical waters and swim through the ocean with great leisurely sweeps of their winglike pectoral fins. Quickly Gray and Hanson lowered the collecting skiff *Sea Colt* into the water from the deck of the barge, started the motor, and sped after the manta.

Gray stood in the bow holding poised a bronze harpoon on a long shaft, and as the skiff gradually overtook the ray he plunged this into the leading edge of one of its great wings. The manta sped forward with a sudden flurry, sending up a great swirl of water and sand behind him and causing loop after loop of harpoon line to run rattling out of the tub in which it was coiled. Gray's gloved hands grasped the line and gradually slowed it down, and the manta, with the restraint on one fin, was forced to turn sideways. As Emil Hanson speeded up the motor, Gray commenced to take in the line hand over hand until the manta, his navigating powers interfered with, was brought alongside the boat. By running the skiff slowly, the ray was then brought alongside the dock and the harpoon barb removed. Then, with the aid of a number of persons who were present, the manta was lifted over and into one of the wire retaining pens.

This latter operation was no easy task since the manta measured a full 10

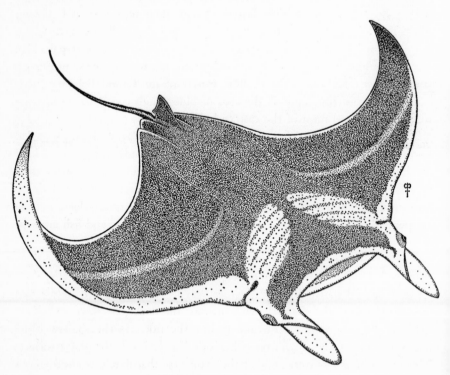

Great Manta, *Manta birostris.*

feet across the wings. It hit the water with a great splash and instantly sent up a shower of foam as it dived and rushed across the enclosure, only to flatten itself against the wire on the far side. Turning, it began to circle the space, this time taking more care to avoid the walls, and before long the great creature had calmed itself and proceeded to drift about in its formerly leisurely fashion. We presented it to the Lerner Marine Laboratory as a gift, since mantas are obtainable from waters adjacent to Miami and the problems attendant on the transportation of one of this size back to the Seaquarium would have been out of proportion to its value as an exhibit. Mantas are also nearly impossible to feed in captivity, since, like the giant whale shark and basking shark, they are plankton feeders, straining the small organisms on which they live from the water by means of their specialized gill-rakers.

The Bimini shore is interesting, mainly because of its great variety of ecological situations. On the Gulf Stream side it is rocky with steep sides in places, while on the eastern, or inner side there are sand and mud flats on which grow mangrove trees with large brightly colored cushion starfishes and needle-spined *Diadema* urchins, as well as the orange-stalked *Condylactis* anemones with their trailing, lavender-tipped, white tentacles resembling bunches of large chrysanthemum flowers, all gathered together among the curving roots of the trees.

On the southern point of North Bimini (the island consists of two parts divided by a narrow channel), is a long, wave-washed sandy spit with several deep potholes just beyond its tip. On the jagged and pitted coral rocks lying to seaward Sally Lightfoot crabs (*Grapsus grapsus*) with blood-red claws scuttle about and enter the water only occasionally, while in the pot-

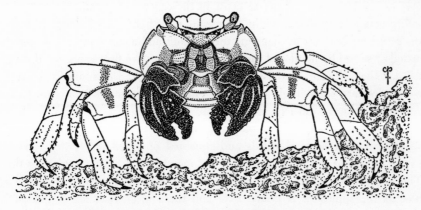

Sally Lightfoot or Rock Crab, *Grapsus grapsus.*

holes live a number of night sergeants, *Abudefduf taurus,* a sandy colored, 6-inch fish with broad vertical bars of dark brown. Preferring rocky holes and a crashing surf to the reef habitat of their near relatives, the sergeant majors (*A. saxatilis*), the night sergeants are less often collected than the latter.

While I am on the subject, I would like to mention that the scientific name of the sergeant major has always been a sort of bugaboo to me, for often I catch myself mentally repeating "Abu-def-duff-sack-sattle-liss" over and over like a voodoo chant until I am unable to get rid of it, and I warn the reader not to dwell on this phrase at too great length. Two other scientific names not easily forgotten are *Vampyroteuthis infernalis* and *Cookeolus boops.* The first is a deepsea octopus relative that is jet black in color with glowing red eyes, and the second is a large-eyed red fish. (The second name of the latter is actually pronounced "bow-ops" and means "cow-eye.") Taxonomists (scientists who classify things), like other mortals, must certainly rebel against conformity at times, and my hat will be forever off to whoever was responsible for the naming of two Mexican salamanders, respectively, *Oedipus rex* and *Oedipus complex.*

Returning to the Bimini reefs, one of our quests at the time was to secure a number of the reef octopus, *Octopus briareus,* which may be found locally in shell heaps and recesses in the coral rock. The species also occurs about the Florida Keys, but the Bimini examples average larger in size. The reef octopus differs from the common octopus (*O. vulgaris*) in having proportionately longer and slenderer arms (not "tentacles," for the latter are found only in squids and cuttlefishes and consist of two highly specialized protractile appendages that can be tucked away in a sheath when not in use), as well as a highly developed umbrella-like webbing that connects the arms and may be used as a sort of net to assist in the capture of prey.

Capturing octopuses at night by means of a light used to be our most successful method, for at that time they are out and about and may be easily netted or seized by hand and tossed into a sack or wire float cage, but during the day they are usually tightly holed up in nooks and crannies in the reef where they are exceedingly difficult to remove, or rather were, before Emil developed a highly efficient means of catching them.

His method involved the employment of a device commonly thought of in connection with hospital wards and consisted of a red rubber bag and a length of tubing to which was fitted a stopcock and a plastic applicator tip. This bag is filled with a concentrated salt solution which is run through the hose as the applicator is poked here and there in crevices about the reef.

Octopuses are highly sensitive to increase in water salinity, and a squirt of brine in one's vicinity almost invariably results in his immediately and hurriedly vacating the premises, trailing a cloud of dark sepia in his wake. Frequently the lair of an octopus (they will often dwell in one particular place for a certain length of time) is marked by an untidy litter of discarded crab shells, loose pieces of coral, and other "junk," and Emil has developed considerable proficiency in locating these while swimming about the shallower reef areas with mask and fins.

In the Bahamas, the natives catch and eat large numbers of the great pink *Strombus* conch, and piles of their discarded shells, which are a common sight locally, make favorite octopus hideaways. We have taken a number of them from a single shell pile, although their capture in such places is frequently far from simple as they will often pull in loose shells to block the entrance to their holes as they retreat.

The octopus, with his goatlike eyes (the pupil is a horizontal slit) and his great dexterity at manipulating objects by means of his suction-cup-studded arms, often gives to the uninitiated layman an impression of being more intelligent than he actually is. A case in point is the story related to me by a man who worked for the collecting department in the past and who was characterized, among other things, by an imagination that surpassed his judgment. This person told me how he encountered a large octopus one day among a pile of shells and other refuse, and, wearing a face mask and carrying a net in his hand, he settled himself on the bottom and prepared to capture it. Immediately the octopus, according to him, wrapped one arm about the neck of a broken beer bottle and drew it suggestively backward, at the same time fixing him with a steady and purposeful gaze. "I wasn't *about* to tackle the critter after that," he explained.

Our newly caught specimens were, as I indicated before, placed either in sacks or wire cages with tight-fitting lids until they could be transferred to special compartments in the live-well of the barge. It is almost unbelievable how small an opening an octopus is capable of squeezing through, and if the slightest avenue of escape remains, they will almost invariably find it in short order. Once an octopus did slip out from beneath the lid of one of the live-wells in the skiff, and when we found it it was quite dead in the bottom of the boat. I was on the point of tossing it overboard when an idea occurred to me.

I had heard that fishermen in the West Indies sometimes catch spiny lobsters by frightening them out of their holes with a dead octopus tied on the end of a stick. I recalled that we had just passed a crevice in the shallow bottom where a number of lobster antennae were protruding, and I thought that here was an excellent opportunity to test this practice and see whether it worked as well as it was reported to do.

Incidentally, the West Indian spiny lobsters (*Panulirus argus*) often gather in large numbers in holes, crevices, and other places, and along the mud flats of the Florida Keys it is a common practice to set out old oil drums, milk cans, and other objects that invite shelter, and these will usually become filled with lobsters within a short time. In these artificial shelters and in natural crevices the lobsters habitually betray their presence by protruding their long, spine-studded antennal "whips," by means of which they are well capable of keeping most ordinary predators at bay, and at the same time setting up their characteristic rasping "zip-zip-zip" sound of irritation which is produced by rubbing a basal spur on each antenna against a roughened stridulating ridge that curves beneath each eye.

Captain Gray once informed me that it was possible to catch spiny lobsters (called "crawfish" in the Keys) on a falling tide by carefully taking an antenna between one's thumb and forefinger, twisting it slightly, and pulling gently. If this be done correctly, the lobster can be "walked" from his hole into the open where he can be caught, but on a rising tide this is impossible as the lobster will brace himself in tightly and the antenna will break off before its owner can be led out. Despite my skepticism at first, I found this to be perfectly true and have tested it many times since, on both a rising and a falling tide.

Now preparing to test another lobster-catching method, I tied the limp form of the dead octopus to the end of a long stick, and with this I waded back to where I had seen the row of lobster "whips" projecting from a long crevice. When I finally located the spot, I bent over and, keeping close watch through a glass-bottomed wooden bucket, I poked the octopus as far up the crevice as I could reach.

I was hardly prepared for what followed. The crevice literally exploded in a frenzied mass lobster exodus, and several of them bumped sharply against my shins in the course of their frantic backward rush. There were actually many more of them than I had suspected in the recesses of the crevice, and as new individuals continued to appear they were joined in turn by large, lumbering giant spider crabs (*Mithrax forceps*) and an odd, flattened locust lobster (*Scyllarides sp.*) that looks suspiciously like the result of a love affair between a lobster and a Volkswagen. Though I have never had occasion to repeat this experiment, I can testify that this process of "spooking" out lobsters with the aid of a dead octopus certainly works to perfection; just in case anyone wants to try it.

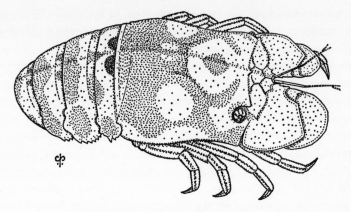

Locust Lobster, *Scyllarides aequinoctalis.*

The remainder of this Bimini voyage, which took place in the summer of 1957, was highly profitable, specimen-wise. From the reefs on the edge of the Grand Bahama Bank we took specimens of the beautiful black trigger-fish or durgon, *Melichthys radula.* Although seen on the Florida side of the Stream only with the utmost rarity, they are so common as to be almost the "trademark" of the Bimini Reefs, and their file-rough bodies of velvety

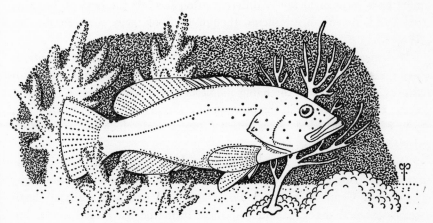

Golden Coney, *Cephalopholis fulva.*

black marked with a neon-blue line at the base of the likewise black dorsal and anal fins make them one of the most majestic of all reef fishes. There, too, we found the golden coney or hind, *Cephalopholis fulva.* To see one of these immaculately golden-yellow sea basses resting among the coral heads is an unforgettable experience, and even more so to bring one aboard on a line or in a trap and see the sun glittering on its body. The high point of our trip, however, came with our rediscovery of the pygmy angelfish which had been lost to science for a number of years. (I shall describe this incident in detail in a later chapter.)

At this point I wish to narrate a personal adventure that culminated in the capture of a rare and most unusual snake. Not only is it one of the very smallest of the family of the so-called giant snakes (*Boidae*), but it has one of the most peculiar traits to be found among living reptiles—its eyes turn blood red whenever it is disturbed. For some time I had heard of but never had seen this *Tropidophis pardalis,* the pygmy boa of South Bimini with its stoplight eyes. Close relatives of this rather variable 1½-foot-long snake are to be found elsewhere in the Bahama Islands, the West Indies, and adjacent mainland areas, and I was determined not to leave Bimini until I had made a personal search for the reptile.

The *Boidae* comprise the boas and pythons which are included in separate subfamilies, due to various technical differences, among them variations in the skull and the fact that most pythons are egg-layers, while the boas bring forth their young alive. Also, their distribution is somewhat different. The pythons are restricted entirely to the Eastern Hemisphere (a small Mexican snake known as *Loxocemus* and formerly thought to be a true python has now been reclassified into a different group), while the boas proper are to be found in both hemispheres, though most of them occur in the New World.

Biologically, the *Boidae* are considered to be among the most primitive of living snakes. They are believed to have evolved from a group of now extinct lizards very much like the living monitors (*Varanidae*) of today, and show traces of their ancestry in the form of rudimentary pelvic bones and a single pair of movable hind claws called "spurs," and which are more highly developed in the male.

While the island of North Bimini is densely populated, South Bimini remains a virgin overgrown land for the most part, and its fauna varies somewhat. Chameleon-like *Anolis* lizards and terrestrial curlytail lizards (*Leiocephalus*) are abundant and these form the main food of the boas. Less inspiring creatures such as centipedes and tarantulas also populate the ground cover of South Bimini, though these factors make it no less inviting. Accordingly, I made preparations for a visit there as soon as an opportunity presented itself.

Although the territory I wished to explore lay within a mile of the Lerner docks, getting there was not simple since a vast flat of gloppy mud which went bare at low tide had first to be traversed, and the shoreline at that point presented a nearly impenetrable barrier of thorny vines, while the bushes and trees held occasional nests of small but particularly neurotic wasps as well. On expeditions of any kind one tends to encounter colorful types of people, and this one was no exception. One of the two individuals who volunteered to accompany me happened to be at Bimini because he was steeped in the lore of the legendary Lost Continent of Atlantis and after years of research and reflection on the subject he was convinced that its remains would eventually be located in this particular part of the world. During the course of the trip he spoke of this and various other things, including earthbound spirits and transmigration of the soul. Since I find all of these subjects interesting whether I concur with the theory or not, the trip was anything but dull.

We left the dock at North Bimini soon after breakfast, crossed the blue channel where the manta was encountered, and headed our skiff toward the far point of South Bimini beyond the mud flats. The sea surface was nearly rippleless as no breeze was blowing and in our path we could occasionally make out a small shark, bonefish, stingray, or now and then, a magnificent white-spotted leopard ray would cross our bow with powerful sweeps of its great birdlike "wings," stirring up clouds of sand and mud as it did so. The tide was already falling rapidly, and about a half-mile short of our intended landing point the water became too shallow for efficient navigation with the outboard, so we shut it off and proceeded to haul the boat the remainder of the way by hand.

This required nearly an hour of seeking the deepest areas of the flat, and meanwhile our feet were sinking into the mud whenever we paused to rest. We finally left the skiff nearly dry at anchor a couple of hundred yards from shore, gathered up our machetes, canteens, cloth sacks, and other gear, and slogged ashore into the steaming thicket ahead.

Once we had beat our way through the first tangle of brush, we found ourselves in a cooler and heavily shaded situation where the top foliage formed an almost unbroken canopy of green overhead and the gnarled, lichen-laden trunks of trees which had weathered many a hurricane rose from the substrate of broken and eroded coral rock to lose themselves by tortuous routes in the overhead matting. What ground there was between the jigsaw coral rock was damp and the air had that cool, musty smell that is a combination of rotting seaweed and punky wood so characteristic of such situations. Here and there were great blue land crabs (*Cardisoma*) which bobbed their eye-stalks and clicked their massive pincers together at us before dropping into the round burrows which pitted the ground at the base of the trees. This latter action was invariably followed by an audible

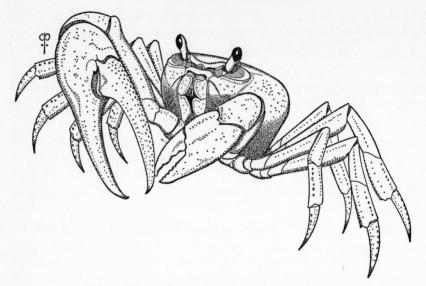

Giant Blue Land Crab, *Cardisoma guanhumi.*

splash or squpping sound, for the lower portions of their holes were filled with water. Adults of this species are either the color and texture of blue celluloid or else dull white, while the young are bright orange, purple, blue, brown, or red and sometimes combinations of these colors, no two individuals being quite alike.

While we were still close to the beach a number of large West Indian anoles (*Anolis sagrei*), brown with dark chevron markings along the back, scurried over the ground and made great leaps from one small bush to another, the males occasionally pausing to nod their heads and pump their expansible burnt-orange throat fans in and out with an air of great importance. When doing this these lizards always remind me of miniature trombone players, and it always seems to me that this activity should be properly done to the accompaniment of a Sousa march.

Here and there between the tree trunks were piles of loose rock, in some cases appearing almost as if they had been gathered and so arranged by hand. We commenced to turn these over one by one, for it was under these flat and porous coral rocks that *Tropidophis* spends the daylight hours, coming forth in search of lizards and other small prey at night.

For a time all that came to light, other than the usual millipedes, small snails, and large sow bugs, were little *Spaerodactylus* geckos, a tiny lizard scarcely longer than his name. These scrambled to the sanctuary of other sheltering rocks almost the moment they were uncovered, and now and then I would see the remains of their ¼-inch-long eggshells, deposited singly under the rocks. Unlike most lizard eggs which are blunt at both ends and leathery, these were hard-shelled and shaped like minute hens' eggs. In fact, they are almost identical in size and appearance to the eggs of a large Florida land snail which I have found under similar conditions.

Moving one particularly large rock aside, I discovered a fairly large hollowed space beneath, on one side of which was what resembled a single turtle egg. This puzzled me, since turtle eggs are not normally deposited under rocks, and this one was too small to be that of a regular sea turtle and too round to be that of a diamondback terrapin, and to my knowledge there are none of the latter in the Bimini area anyhow. Mentally eliminating the possibility that it might be that of an iguana (none occur on Bimini), I reached for the object so as to examine it more closely. The move was never completed. *"Tarantula!"* shouted one of my companions as he batted my extended hand aside. For, unseen by me, a large female tarantula was crouching in the bottom of the depression, her hairy body closely matching the ragged dead leaves and other vegetation. Her foremost legs were actually resting on either side of the silken egg case, and, had it not been for the alertness of my companion, I would almost certainly have been bitten, though the dangerous properties of tarantula bites, like many other things, have been considerably overrated.

Having no wish to harm the watchful mother and her developing brood, I carefully replaced the rock, and, needless to say, proceeded in my search with greater caution. Several more tarantulas, most of them with egg cases in various stages of development, came to light, and once we found a swarm of pale chartreuse, waxlike tarantulets emerging from a case. Like most spiders large and small, these tarantulas were slow to anger, although their strong protective instincts regarding their egg cradles made them potentially more dangerous at this time than at any other.

Suddenly, another rock on being moved aside revealed a shiny, almost black snake about 3 feet in length. This unexpected prize was a boa, though not the species I was searching for. We had chanced upon one of the slender Bahaman boas (*Epicrates striatus*), which is the only other snake native to Bimini and which sometimes reaches a length of 6 feet. Various other species of *Epicrates* are found throughout the West Indies wherever the pygmy *Tropidophis* likewise occurs. Many of the former are characterized by the presence of sensitive pits or pores located between the scales on the lips. These pits, which function in the same manner as the facial pits of poisonous pit vipers such as the rattlesnake, are heat-sensitive, and by means of them the snakes are able to locate warm-bodied prey such as rats and small birds at night.

Once this heat reaction on the part of a boa was demonstrated to me in a dramatic way. From time to time Fanny and I have kept various tropical tree boas, which have highly alert and nervous temperaments and will strike immediately if any warm object approaches too closely. The prize of our collection was a beautiful 3-foot green and white emerald tree boa, *Corallus canis,* which lived on a driftwood branch suspended on wire from our porch ceiling for several years. Unless removed by hand the boa never left his perch, although at night he would explore the branch from one end to the other. On one occasion I reached for him, only to have him lunge at me most unexpectedly and deftly snatch my lighted pipe from between my teeth. In doing so the unfortunate snake received a mouthful of hot ashes, but in a few days seemed none the worse for his experience. Needless to say, that was the last time I smoked in his immediate proximity.

When I picked up the *Epicrates* I found him quite gentle and disinclined to bite. I had seen this species before, but the Bimini specimen was darker than any of the others, almost obscuring the normal pattern of close-set wavy dark bands across the back. I placed him in a sack which I tied about my belt, and continued to turn over rocks one after another.

At last the time was drawing near when we would have to return to our boat and I was afraid that we would have to abandon our search for the *Tropidophis* at least for the time being, when I heard the cry of "Pygmy!" Turning to where my companion indicated, I saw what at first looked like a small, blackish disk lying on the ground where a rock had just been moved. There, lying in a neatly arranged and important looking coil, was our diminutive boa.

The snake was about 12 inches in total length, quite stout, and had a very short and blunt-tipped tail. The forward two-thirds of its body was dark brown marked with yellow in places, and there were rows of black dots along the back and sides, while the hinder portion of the body and tail were quite black. As I held the little reptile in my hand it gently twined between my fingers and I marveled that here was a true relative of the great pythons, boas, and the anaconda of the jungle compacted into a form smaller than the average garter snake.

I took a closer look at its head. The eyes were copper colored with tiny black vertical pupils, adapted as in all typical boids, for night vision. As yet the snake showed no inclination to turn his eyes red for my benefit, so I tapped him lightly on the top of the head several times with my forefinger.

Reaction was almost immediate. Both eyes commenced to turn perceptibly pink, then deep pink, and finally the pupils disappeared completely as they became red as two glittering rubies. The boa then opened his mouth slightly and a small amount of fresh blood ran out and formed a large drop in the palm of my hand. Immediately thereafter the eyes quickly faded to their normal color, the entire cycle having taken place in the space of little over five seconds.

Since all snakes lack movable eyelids and have the eye covered instead by a perfectly transparent scale called the "spectacle," some mechanism in this species evidently causes a quantity of blood to well into the space between the spectacle and the eyeball proper, and then causes it to promptly disappear after the mouth-bleeding occurs. Just what purpose, if any, is served by this strange habit pattern is open to question. The North American hognosed snake (*Heterodon*) will often feign death by rolling on its back when danger threatens, and likewise *Tropidophis* will, for a few moments at least, cause itself to look like a badly injured snake. Whether this action would under natural conditions successfully protect it from predators is doubtful, but it would be an interesting subject for further study.

Pygmy boa of Bimini, *Tropidophis pardalis.*

Incidentally, a similar instance of spontaneous bleeding involving the eyes takes place now and then in the Western horned "toads" (actually, they are lizards), *Phrynosoma,* and I have witnessed this on one occasion. When alarmed, the horned toad is capable of *projecting* a tiny but powerful stream of blood from the corner of its eye, and on the occasion cited one of them spattered the back of my hand with small droplets of blood so quickly that at first I did not realize where it came from. Since two entirely different reptiles have independently evolved a unique and startling mechanism involving the spontaneous emission of blood, there may be a similar purpose involved in each case.

My *Tropidophis* repeated his performance several times after that, although I hesitated to use him as a subject for demonstration too often for fear that he would lose too much blood in the process. Several days later I sent both boas to my wife in Miami by way of the expedition photographer, who returned by plane. We followed shortly thereafter with our live-wells laden with new marine specimens which were soon placed on exhibit in the Seaquarium tanks, and the two boas thrived in our home collection for some time thereafter.

# CHAPTER 11

# MANATEE FAIR

*A Mermaid Comes to Life. I Make Friends with "Cleo." Feeding Problems. "Cleo" Drinks from a Garden Hose. Scrubbing a Sea Cow. Birth of "Chloe" and the Capture of Another Orphan. A Tragic Ending*

We named her "Cleopatra" because she was so beautiful. Her body was fresh and glistening as she emerged from the river, and her breath came forth in a languid sigh. Her skin was gray and pebble-toned and covered all over with delicate, silky hairs. Her eyes were minute, black, and oozed gluey tears as she watched me, and her lips shuddered slightly, for they were dragging on the ground. This was the moment I had long awaited; she was in the net, the most beautiful sea cow I had ever seen!

Ever since the loss of our baby manatee mentioned in Chapter 2, I had hoped that we might secure another specimen for the Seaquarium. Since they are rigidly protected by law, it was necessary to obtain a special permit from the Florida State Board of Conservation, and having secured this, it was necessary to wait for some time in order to locate a suitable specimen that could be captured—or, rather, in a location where it could be netted, since this was an impossibility in most of the jagged rock-walled canals where they were to be found.

We had made a number of unsuccessful attempts to net an immense sea cow that paid periodic visits to the Seaquarium boat slip on the rising tide. Unfortunately, this old-timer was far too wary; we could never get close to him, although we marveled at his vast brownish bulk adorned with barnacles in the manner of a sea turtle. Although manatees normally surface and "blow" silently, old "Ferdinand," as we came to know him, would snort in a manner that seemed absolutely contemptuous, and although no gentler creature exists in the sea we knew we would really have our hands full if we ever succeeded in surrounding him with a net (which we were never able to do).

Once we managed to enclose a family of three that were browsing on sea grass at the edge of a channel, but since the lead-line of our net rested on soft mud, they easily worked their way under it and left in a great swirl of mud. Another time we had a mother and calf enclosed in the net, but the

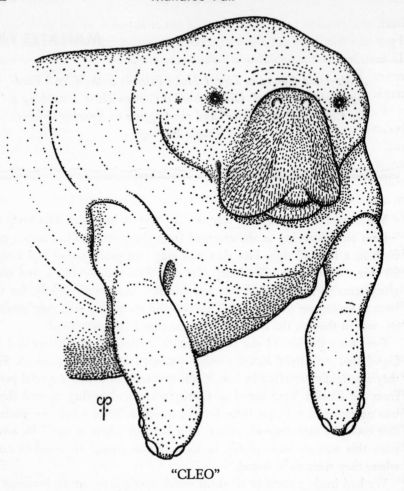

"CLEO"

net filled with mud and grass and rolled under when we tried to raise it, and again our quarry escaped.

I was becoming more and more impatient, because this was the main item still lacking in our collection and we were becoming increasingly aware of how difficult they were to secure. A dolphin is fairly easily entangled in a net because of its angular fins and flukes, but a manatee is a rounded, blimp-like creature and nearly as difficult to snare as a bag of wet cement.

Finally, one day in March, 1957, we received a telephone call from some persons who had located a large manatee near the end of a system of canals that connect with the Miami River. Captain Gray and I drove out to investigate, and found the creature in a spot that made it appear available for capture—if only it would remain there long enough. Walking along the bank to a position far enough ahead of the manatee so as not to disturb it, I put on a face mask and fins and entered the water. I found the canal about 12 feet deep at that point and with a smooth bottom free from entanglements. It all looked quite promising, so we returned with the Seaquarium truck, a heavy net, and plenty of extra help.

We knew we would have to move fast and enclose the manatee before it became frightened. One of our men swam across the canal as quickly as he could, dragging a long rope behind him, the other end of which was attached to the net. In no time at all we had our quarry bottled in, and seconds later the sea cow was in the bag of the net, pressing against it with so much force that the cork line was pulled completely beneath the surface. Giving the net some additional slack, we waited until the beast was thoroughly entangled, and then, with the help of a lifting crane we had hired for the purpose, we hoisted it into the bed of our truck, setting it carefully on a heavy mattress. On the return trip to the Seaquarium I rode with her (she was a female) in the back of the truck. Moreover, she looked as if she were pregnant, and I was delighted over the possibility of an addition to our collection.

At the Seaquarium we again hoisted her, still wrapped in the net, into the shallow receiving flume between the two large tanks. As we cut the netting and freed her, she came to life in a spectacular manner (having lain nearly motionless in the truck), raising great waves as she swam about rapidly from one end of the flume to the other. After a few minutes she quieted somewhat, although she remained quite nervous until dark, frequently rising to the surface to breathe.

Next morning, on arriving for work at the Seaquarium, I rushed up the stairs to the top deck to check on her condition. Our manatee was lying stiff and motionless on her back on the floor of the flume! I was dismayed. She had seemed to be in such good shape the night before. Had she died of shock as some sea mammals do, or had she possibly suffered rough handling during capture? While I was pondering this, I thought I saw one of her flippers move perceptibly, and a moment later, still upside down, she began paddling languidly about the flume, finally rolling over to an upright position, coming up for several breaths of air, and then once again assuming her strange position of lifeless repose.

"Oh, NO!" exclaimed a voice from behind me. Turning around, I saw two of our tank divers who had just arrived on the scene, their faces the picture of tragedy. "What happened?" they asked. I turned away so they couldn't see that I was chuckling to myself, for I had just received the same shock. The manatee was swimming again, but by this time my companions had turned away to break the sad news to another person who was ascending the stairs. "Deader'n a doornail," said the first man, but his voice broke abruptly as he indicated our very-much-alive sea cow with a sweeping gesture of his hand.

"Cleopatra" was her name, soon shortened to "Cleo," and we all became immensely fond of her. During the first few days of her captivity I spent considerable time in the flume with her, swimming alongside her, wearing a face mask. She was shy, but not too frightened at my presence, and when I was able to approach her closely enough to touch her, she would shudder slightly with a tiny, plaintive squeak and turn away. The sound was identical to that made by the first orphaned baby I had caught while the Seaquarium was still being built, and while almost inaudible at the surface, I could hear it very clearly underwater. The sound was made, as I have said, to the accompaniment of a slight shudder, but since no air bubbles were to be seen nor did the mouth appear to move, the sound must originate well back in the animal's throat.

Although I covered the surface of the flume with fresh lettuce and cabbage trimmings each night and cleaned them away each morning, there was no indication after a week's time that she had begun to feed. Moreover, she seemed to me to be losing weight and I was becoming worried. I was aware of the fact that captive sea cows are usually stubborn over shifting their diet to foods they are unused to. Paradoxically, "Cleo's" natural food, which consists of various marine and freshwater grasses, was growing in great abundance close to the Seaquarium, but it would be difficult to gather and terribly messy besides, as considerable quantities of this rough forage would be required. It was unthinkable to attempt to fill the flume with all this wet hay, which would unavoidably drift into the main tanks.

Nonetheless, she was going to have to feed soon or risk starvation, so as an emergency measure I took a rake and a couple of tubs and gathered up a large quantity of *Naias* grass from a nearby canal. This is a fine, wispy, green waterweed often used to decorate home aquaria, and manatees consume large quantities of it whenever they can find it growing abundantly enough. As I placed bunches of the *Naias* in the flume I wondered if she would feed at all, for her digestive processes were in a state of temporary cessation. To my relief she started consuming it at once, and in the space of a minute had polished off the result of my hour and a half of work, and was looking around expectantly for more. Instead, I offered her some lettuce, which she scorned.

To keep her in *Naias* would require the full-time work of two men, an obvious impracticability. I then turned to water hyacinths, a leathery green plant whose air-filled floating leaves line the ditches and canals of the Florida Everglades. She accepted the hyacinths as readily as she did the *Naias,* so we began to make twice-weekly trips into the Everglades for this staple until such time as we could wean her over to lettuce and cabbage, which were easily obtainable from local markets.

Since manatees frequently leave the sea to travel up rivers (as "Cleo" had done when we caught her) and there drink fresh water, I began to wonder how "Cleo" was faring in this respect, being kept permanently in full-salinity seawater. Certain marine reptiles and sea birds have salt glands provided with ducts for the ejection of surplus body salt, but to my knowledge nothing comparable is known to exist in the sea cow. Deciding to see if she was interested, I attached a garden hose to a nearby tap, turned on the water to a low stream, and dangled it into the flume so that the water played across her nose. To my delight, "Cleo" took the hose in both her flippers and held it against her mouth!

She was still having some difficulty manipulating it, but I found that if the flow were cut down to just a slight trickle she could hold it with little

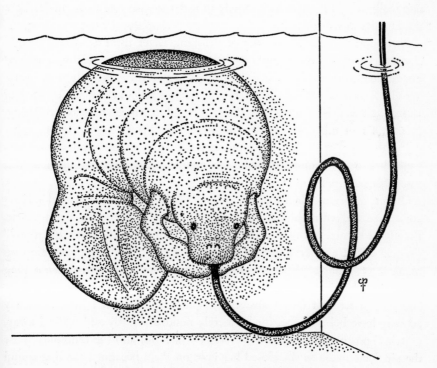

"CLEO" drinking fresh water from a hose.

trouble. She drank water in this manner for almost a half hour before dropping the hose. I began to "water" her every other day, and she would rest on the bottom or in mid-water, holding the hose in her flippers from five to ten minutes at a time. This performance was remarkably human to behold, for the flippers of a manatee, though short and lacking fingers, are jointed much as our own arms, and when they push grass into their mouths or paddle themselves leisurely through the water, one can begin to believe that these unfortunately dim-witted creatures may after all have given rise to the legend of the mermaid.

I hate at this point to have to discourage romanticism in favor of cold fact, but I must note that, while "Cleo" may have been a passable mermaid in certain respects, in others she most definitely was not. I have seen drawings of female sea cows that were obviously executed by individuals whose imagination was greater than their factual observation, for they were depicted as having quite voluptuous breasts. "Cleo," though mature and apparently gravid as well, could not, through any stretch of the imagination, be said to have a glamorous figure. In fact, in all the manatees that have come under my personal observation—and there have been quite a few—one really would have to look closely in order to distinguish the males from the females in this respect.

Returning to "Cleo's" manner of drinking water from a hose: this sight always seemed to baffle visitors to the aquarium. For some reason, it seemed implausible to them that she was drinking water while actually underwater herself. Repeatedly I would explain to curious onlookers that the kind of water she was drinking was not the same kind in which she was swimming. In fact, I remember that as a youngster in St. Petersburg I used to enjoy doing this very thing myself—sipping water from a hose while swimming beneath a dock, though I doubt that many others have indulged in this enjoyable pastime.

On one occasion, when I was watering "Cleo," a somewhat cynical-looking gentleman walked up beside me and stared long and silently at the spectacle. Finally he turned in my direction and said, "Mind if I ask you a question?" "Not at all," I answered, prepared to deliver my customary dissertation on manatee hydraulics. "What are you putting into it?" he inquired. Something about the phrasing of his question deflected me from my usual response, and with a straight face I answered, "Gasoline." For all I know, he may actually have believed me, for he merely nodded slightly and walked away.

"Cleo" prospered on her diet of water hyacinths, and the crumping noise the air floats made as she closed her jaws on them became a familiar sound in the flume. As I said before, the food of manatees is secured both with their flippers and their divided and highly mobile upper lip, which is covered with short bristles resembling the stubs of goose quills. There are no front teeth, chewing and grinding being done entirely by the heavy, flat, rear molars. It is in the shape of the skull and the lower jaw especially that manatees resemble elephants, and the skin color, texture, and arrangement of hairs is also reminiscent of a young elephant. It is easy to look at the flattened flippers with their tiny flat nails and picture them as having evolved over the ages from the feet of the same river-browsing herbivore that gave rise to the mighty mastodons, mammoths, and modern elephants in a different direction.

Between her hyacinth meals and hose waterings, "Cleo" would leisurely paddle herself, often with just one flipper at a time, in a circular path around the flume, frequently pausing and "playing dead" on her back for a minute or so. Though I have observed a number of captive manatees before and since, I have never seen another one behave in this manner. Although she had apparently gained back the weight she lost while fasting, she did not appear to be quite so plump as during the first few days of her captivity, and at this time we fairly well abandoned the hope that she might be pregnant.

Eventually, it was time to move her from the flume to a new 15- by 30-foot oval tank which we had built for her from reinforced concrete on the Seaquarium grounds. We again had to tangle her in a section of netting and place her in a large metal and canvas cradle and lift her onto a mattress in a waiting truck, drive her to the new tank, and slide her into the water. This was a process that she didn't enjoy in the least, and she softly squeaked her objections as we hoisted her great bulk from one tank to the other, her viscous tears—actually a secretion to protect her eyes from the wind—flowing freely. (I have read that the tears of her Indian Ocean relative, the dugong, are valued as a native love potion, though I cannot imagine how this tradition ever got started.)

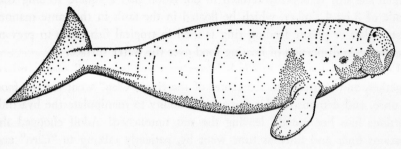

Dugong, *Halicore dugong.*

Her new tank was fitted with two separate water lines—one for fresh and one for salt water, so that we could supply her with any desired amount of salinity, and by alternating one kind of water with the other, we could retard the growth of algae as well. However, some algae still grew, not only on the sides of the tank, but also on "Cleo's" head, back, and tail, so it was necessary to drain the water from the tank at intervals and go over the walls and "Cleo" herself with a heavy scrub brush. Later, it was discovered that the best remedy for this situation was to include several large mullet (*Mugil cephalus*) in the tank with the manatees, as they would keep the algae closely cropped at all times, and the manatees seemed to enjoy the fish "grazing" along their broad backs.

Likewise, "Cleo" appeared to enjoy her scrubbing. This was usually performed by one of the divers or tank attendants, but occasionally I would do this myself. "Cleo" was remarkably cooperative at this time, and even with the tank quite emptied of water she was easy to manage and would roll from her stomach to her back and over again at a slight nudging on my part. With a hose in one hand and a brush in the other I would often sit astride her back or flat tail while I scrubbed. Oddly enough, if there was enough water remaining in the tank to float her, "Cleo" usually objected to being handled. Often while lying on her back "Cleo" would cross her flippers on her chest, eyes closed, wearing all the while an inscrutably peaceful expression, and at such times I was tempted to place a white lily on her bosom for effect.

She would still eat nothing but water hyacinths, and her care was at this time turned over to Adolf Frohn, the Seaquarium's Director of Animal Training. Adolf was born in Germany of a family of professional animal trainers, and his great persistence, attention to detail, and devotion to his animals have won him some remarkable achievements and the renown of being the first man to successfully train the bottlenosed dolphin in captivity.

Adolf's first undertaking was to induce "Cleo" to eat lettuce and cabbage, which she still stubbornly refused to do. Adolf had a square feeding tray made of 2 by 4 timber, which he floated in the tank in the same manner that a glass or plastic feeding ring is used in tropical fish tanks to prevent the too wide dispersion of floating food over the water surface.

Lettuce, cabbage, and hyacinth leaves were cut into small pieces, mixed together, and poured into the center of the ring. "Cleo" went for the food at once, and demonstrated a remarkable ability to manipulate the hyacinth portions into her mouth, leaving the rest untouched! Adolf chopped the portions finer and finer as time went by, patiently talking to "Cleo" and gently patting her as she fed, until at last she was accepting the lettuce and cabbage, which remained her diet from then on.

"Cleo" continued to thrive and be admired and photographed by hundreds of daily visitors, although she never became as tame as we had hoped. She was still reticent about being touched. She would, however, frequently feed from our hand, and visitors who were permitted to feed her enjoyed being tickled by her blunt quill-like bristles and always marveled at her tiny eyes and valvular nostrils, which were located on the very top of her nose.

On August 27 came the exciting day. On arriving at work, I was informed that "Cleo" had given birth during the night, and the tiny calf had been discovered by the watchman making his morning rounds! Had we but known, we might have observed or even photographed this event, which has never been witnessed and scientifically recorded. Only a short time before, we had decided that she was definitely *not* pregnant!

The small size of the calf at birth (35 pounds) had evidently fooled us. The baby stayed by its mother's side most of the time, although it would occasionally swim about at the surface of the tank. Its color was darker than that of "Cleo" herself, and its skin fairly soft at first, although this became rougher and more pebbly within a couple of days after birth.

I weighed the youngster (which proved to be a female) by lifting her out of the water and placing her in a large enameled pan on a scale. During this process, "Cleo" seemed not to mind our handling her baby, which was certainly one of the cutest baby mammals I had ever seen. It appeared to have had a very short umbilical cord, and I wondered if manatees, like dolphins, are normally born tail first in order that there be no danger of their drowning during the birth process.

Now in looking at "Cleo" I could see that the placement of her nipples, which were nearly in her armpits, made for a handy arrangement, for it seemed logically apparent that this would allow the baby to nurse and still be able to breathe at the same time the mother rose for air, which was usually about once a minute. However, for some reason we were to be forever thwarted in our attempts to witness the feeding technique, for at no time did we ever actually see "Cleo" feed her baby. Apparently this must occur quite rapidly and at very infrequent intervals (as it does in the case of rabbits, for instance), or else it must occur at night when nobody is close by to disturb them. I approached the tank as stealthily as possible on some nights with a flashlight, hoping to catch the youngster in the act of nursing, but always the two would simply be swimming about slowly together, or resting side by side on the floor of the tank. I left instructions with the night pumpmen and watchmen to keep an eye out for any sign of feeding activity, but to no avail.

Yet the baby was obviously being fed, for she continued to grow fairly rapidly and she soon became quite plump as well. Considerably more fearless than "Cleo," the baby would readily allow herself to be fondled, and I delighted in lifting her partway out of the water by her tiny flippers. When I did this, she would often roll her small eyes upward so as to show the whites, and she seldom made any resistance on the occasions when I would remove her from the tank for weighing, although manatees, like dolphins and porpoises, are totally aquatic and never leave the water for any reason, so that removal from it, no matter how briefly, must be a most unnatural experience for these mammals.

The calf not only grew but was apparently browsing on algae as well, for her nose and lips were showing constant green stains. Finally we noticed her nuzzling and apparently swallowing some of the algae that was growing on the wooden feeding ring (which we still used for "Cleo" since it kept particles of floating food from spreading all over the tank surface). This indicates that young manatees are evidently quite precocious, as she was still only just a little over a month old when she commenced to do this.

Then, on September 27, a remarkable coincidence occurred. I received a phone call from the Coral Gables Police Department stating that a young and apparently orphaned manatee had been observed that day swimming about the keel of one of the department's patrol boats, which lay tied to a dock in the Coral Gables Deep Waterway, about 5 miles from the Seaquarium. The corpse of a large manatee had been seen floating by some time earlier, apparently killed by collision with a boat, and it appeared that this might have been the baby's mother.

Captain Gray and the truck were out making a call that afternoon, and experience has taught me to take advantage of any opportunity, if at all possible, without any delay. Recalling my successful capture by hand of the first orphaned manatee, I decided to repeat this event, if possible. I placed a large dipnet in the back of my car, and then rang up my wife on the phone. "Fanny," I said, "put on your swimsuit right away. We're going to catch another manatee!" "Oh, wonderful!" was the reply. "I'll be all ready!"

As we arrived at the dock I saw a ripple at the surface of the water by the stern of the boat. I had changed to my swimming trunks and was carrying the dipnet, and on boarding the boat, I saw the little sea cow disappear beneath the keel. Walking around, we spotted it as it appeared on the other side. This one looked the exact size of "Cleo's" baby, and appeared to be in good health, not showing the emaciated condition of the first little one in

Hurricane Harbor. As it again came swimming leisurely toward the stern, I raised the dipnet above it to attempt to slip it over the manatee's head, but at that point it saw me and stopped swimming, lying close by the side of the boat with its head at the surface and its tail curved down beneath it.

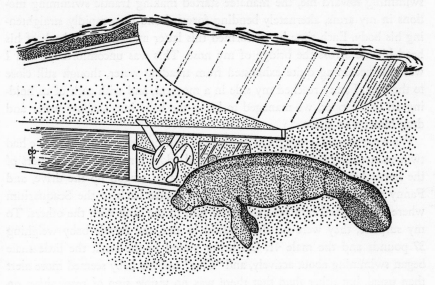

Young Manatee under keel of boat.

In this position it would be difficult to net and we might lose it. On the other hand, it seemed quite unafraid and its flippers were within easy reach of my arms. Remembering the comparative simplicity with which I had secured the Hurricane Harbor specimen, I dropped down on my knees, reached over the rail, and grabbed it firmly by each flipper. Then, straightening my back, I prepared to haul it aboard with one continuous motion.

Somehow or other, the exact opposite happened. The manatee instantly turned a half-somersault and pulled me into the canal headfirst without even a chance to call to Fanny, who stood some distance behind me. With a crash of foam I plunged downward into the dark water, still retaining my grip on the creature's wrists. He may have turned the tables on me, I remember thinking, but he's not going to get loose from me so long as I can hold my breath! (The fact that this obviously would not be forever did not occur to me at the time.) I was stubborn and determined, and I was going to take him back to the Seaquarium, and that was that.

After being pulled this way and that by the terrified little manatee, we both broke surface, which was lucky, since I was already beginning to choke on the water I had inadvertently swallowed during our descent. Twice he all but twisted out of my grasp, and I was actually surprised at how strong he was. Finally I managed to pull him against me and locked my arms around his chest, meanwhile shouting to Fanny for assistance. As she came swimming toward me, the manatee started making frantic swimming motions in my arms, alternately bending forward and then rapidly straightening his body. Each time he performed this latter maneuver, the back of his head hit me across the bridge of my nose. This was uncomfortable, and I was also becoming quite exhausted from treading water, though still close to the boat. Fanny reached my side in a moment, and with each of us holding on to a flipper, we managed to bring the baby into shallow water and drag him up on shore.

We were especially delighted to discover that he was a male. Now we had twin manatees! Now if only "Cleo" would adopt him also! The owners of the house behind the dock brought their station wagon up the drive, and Fanny and I rode in the rear with the manatee back to the Seaquarium where we weighed him before placing him in the tank with the others. To my surprise, they were nearly identical in size, the female baby weighing 37 pounds and the male 41. On being placed in the tank, the little male began swimming about actively, and "Cleo" and her baby seemed more alert than usual, but other than that there was no visible sign of recognition on the part of any of them, being the inscrutable beasts that they are.

Next morning, both babies were resting on the bottom, one on either side of "Cleo," and from then on both youngsters usually swam close together, either side by side or in tandem, occasionally making endless circles of the tank while "Cleo" dozed on the bottom. Within a few days it was apparent that "Cleo" had adopted the newcomer as her own, as he was noticeably plumper and looked well on the way to outgrowing his foster-sister. He was becoming quite active as well, although he never became quite so tame as the little female, who had been used to human handling from birth.

Still, we were unable to catch "Cleo" in the act of nursing either baby. This will always remain a mystery to me, as they were under observation most of the time and sooner or later one would have expected to obtain a glimpse of this process. For that matter, neither did we ever see her prod or nuzzle the babies as mammalian mothers customarily do, nor did she ever show the slightest objection (or any awareness of the fact, for that matter) when we removed either baby from the tank for measuring and weighing. In natural history books on the subject of Sirenians (manatees and dugongs), one almost invariably finds the statement: "They are said to clasp their young to their bosom as they rise out of the water to breathe." While I will not deny that this is a possibility, I have never seen any behavior of this sort during the time I observed "Cleo," as well as another manatee mother with a baby at a Florida aquarium. However, it would be presumptuous to say that this never happens, since, for the same reason that I have never personally seen it, I could equally well assert that they do not nurse their young!

The fact is that much remains to be learned about the Sirenians, which are perhaps the most atypical of all aquatic mammals in that they are individualists and totally unlike any other creatures in the world. Lacking the amazing intelligence of dolphins, the aggressiveness of sea lions, and the playfulness of the seal and the otter, they nonetheless have a unique sweetness and charm that is entirely their own.

The two babies grew rapidly in the tank during the following month before I went on vacation. I had a great sense of pride in having been able to add another member to the family, as I have never heard of this having been done anywhere before. I left them for what was to be two weeks with considerable regret, as I didn't wish to miss the opportunity to make any additional observations that might contribute to general knowledge concerning the habits of manatees.

On returning from vacation late in October, I arrived at the Seaquarium with a certain feeling of foreboding—almost a premonition—that something detrimental had happened to them during my absence. Nonetheless, I kept telling myself that I was just a chronic worrier and that my anxiety was simply due to my emotional involvement with their progress.

Unfortunately, my worries were only too well founded. All the manatees became sick soon after my departure, and the little female had become progressively thinner and had died two days before my return. Moreover, "Cleo" was going blind in one eye, a thing that should have tipped me off to the true nature of their condition. But anyhow it was too late. "Cleo" died the next day, and several days later the little male died too.

By then I had my suspicions, and I had the manatees autopsied by a local vet, who discovered the truth. During my absence from the Seaquarium and strictly against orders, one of the maintenance personnel had sprayed the area adjacent to the manatee tank with DDT and Chlordane in an effort to kill mosquitoes, and airborne oil droplets containing these deadly poisons had settled on the water surface. The chemicals were gradually absorbed by the manatees who could not tolerate them.

"Cleo's" body was frozen and shipped to the University of California for scientific study. Eventually we did obtain some more manatees, but the untimely death of our family remains one of the saddest events of my experience, as "Cleo" and the babies will always be, to me, irreplaceable.

# CHAPTER 12

# PINK PIRANHAS AND PROBLEM PETS

*A Shark of Another Color. Arrival of the Piranhas, and the Odd Effect of Their Diet. Feeding Sharks with a Grease Gun. Electric Eels and Other Shockers.* Dermocheles, *the Largest Living Turtle*

A knock sounded at the laboratory door. Opening it, I met a news reporter carrying a notebook and camera. "Are you the curator?" he asked. I told him that I was. "We understand that you people have a pink shark," he went on. "Is this true?" I nodded, adding that we actually had two of them. He shook his head, puzzled. "Pink elephants I've heard of, but a *pink shark* . . ." He looked around my office as if he expected one to creep out of the woodwork. "Tell me, are they a special kind of shark, or what?" "Well, they're really quite ordinary sharks, or at least they were to begin with," I explained, "but we have been turning them pink in the interest of science. Come along with me and I'll show you how it's done."

It all really started with our piranhas. We had recently added four freshwater tanks to the Seaquarium exhibit, and decided to turn one of them into a special piranha display, since these interesting fish were always being inquired about by the general public. There is considerable popular lore on the subject of piranhas, and, as is true in the case of sharks, a great deal of this is exaggerated or misconstrued in the popular mind. For one thing, there exists the common idea that the piranha is a very small fish. Most specimens seen in the tanks of aquarium importers have been small, from 1 to 4 or 5 inches, but at least two species exist which are said to attain a length of over a foot in the wild, and since the piranha is a quite robust fish for its length, a two-footer would be quite a sizable specimen.

Secondly, their actual danger to man seems to be grossly overrated, and ever since Teddy Roosevelt first reported on their legendary bloodthirstiness in his writings on South America, piranhas have held a special place in the public imagination. Not having firsthand knowledge of these fish, I called on Dr. James W. Atz, Assistant Director of the New York Aquarium. Atz informed me that this danger varies considerably with the various species (which occupy different habitats), as well as the conditions under which they are found in the wild. In areas well removed from native villages and the like, one may usually go swimming in safety in piranha-infested waters, while, on the other hand, in the rivers adjacent to villages where garbage and the leavings of meals and butchered animals are dumped into the river as a matter of course, the piranhas soon become quite fearless and frequently rush to attack when anything disturbs the water.

There are actually several species of "true" piranhas, all belonging to the genus *Serrasalmus,* though they differ somewhat in size and appearance. The smallest and slenderest of these is *S. rhombeus,* until recently quite frequently kept on hand by tropical fish fanciers. *S. spilopleura* is somewhat larger, up to 6 or 7 inches and similarly colored, being metallic silvery with irregular black dots on the sides and acquiring a flush of bright orange-red on the belly, breast, and lower part of the head when adult. This species is the "typical" piranha of the aquarist, being imported even more frequently than the former.

*Serrasalmus nattereri* is the first species large enough to be placed in the "maneater" class, as it grows to nearly a foot long. In coloration it is nearly identical with *S. spilopleura,* and differs mainly in having a slightly longer and lower dorsal fin, a more rounded forehead, and a slightly shorter but thicker lower jaw. *S. piraya* and *S. niger* are much larger, but quite rare in aquarium collections. The most impressive species in appearance is, in my opinion, *S. niger,* which is called the black piranha. At the time of writing there is an 18-inch specimen in a tank at the John G. Shedd Aquarium in Chicago, and it is indeed a devilish-looking brute. Its color is largely dark metallic gray, over which one may see occasional silvery flecks, and it has a most purposeful set of jaws and teeth to match its size.

Aquarists who have kept piranhas know that it is nearly impossible to keep a small number of them together, unless these are quite young specimens. If two are placed together for any length of time, one will almost invariably be killed by the other. If three are placed together, one will usually be killed quite soon by the other two, one of which will then proceed to win dominance over the other, harass, and eventually kill it. If four are confined in the same tank the same thing will inevitably happen, though it will take a longer time. Five or six in a group may get along quite well for a time, but once their number starts decreasing, the chances are that it will rapidly dwindle until one battle-scarred victor is left.

If, however, 10 or 12 piranhas are placed in the same tank, and especially if they are well fed, the chances are that they will get along beautifully. Above the "critical" number, which seems to be in the neighborhood of six, the individual action becomes more defensive than offensive, provided that they are not too closely crowded and especially if there is plenty of room in which to swim and hide. The reason for this, in my opinion, is that in the larger group each fish is in the position of being highly outnumbered by the rest, which acts as a damper on his normally aggressive behavior.

In one of our 500-gallon corridor tanks we built side walls of pitted rock and decorated the floor with the same, adding pieces of water-soaked wood here and there until we had a simulated tropical river scene. Since our piranhas were being held for us by a local importer, we hastened to finish the tank as soon as possible. Our specimens were 24 spotted piranhas, *Serrasalmus spilopleura*. They measured from 3 to 4 inches in length and I brought them to the Seaquarium tied up in two large waterproof plastic bags, 12 piranhas to each bag.

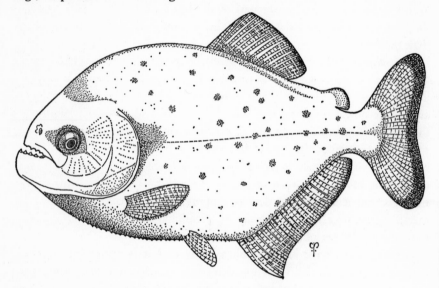

Piranha, *Serrasalmus spilopleura*.

When I released them into the tank, I could see that they were quite hungry, as their bellies were thin and their fins and tails were ragged in places where they had nipped one another in their close-crowded quarters. In order to feed them immediately, I put 200 *Mollienesia,* one of the easily obtainable local topminnows, in the tank with them. The piranhas started chasing and catching them at once, and within an hour nearly half of them were gone. The next day the piranhas were fed meat, although perhaps a dozen or so *Mollienesia* were left. From then on they received no additional live food except experimentally, although a half dozen *Mollienesia* continued to live in the tank, unharmed, along with the piranhas for quite some time afterward.

This illustrates a very interesting fact in regard to the relationship of certain predatory animals and their prey. Through not being eaten immediately the remaining *Mollienesia* became more and more familiar objects to the piranhas, until they no longer were sought after as food. Just why this occurs I do not know, but other aquarists have observed this phenomenon repeatedly. If other fishes are introduced as food objects into a tank and not eaten immediately, the less becomes the likelihood that they will be eaten at all.

This is similar to the situation when a new boy moves into a neighborhood and finds all his potential companions picking fights with him at first, but, as time goes on, he is accepted as one of the gang. This relationship may not necessarily be of a predator-prey nature, for almost invariably when *any* new fish is introduced into a tank, he is chased and sometimes killed by the established residents.

In introducing new specimens to an average-sized tank, I sometimes remove the original inhabitants for a day while the new ones acclimatize themselves to their surroundings. When the old specimens are re-introduced after a day's time they have "forgotten" their territorial claim rights and so no fight ensues. Were I to withhold them for a week or more, they would in all probability be attacked by their replacements, who by that time had established territorial rights of their own. In the case of the main tanks where it is impossible to protect the newcomers, I have used various stratagems to counteract the initial attack-response of the established specimens. Two methods that work fairly well are to introduce the new specimens at night or else right after the old ones have been fed, when they are least likely to attack.

In the case of predators and their potential food, any new *Mollienesia* that I experimentally placed in the piranha tank were immediately chased and eaten by the latter, while the acclimatized *Mollienesia* looked on, unconcerned and unafraid. This seems to be such a predictable phenomenon in the predator-prey relationship that I am convinced that, had enough Hebrews been dumped at one time into a lions' den, at least one Daniel would in each case have eventually emerged.

In feeding the piranhas generally, I decided to experiment. Their appetite and preference for fresh meat was, of course, legendary, so I set about to try them on various food items, such as fresh fish, horse meat, beef heart, beef liver, and bloody and fragrantly oily steaks cut from a young pilot whale that had recently been found stranded on a nearby beach and had died soon after being brought to the Seaquarium. As might be expected, the piranhas partook readily of the entire menu, but seemed to prefer the fresh fish fillets to anything else! (This is really not so surprising when one stops to consider that fish is what they are able to obtain most readily in nature.) Once a day we would hang a large blue runner fillet in the tank on a wire, and the piranhas would surround this, shaking it violently as they all bit hold and vibrated their heads from side to side with a fluttering movement of the tail. This activity is quite characteristic of feeding piranhas, and enables them to "saw" their way through tough flesh after having a firm bitehold.

This manner of feeding created considerable interest on the part of the public who witnessed it, and the entire fillet would usually be consumed within 15 minutes' time. Often I would be asked what we were feeding them, and when I replied that we fed them on fish, almost invariably I would be asked why we didn't give them raw beefsteak, as this was what the public seemed to think they required. One day I was watching them eat and thinking meanwhile how much more spectacular the feeding would be if they were actually eating bloody meat instead of the pallid fillets. Suddenly, what seemed to be a brilliant thought crossed my mind, and I wondered why this hadn't occurred to me before.

First, I procured a small jar of alizarin crimson. This exceedingly penetrating dye consists of small crystals of a dull orange hue, but when dissolved in water a deep red results. I filled two-thirds of a gallon glass jar with water and put in a spoonful of the alizarin dye, setting it on a shelf directly behind the piranha tank. I next instructed the feeders to dip each fillet for a few moments in the dye before suspending it in the tank.

The results were most spectacular, to say the least. Since the dye was harmless when swallowed, I knew it wouldn't harm the piranhas, and the effect was exactly as if they were gobbling fresh steak; and even as the excess dye mixed with the water in the tank it gave the effect of blood (between feedings this would all wash down the drain, as water flowed constantly through the tank). I must admit that this mild form of deception I was playing upon the public may not have been exactly cricket, and I have always abhorred any form of nature-faking in animal exhibits. I rationalized my way out of this by assuring myself that, after all, the piranhas *would* eat bloody meat if we gave it to them, so we weren't actually implying anything contrary to their natures.

By now the initial injuries the piranhas had inflicted on one another had completely healed, although now and then a certain fish might appear with a fresh bite out of a fin or tail, or sometimes his back. An interesting fact about this was that all of these wounds healed with phenomenal rapidity, in about half the time it would take the average fish to recover from a bite. On one occasion I noticed a certain piranha with a deep chunk taken out of his back directly behind the head, and in just about a week this had healed and the scar had filled in so that the original site of the bite could be seen only on the closest scrutiny. Apparently this is a natural provision to aid a type of fish that is in almost constant danger of being nipped accidentally, or deliberately, by its companions. Were the injuries so inflicted more slow in healing it is conceivable that some individuals might spend the greater part of their existence in a state of slow recuperation.

Not only did our piranhas recover from their injuries, but they were growing rapidly as well. Now they were eating at least two large fish fillets a day, and would have eaten more, except that we did not wish to overfeed them.

One afternoon Ed Nichols, my assistant, came into the laboratory with a slightly puzzled look on his face. "I wonder if I'm seeing things," he said, "or are our piranhas turning pink?" "Turning pink?" I asked, incredulously. "They sure look pink to me," was the reply. I hadn't paid really close attention to them for several days, but now I hurried to have a close look. Ed was right, they *did* look pink! On closer scrutiny, I saw that each scale on the fishes' sides had a tiny red border, and that each one of their fin-rays looked like a thin red line. They were absorbing the alizarin dye into their systems!

Within three days following this discovery, the piranhas were pink beyond all question. True, this gave them a rather festive appearance, but by now people were beginning to ask questions, so somewhat regretfully, we discontinued the dye and from then on we used undoctored fillets lest our piranhas became veritable red herrings. I had no idea as to how permanent their condition might have become, but the color slowly faded until after two weeks it was no longer noticeable.

A short time afterward, this same principle was put into practical use. A visiting scientist was making a study of the development of the skeleton in sharks, and since the cartilaginous skeletons of sharks are preceded in their development by substances containing calcium, which also precedes the development of true bone, alizarin dye was to be fed as a sort of "tracer" to young sharks with the hope that all their calcareous structures would eventually take up the dye and that they could later be killed, sectioned, and their minute anatomy be prepared and studied in the form of microscope slides.

For this experiment we selected young nurse sharks, *Ginglymostoma cirratum,* since these were easily obtainable and extremely hardy in captivity, besides being avid feeders. However, they showed a reluctance at first to take food that was heavily stained, so we made up a semiliquid mush of dyed ground squid and fish, which we administered to the sharks by means of a compression gun of the type used to lubricate machinery, to which was attached a heavy plastic tube.

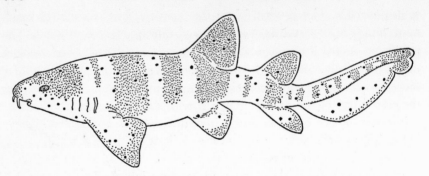

Young Nurse Shark, *Ginglymostoma cirratum*.

Nichols would hold each shark in turn while I forced the tube down its throat and administered the formula, to which we had whimsically applied the name of "Lydia Pinkham's." After a couple of weeks the dermal denticles (enamel-covered toothlike structures in the skin which give sharks their characteristic rough texture) were turning pink, and before long the sharks themselves, each about 3 feet long, were a bright shade of magenta all over. The experiment was a success, and these were the specimens the reporter had come to photograph. Although these and subsequent specimens were later sacrificed in the name of science, one was eventually spared for exhibition in one of our corridor tanks, and here he retained his unsharklike color for some time.

At the same time we acquired our piranhas, we obtained from the same source seven specimens of the electric eel, *Electrophorus electricus*. Although eel-like in shape, these unusual fish have no relationship with the true eels, but instead are freshwater fishes allied to the knifefishes of the Family *Gymnotidae* and not too distantly to the Characin group, a great division which also includes the small, brightly colored tetras which are so sought after by tropical fish fanciers, and likewise includes the piranhas themselves.

Aside from their highly developed electrical powers, the electric eels differ from the true eels (*Apodes*) in their manner of swimming and in a number of anatomical characteristics as well. For one thing, they are nearly all tail and it is this that contains the electric organs of which there are three pair. The other internal organs are highly compacted and the digestive tract is doubled back upon itself in such a manner that the anal opening appears to be under the fish's throat, immediately beneath the gills.

Whereas true eels and most other elongate fishes swim in a lateral or serpentine fashion, the electric eel can move forward or backward in a straight line by rippling the very long anal fin, which runs nearly the entire length of its underside. This is what I term the "conveyor belt" manner of swimming, and it is an exceedingly graceful and efficient method to watch. The electric eel is able to change direction instantly by reversing the rippling action, and it glides back and forth across its tank in this manner with a minimum of effort.

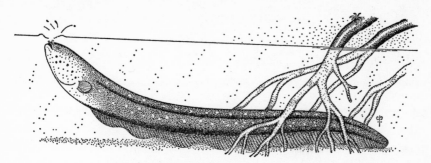

Electric Eel, *Electrophorus electricus.*

As in certain of the Characins, the electric eel is largely an air-breather as its gills have a reduced function and it must rise often to the surface for a gulp of air. In certain other air-gulping fishes such as the freshwater gars, the internal swim bladder is provided with a tube leading to the throat, and so serves as a supplemental lung. However, no such arrangement is to be found in the electric eel, which absorbs some oxygen directly through the vascular lining of its mouth.

For its electrical powers this fish has become legendary, because it is the most powerful of all of the several kinds of fishes which are capable of delivering a perceptible electric shock—including the electric rays, electric stargazer, and one other freshwater fish, the electric catfish of Africa. The electric eel has been recorded as delivering shocks in excess of 600 volts, which makes it definitely dangerous to man. A classic and oft-repeated story is that of horses being killed while fording streams in eel-infested waters, but this must be qualified by stating that individual animals appear to differ widely in their electrical tolerances, and horses are especially sensitive to electrical shock, while certain lizards, on the other hand, can survive shocks that would quickly kill a man.

In order to demonstrate the powers of our specimens, I devised a special apparatus for their tank, which was 7 feet long and 4 feet wide. The water depth was held to 20 inches so that they could easily rise for air, and in the open space above the water I set jagged rocks over which the incoming water gave the effect of a miniature waterfall. Projecting up from the floor of

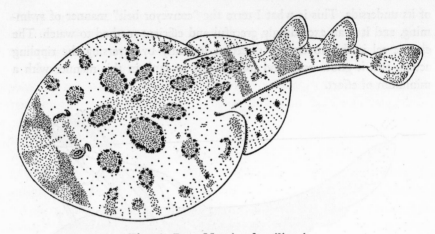

Electric Ray, *Narcine brasiliensis.*

the tank were large gnarled branches of natural driftwood, on which I planted a number of tropical air plants or Bromeliads and native orchids from the Everglades, until the over-all effect was like that of looking into a cross-section of a tropical swamp. To the front of the glass, about 6 inches above the water line, I attached two rubber suction cups 2 feet apart. These supported a length of clear plastic tubing inside of which was a heavy aluminum wire which curved downward to the bottom of the tank at each end, where it was soldered to a mat of copper mesh. In the center of the tube, between the supporting suction cups, wires rose in a broad loop through a slit in the plastic. It was my intention to attach a bulb at this point that could be illuminated whenever one of the eels discharged.

Now, a few facts about the nature of their electricity must be explained. While the voltage of the eel is very high, the direct-current amperage is very low, less than 1 ampere. This may be compared to a very small stream of water flowing at extremely high pressure. Since the individual pulses of current last only about one two-thousandth of a second and only three to seven pulses are given out at a time and these are completed in several hundredths of a second, an ordinary light bulb has no chance to heat up to the point where it will emit visible light. Something sensitive to the feeble amperage and with a light-lag must be used, and a small argon lamp serves this purpose admirably.

When I attached a small 2-watt argon jiffy lamp to the gap created by cutting the aluminum wire at the top of the loop and prodded one of the eels on the head and tail simultaneously with the two wire grids, the argon lamp would emit its ghostly purplish glow for a fraction of a second, as the contained gas retained its ionization for a brief moment following the eel's discharge. Repeated proddings would evoke several additional flashes of the bulb, but usually the specimen would cease to shock after several successive tries. Then I would select another specimen. With the apparatus firmly attached to the front glass there was still enough flexibility of the free ends of the plastic-enclosed wire to allow the copper grids to be moved sideways in order to contact the eels.

Under normal conditions the eels never released their strong current unless deliberately prodded, so it was impossible to set up any sort of program for the public that would be really effective, especially since not more than 15 persons could get a good view of the tank at the same time. Nonetheless, the system worked well enough to give me hopes of modifying it in the future in some way so that a continuous or nearly continuous demonstration of their electrical powers could be maintained.

Such a demonstration has been effectively carried out at the Cleveland, Ft. Worth, and New York Aquariums to date, but it makes use of a little-known secondary purpose to which the electric eel puts its electricity—that of navigation. In addition to its main defensive and offensive battery, the eel has a much smaller one known to scientists as the bundles of Sachs, which puts out, while the eel is swimming, a nearly constant series of low-intensity "pings" which work as a sort of sonar, striking any nearby object and bouncing back to the fish, who receives them through a specialized series of pores on its head. While the young have fairly well-developed eyes, the adults are nearly blind and must depend almost wholly on this sonar for navigation and the location of food.

At the aquariums mentioned, two sensitive electrodes placed in the tank are connected to an oscilloscope which traces a visible path of the "pings," which run from 20 to 50 per second, on the face of a luminous screen. The current may also be fed into a loudspeaker, and when this is done a sound remarkably similar to that of a small outboard motor may be heard when the eel is swimming full speed. (Of course, this sound is an "artificial" one, being produced entirely by electrical energy, and not by any actual noise made by the fish.)

While working about in the tank, I always had a dread of receiving a shock by accident. Fortunately, this never happened, though once I did receive a perceptible jolt that made my arms tingle when I deliberately handled a 4-foot specimen with a pair of what turned out to be insufficiently thick rubberized gloves. This, by the way, brings me to a pet phobia of mine: I am unusually jumpy about electricity and have been ever since I inadvertently grabbed hold of a live wire as a child and received a painful, if not serious, shock. Since then I will have nothing whatever to do with wiring fixtures if I can help it, and even touching a metal object after walking about on a thick rug will cause me to flinch.

Since I consider electricity to be the invention of the Devil, it is not surprising that I have had some rather bizarre experiences with it. Once, during my early college days, I volunteered to minister to an ailing boa constrictor at a local wild animal compound. The snake, a 9-footer, was suffering from a condition known as canker-mouth, which is fairly common among large captive snakes that have not fed for some time, and while the disease is fairly easy to treat in its early stages it is almost invariably fatal if left unchecked.

This particular boa was in a large electrically heated cage fitted with a sliding door, and it was my custom to visit it every other day and swab its gums with Listerine after removing any loose teeth with a pair of forceps. My patient was showing marked improvement, and owing to its rather lethargic wintertime condition, it offered little resistance to being handled. On this particular occasion I had opened the door, seized the boa by the neck, pried its mouth open with the fingers of one hand while I poked about for loose teeth with the other, when I suddenly received a shock that ran up my arms through my body and down through my legs and left me tingling for some time after. What had happened was that the snake, grown restless, had somehow worked its tail into the wiring of the heater and had formed a direct connection, by way of me, to the ground. I will say that the boa took it much better than I did; in fact, he hardly budged.

On another occasion, in 1947, I was working as assistant to the curator of the oceanarium at Marineland, Florida, and was engaged in cleaning a 100-gallon tank containing several octopuses. The tank was provided with a removable screen top in order to prevent them from climbing out, and it was our custom to place a wooden partition in the center of the tank during cleaning and work on one half of the tank while the octopuses were confined in the other. This was a necessary procedure, since, after a short while in captivity, octopuses become fearless and highly curious, and will seize hold of one's hand or any brushes or other paraphernalia that comes within their reach, considerably hindering the cleaning operation in the process.

On this occasion I was engaged in scrubbing an accumulation of algae off the front glass of the free side of the tank with a piece of steel wool bound to a stick, when one of the octopuses behind the barrier rose to the surface, and, inflating its bulblike body, sent several spurts of water in my direction. This was a rather frequent occurrence, and since I was wearing only bathing trunks at the time, I paid little attention to it. By happenstance the final water jet came in contact with a 100-watt light bulb over the tank. This exploded practically in my face with a great flash of light, and because the stream of salt water made a direct connection between the lighting fixture and the wire tank cover on which my hand rested, I received a terrific jolt in the process. Needless to say, this was the last time I cleaned the tank without first unscrewing the bulbs and covering the lighting fixtures.

The awesome powers of the electric eel and my own personal feelings on the subject of electricity notwithstanding, I have always had a special fondness for these animals, mainly because of their deliberate and purposeful actions and their truly majestic manner of swimming.

Very little is known of their life history to date, beyond the fact that they appear to migrate to swampy areas for the purpose of breeding during the rainy season, and on returning, one of the parents will be seen to be accompanied by a great mass of fingerling young, who remain close to the head (the electrically positive end) of their guardian until they acquire full electrical maturity at the length of several inches. (Just how much direct control the parent maintains over its brood I have no idea, but one can well imagine the serious consequences, should any of them ever try to get out of line.) Much still remains to be learned of these creatures, and doubtless considerable research into their nature and habits can continue to be carried on in the aquarium as well as in the field.

In the aquarium, there are certain creatures that never seem to survive for more than a short while due to something in their make-up that resists adaptation to confinement. A case in point is that of the giant leatherback turtle or luth, *Dermochelys coriacea*. This is the largest of all the sea turtles, reaching a weight in excess of half a ton and a length of 8 feet. It has no near relatives, and scientific opinion varies as to whether it is a primitive holdover from prehistoric times or the descendant of a more modern type of turtle whose shell has undergone degeneration in keeping with its swift movements in the open sea.

At any rate, this turtle has virtually no shell, this being replaced by a bone-supported, tough, leathery integument reinforced by seven bony ridges running the full length of the upper side. In captivity, no adults of the luth have survived more than a week or so, owing to the turtle's inability to adapt itself to a tank with confining walls. I have seen specimens in a large tank of the oceanarium type swim repeatedly into the side walls at full speed, so injuring their heads and flippers that they either soon died or eventually had to be released, while refusing all food in the meantime. In this form of behavior they resemble certain fishes, such as the giant pointed-tailed ocean sunfish previously mentioned in Chapter 9.

At sea, the leatherback turtle is known, like the sunfish, to feed on jelly-fishes to a considerable extent, although it is hard to visualize how much in the way of genuine nourishment can be obtained thereby, as the ratio of organic matter to water in the bodies of these latter creatures is small indeed, and, judging from the great activity of the swimming leatherback, its metabolism must be much higher than that of the ordinary sea turtles. Undoubtedly, they must consume a large quantity of other material as well, and their dissected stomachs have indicated that they also normally eat fishes, crustaceans, and a certain amount of seaweed.

Usually solitary creatures, leatherbacks will nevertheless sometimes con-gregate in large numbers among jellyfish swarms. Once a large group of them were observed from the air, swimming about in shallow water along the northern shore of the Gulf of Mexico near Ft. Walton, Florida. Closer investigation showed that they were all engaged in feeding on large *Sto-molophus,* or cannon-ball jellyfishes. These particular jellyfishes appear in great numbers along the Florida coast at certain times and are well named, for they are nearly round, being much the size and shape of the average grapefruit, and are almost as solid as well, for they can be lifted from the water without breaking apart.

Where ordinary sea turtles have an upper jaw that slightly overlaps the lower and forms a single hooked beak in front, the leatherback has a double hook with a deep notch in the center. The greatly developed flippers are smooth-skinned and clawless in the adult, and the short tail is vertically flat-tened like a sort of rudder. The color of the upper surface varies from steel-gray to nearly black. This combination of characters, together with the lack of the usual horny plated shell found in most turtles, serves to instantly distinguish this species from all others.

One night we obtained a large female luth from a shrimp fisherman who entangled it in his net quite by accident as he was fishing close to the Sea-quarium. This happened during a time when the Shark Channel was nearly empty of specimens, so we released the turtle (which we named "Claire Boose Luth") there in hopes that, like the large sharks, it would orient itself upstream and learn to avoid collision with the side walls.

Unfortunately, this wasn't successful. The turtle swam about hugging the outer wall from the first, and within a couple of days we were forced to remove and free her before she had injured herself fatally. It then ap-peared to us that any attempt to keep a large one for any length of time would be a futility, though I continued to hope that through some stroke of luck we might be able to obtain a young one, since a hatchling had been kept alive for several weeks the year before at Marine Studios, and I had

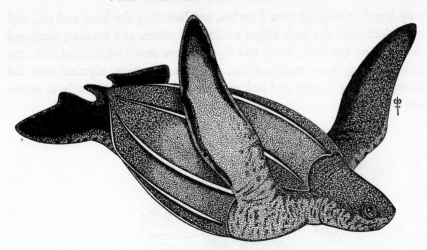

Giant Leatherback Turtle or Luth, *Dermochelys coriacea.*

read where a Dr. P. E. P. Deraniyagala of Ceylon had managed to rear a few to a fairly large size. This he did by keeping them in a rather large tank and patiently feeding them on finely chopped fish until they gradually became acclimatized to their artificial surroundings.

I did not have long to wait, for the following summer, in 1957, we were presented with 12 hatchlings by the Florida State Board of Conservation. According to all available reports, the leatherback only infrequently lays its eggs along the Florida coast, but on this occasion one had been discovered by poachers in the act of depositing eggs in a large hole it had scooped in the sand above the tide line on Jupiter Island near Ft. Pierce. Since turtle eggs have acquired a traditional value far in excess of their actual culinary merits, these are eagerly sought after by local residents of the beach areas, and despite Florida law which strictly prohibits such activity in the name of conservation, poachers occasionally patrol the beaches in jeeps and other vehicles during the laying season for the purpose of plundering turtle nests, sometimes not even waiting until the female has laid but butchering her on the spot.

Fortunately, in this case the poachers had been apprehended and the eggs confiscated and subsequently hatched in containers of sand by the conservationists. Most of the young were eventually returned to the sea, but the aforementioned specimens were given to us in order that we might attempt to rear them.

The babies were remarkable little creatures, not only in their shape but in their coloration as well, being mainly black and white. They each had a body length of slightly over 3 inches, not including the head and tail, and were black with the back ridges outlined in white, and between these and elsewhere on the body, head, and flippers were small whitish dots. On the underside they were mainly white, and this coloration, together with the immensely long flippers and lack of shell, likened them strikingly to miniature penguins.

Baby Leatherback Turtles.

Dividing them into three groups of four each, I placed them in three 10-gallon glass aquarium tanks provided with running seawater. True to their nature, they bumped the glass constantly and often remained for minutes in one position with snout pressed against the glass and their long clawless flippers flapping up and down like wings, in a futile attempt to swim forward. Because of their small size and the smoothness of the glass, I felt that they would be unlikely to injure themselves in this manner. Some of them already had injured snouts where they had previously scraped them on the sides of a concrete tank, and I treated these with penicillin ointment and within a few days their injuries had healed, although they continued to bump the glass with as much vigor as before.

Reading Dr. Deraniyagala's account of rearing his Ceylon specimens, I decided to start them out on ground squid, clams, and fish. As an extra "psychological persuader" I placed two hatchling Atlantic loggerheads, *Caretta caretta,* in each tank with the leatherbacks. It was my hope that, since the latter adapt especially well to captivity and are good feeders, their presence might somehow set an example to the leatherbacks.

Baby Loggerhead, *Caretta caretta.*

Whether or not this actually happened I cannot say, but within two days all the leatherbacks were feeding with gusto. I noticed, however, that their feeding behavior was just as erratic as their constant attempts to swim through the glass walls of their tank. While the little loggerheads would attack the morsels with deliberation, the presence of food would instantly cause the leatherbacks to open their jaws widely and snap about haphazardly in all directions until they got hold of something, it seemed to me, by sheer happenstance. They fed in this manner from this time on, and it wasn't until about three weeks later that their continuous flapping about and nose-bumping began to abate somewhat.

They put on weight rapidly from the first, outstripping the loggerheads in their growth. Deraniyagala's success with these creatures gave me added hope that I might rear them to a size where they could eventually be placed in one of the display tanks, but for the present they were confined in my private laboratory, and Nichols and I took turns feeding them twice daily.

At this time occurred one of those remarkable coincidences which I personally experience only occasionally. One day, shortly after I had fed the turtles, I answered a knock at the laboratory door. In came a dark-complexioned, scholarly gentleman who introduced himself as Dr. Deraniyagala from the Colombo Museum in Ceylon! To say I was astounded would be an understatement for I had no idea even that he was visiting the States, much less the Miami Seaquarium at this time. He explained that he had come to Miami to visit a friend he had met in Ceylon, and that this friend, who also knew me, had suggested that he visit the Seaquarium before he left.

It was Deraniyagala's turn to be surprised when I showed him the *Dermochelys* turtles in their tanks on a wooden table behind my desk. He was very intrigued with them and wished me luck in my attempts to rear them, as he had successfully done. I explained to him that a couple of things were happening to the turtles at this stage which caused me some surprise. First of all, on hatching they were completely covered with a mosaic of tiny, closely set scales or plates in place of the smooth, leathery skin of the adults. I had expected these scales to become gradually smaller and less distinct as the turtles increased in size, but for a time they remained as much in evidence as ever, with no sign of becoming resorbed. Then one day I noticed that two of my specimens showed irregular grayish patches on the limbs and body, and the following day all the remaining turtles were thus afflicted. Thinking that this might be some sort of skin infection, I rubbed the "afflicted" parts with penicillin ointment in an effort to arrest the condition, whatever it might be, when I noticed that the scales were rubbing off in patches, actually being shed instead of becoming overgrown by the skin as I would have expected.

After all the scales were shed, the white stripes and spots that marked the little turtles were brighter and more clear-cut than ever, exactly the opposite of what I would have expected, since the adults are quite devoid of any markings. Dr. Deraniyagala explained that both these phenomena were quite normal, and in addition he showed me a photograph of a leatherback turtle he had reared in a tank for well over a year. This one appeared to have a "shell" length of about 2 feet and at this stage its markings were even bolder in appearance, its pattern of white stripes and intervening spots reminding me strongly of the pattern of the great whale shark, *Rhincodon typus,* which also spends much of its time at the surface of the open sea.

Just why these turtles should develop a progressively more strongly marked body pattern as they increase in size, only to lose it altogether as an adult, is something of a mystery, though it may possibly correlate with some change in diet or habits, or it may be that the pattern serves some sort of protective function at this time in their lives when they still lack the immense bulk and speed of the adult.

Following Deraniyagala's visit the turtles continued to feed and to increase rapidly in size. I was prepared to move them to a roomier tank, but after I had kept them for about a month and a half they began dying off for no accountable reason. Within the space of several days a specimen that had previously been feeding well would cease to eat, rapidly become hollow-bellied, and expire. One after the other of the turtles followed suit until only three were left, and these in turn expired almost simultaneously a week later. Perhaps something in their diet was insufficient, or it may have been that the size of their aquarium curtailed their normal swimming activity too tightly. At any rate, I was unable to rear them to a larger size, and was deeply disappointed at the loss of these prize reptiles which are a worthy addition to any collection.

Hawksbill Turtle, *Eretmochelys imbricata.*

Perhaps as more is understood concerning their natures, these and other "difficult" creatures can eventually be added to the ever-growing list of animals that can be kept successfully under aquarium conditions. It is problem pets like these that offer a true challenge to the aquarist, and although the public may become more excited over meat-eating piranha fish or eels that light bulbs, the aquarist, with his sympathy for and understanding of the ways and requirements of his charges, frequently achieves more rewarding satisfaction in the solving of problems of this type.

# CHAPTER 13

# THE OCTOPUS IN CAPTIVITY

*Egg-Braiding and Maternal Care. Poisonous Bites and Color Changes. Strange Love Life of the Octopus. Hatching the Young. Collecting Octopuses at Night and the Episode of the Singing Sewer. A Mystery Specimen. Freezing a Giant Octopus for Shipment. A Flying Squid and the Discovery of* Pick- fordiateuthis

A crowd had gathered in the gallery before the rock-lined tank where the octopuses were kept. One of our large *Octopus vulgaris* had been laying eggs all morning and this spectacle never failed to attract considerable attention, partly because of the unorthodox manner in which it was done. Egg-laying with this particular specimen had become almost a weekly occurrence, although no young were ever hatched since she invariably devoured the eggs a short time later. It would do no good to take the eggs from her, or vice versa, since constant maternal care which includes turning them about with her arms and blowing streams of water over them to provide adequate oxygen, is necessary for their successful development.

Octopus eggs are small, numerous, and teardrop-shaped, and have at their pointed end a short, tough thread for attachment to some solid object. In this case the octopus had glued the first threads to the front glass by means of an adhesive substance and was proceeding to take the eggs in her basal suckers as they appeared one by one and to braid their threads together like a string of firecrackers. After the first string had reached the length of about 3 inches she started a new one close to the base of the first. Now and then she would pause in her work, eat a few eggs reflectively, and then continue to add others to the growing string.

The reproductive habits of the octopus are among the strangest to be found anywhere in the animal kingdom. In order to understand them fully, one must first have a basic understanding of the octopus and its anatomy. Although it bears practically no resemblance to its relatives the snail, the clam, and the oyster, the octopus represents a highly specialized type of mollusk, called a Cephalopod, or "head-footed one." Since the octopus normally rests in a halfway upside-down position, the true relationships of its body parts can be confusing to the layman, but if it is laid on its side with

*Octopus vulgaris* guarding eggs.

all its arms trailing in one direction, they may be somewhat more easily understood.

The large, bulb-shaped portion of the octopus is its body. This is provided with no appendages, but beneath the slight constriction that serves as a neck is a wide transverse slit called the mantle fold, into which water is taken into the mantle cavity where the feathery gills are located, and expelled through a short, muscular tube known as the siphon, by means of which the creature may jet-propel itself (backward) on occasion. The head of the octopus is about one-third the size of the body and bears the eight muscular arms which in most species are studded with a double row of suction cups, though a few kinds have but a single row of suckers on each arm. In the center of the disk formed by the united arm bases is the mouth, which consists of a retractable horny beak enclosed in a fleshy sheath. There is a radula, or spine-bearing tongue which lies coiled like a watch spring and the posterior salivary glands secrete a highly toxic poison which is capable of quickly paralyzing small fishes, crabs, and other animals which form the octopuses' prey.

Although octopus bites of humans are exceedingly rare, I was once bitten on the forearm by a small species (*Octopus joubini*) which I had found hiding in a scallop shell from the bottom of Boca Ciega Bay in St. Petersburg. I was allowing this tiny octopus with a 4-inch spread of arms to crawl along my arm, when suddenly it stopped, appeared to bear down, and almost instantly I suffered an intense, burning pain like a hornet sting, which lasted for an hour or so. Presumably the bite of a large octopus could be quite dangerous in most cases, and at least one death from this cause has been reported to date.

Pygmy Octopus, *Octopus joubini.*

In addition to its venomous bite, the octopus carries a sac of sepia, or octopus-ink, within its mantle cavity, and this substance, which tends to form a fibrous clot when ejected into the surrounding water, has an anesthetic effect on the visual and olfactory senses of fishes, being a highly efficient means of protection. Many books refer to this ink as being used as a protective "smoke screen" by octopuses and squids. In some cases I have seen it apparently thus employed, but more frequently I have seen the animal who ejected it instantaneously fade to a whitish color (no other living creature has such rapid powers of color change) and rush away from the ink blob, which, as I have said before, tends to retain a definite shape and appears to act as a "dummy" to distract attention from its owner, who is meanwhile beating a hasty retreat.

In preparation for the mating act, the male octopus develops a peculiar ridged spoon- or pad-shaped structure, called a hectocotylus, on the tip of one of his arms, usually the third one on the right-hand side. The hectocotylized arm is believed by some to be employed to stimulate the female preparatory to mating, and there is some evidence for this. However, its primary function appears to be to transfer the sperm cells, which are enclosed in small gelatin-like capsules called spermatophores, to the mantle cavity of the female.

The hectocotylized arm not only bears its strange applicator at its tip, but also has a longitudinal groove extending from the region of the hectocotylus to its base and into the mantle cavity. It is up this groove that the spermatophores travel before being implanted within the female by the hectocotylus. Soon after the female receives the spermatophores, these rupture or explode, fertilizing her developing eggs. The size of the eggs as laid often has little to do with the size of the adult of the species that produced them. Thus, the tiny *Octopus joubini* produces eggs nearly a quarter-inch long, rivaling those of the larger reef octopus, *O. briareus*. The largest of all the local Atlantic species is *O. vulgaris* whose body commonly reaches the size of a grapefruit, and specimens from deep water may be much larger. The eggs of this species, however, measure about one-eighth inch in length and a great many more are laid at one time than in the case of the others just named.

On one occasion my wife and I found a reef octopus under a flat rock guarding its eggs which were in the "eyed" stage; that is, the eyes of the developing embryos were already visible in each case as a pair of tiny red dots. Part of this clutch of eggs was removed from its rocky attachment and placed in clean seawater in a glass vessel under a constant air-jet made by bending and drawing a piece of heated glass tubing into the desired shape and attaching this to a small compressor pump. Although eggs kept under this artificial set of conditions almost invariably fail to hatch, it was hoped that, due to their being well along in the process of development and the large quantity of air with which they were supplied, these might hatch of their own accord.

In about a week we were rewarded by the first youngsters making their appearance. As they emerged they would often leave the remnants of the yolk-sac behind them in the empty egg case, but more often this would remain attached to the mouth in the center of the short stubby arms. Their bodies were fat and bulbous, and at first the hatchlings were free-swimming in habit, jetting themselves about their glass bowl with steady pulsations of their tiny siphons. Although the yolk-sacs appeared still to contain food material, these were eventually detached in their entirety instead of being gradually adsorbed, and the floor of their bowl became covered with the remains of these little jettisoned fuel tanks.

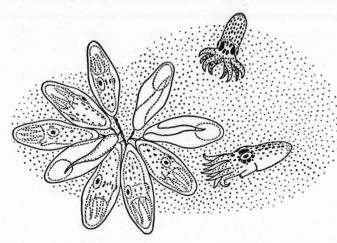

*Octopus briareus* eggs and hatchlings.

Immediately on hatching, the little octopuses demonstrated their ability to emit tiny puffs of ink whenever they were disturbed, and the power of instantaneous color change was similarly developed. With the exception of a few primitive and aberrant forms, all Cephalopods (the class to which cuttlefishes, squids, and octopuses belong) possess a color-changing ability that is rivaled by no other living creature. Scattered throughout the skin are vast numbers of chromatophores, or pigment bodies which may be either expanded or contracted by means of tiny muscle fibers attached to their peripheral edges. The individual chromatophore varies in size from nearly invisible to about twice the size of a pin's head, and they are of varying colors such as black, dark brown, light brown, yellow, orange, and red, though no single species possesses all these colors at once.

The adult octopus will frequently "blush" when disturbed, this consisting of a momentary darkening of the brownish colors around the eyes and elsewhere on the head and body, and when badly frightened may blanch altogether for a few seconds, becoming pearly translucent white all over. At other times the creature will turn a solid red-brown or blackish brown, and while actively moving about will show waves of living color playing lightly and constantly over the surface of its head, body, and arms. In the related and more active squids most of the chromatophores are large enough to be easily visible to the naked eye, producing a sparkling effect as they expand and contract.

Despite the fact that the young reef octopuses emerged from their egg cases in good shape and their supply of fresh seawater was changed frequently, all but one died in the space of several days. The sole survivor thrived for about two weeks, during the first of which he rapidly underwent a change in habits and appearance. After two or three days of an active, free-swimming life he began to rest on the glass sides of the bowl more and more while his lemon-shaped body actually shrank and his arms rapidly grew to the proportions (in miniature) of the adult. Finally he took to spending most of his time in concealment beneath a small fragment of coral on the bottom, but venturing forth with enthusiasm whenever newly hatched brine shrimp or other minute crustaceans were placed in the water with him. His ultimate death as in the case of the others could not be attributed to any particular cause, but gave additional testimony to the fact that octopuses are generally difficult to keep for any extended period of time in captivity.

Like those of the reef octopus, the much smaller young of the common *Octopus vulgaris* undergo an initial free-swimming stage wherein they gradually undergo a change in appearance, while on the other hand the newly hatched pygmy *O. joubini* emerges as an almost exact duplicate of the parent and foregoes the active swimming stage. This latter species is one of the hardiest of all in captivity, and its small size makes it possible to maintain it in the home aquarium. Reynolds Moody, an acquaintance of mine, once had one of this species in a 10-gallon glass aquarium fitted with a sub-sand filter in his living room. Here the octopus laid a clutch of eggs over which she watched and carefully tended, fasting all the while (which is the usual case with brooding females) until they hatched. A day or so later she died, which again frequently happens in captivity and perhaps in the wild as well. This may be the first time octopus eggs have been laid and hatched in a home aquarium, but it should not be especially difficult to duplicate this event with this particular species.

We have collected a number of pygmies by seining them at night in the grass beds at Bear Cut, between Virginia Key and Key Biscayne on the Rickenbacker Causeway at Miami. These same beds yield many other interesting forms of marine life, and from them Fanny and I have obtained certain species that we have only rarely found elsewhere, including baby cornetfish, *Fistularia tabacaria,* which are elongated like pipefishes and have a peculiar filament which runs through the middle of the tail fin, trailing behind as the fish swims.

In connection with this Bear Cut area, I must now tell of a most improbable incident that befell us one night. The City of Miami Sewage Treatment Plant, as I have mentioned in an earlier chapter, is located on Virginia Key

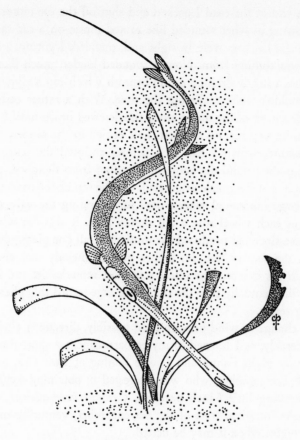

Young Cornetfish, *Fistularia tabacaria.*

on the opposite side of the highway from the Seaquarium. This plant processes local sewage which is conducted to it by way of a pipeline in the floor of Biscayne Bay before discharging the purified effluent far out to sea by means of a similar line. The area occupied by this plant and its grounds includes some shoreline on the side of Bear Cut opposite where we do most of our collecting, and this shoreline is reached by way of a meandering gravel road. I had visited this area a number of times without noticing anything particularly unusual about it until one day Bob Parker, a friend of ours who has also collected in the area, asked me if I had ever happened to be there on a windy day. When I told him I hadn't, he advised me to try it some time, as I would be in for an odd experience.

One afternoon a short time later, when a fair breeze was rippling the Cut, I decided to drive over and discover what he was talking about. When I reached the end of the road I parked and shut off the car motor. I was immediately aware of what sounded like muted music on a car radio nearby. However, no other cars were in sight and, puzzled, I got out to see where the music was coming from. Now it sounded louder, much like a bagpipe cadenza with a steady droning sound beneath which ran a rippling melody, though I couldn't quite make out the tune. With a rather eerie feeling, I followed the source of the music along the deserted beach until I came upon a large boxlike structure of concrete, half buried in the sand.

This structure, which I had seen before, enclosed the gate valves that control the underground discharge line leading from the sewage plant, and it was from it that the music originated. On the top of the concrete platform were two large horizontal wheels used for operating the valves, and from the center of each wheel rose a tall slotted pipe. It was the wind blowing through these slots that produced the music, the tall one giving off a droning sound and the shorter one the higher pitched melody that changed with variations in the breeze. The effect was most remarkable, and I hope that someone will eventually take the trouble to tape-record this phenomenon of the singing sewer.

A slight change in wind velocity (and possibly, direction) alters the situation considerably, as I learned to my embarrassment a short time later. On this particular night Fanny and I were seining at Bear Cut, assisted by a friend, Bob Longenecker, who was interested in obtaining some specimens of the interesting little 6-inch pearlfish, *Carapus bermudensis,* which lives by day in the intestinal tract of the sea cucumber, venturing out to forage around at night, when it may be netted.

Sea cucumbers are members of the phylum Echinodermata, which also includes the starfishes and sea urchins. Although superficially appearing to be rather low on the totem pole of life, indications in the early development of these creatures suggest that they may be close to the main stem of invertebrates that ultimately gave rise to backboned animals. The sea cucumber, which derives its name from its shape, is proverbial from its habit of ejecting all its insides when disturbed, only to grow them back at leisure. Dried, the flesh is known as bêche-de-mer to epicures of the Far East.

Since the cucumber breathes by the process of taking in a quantity of water through its anal opening and then expelling it, the little *Carapus* fish gets plenty of oxygen and does not live in such raunchy surroundings as might be otherwise imagined.

We had a number of pearlfishes in our collecting jars and, as it was getting late and increasingly windy, we decided to leave for home. At this point I suggested that we all go listen to the singing sewers before retiring.

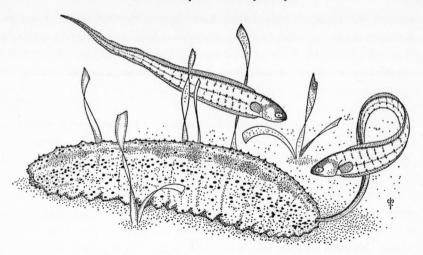

Pearlfish, *Carapus bermudensis,* entering a Sea-Cucumber.

Fanny, who had heard them previously, was enthusiastic, while Bob, who had not, was considerably puzzled at my proposition. Anxious to introduce him to this unexperienced delight, we drove across the bridge spanning Bear Cut and turned off on the road leading to the shoreline where the gate valves were located. When we reached the spot, alas, the wind was blowing a minor gale from the east and the pipes had lost their melody, producing in its place a dismal and monotonous hum quite devoid of any inspirational overtones.

On turning back to the car we saw that we had been followed. Two bright headlights cut the darkness a half block behind us, and the shape of what proved to be a police cruiser slowly pulled up to the rear bumper of our car. An officer got out. I recalled that we were technically trespassing, and I remembered reading in the papers of somebody having recently been robbed at the point of a gun while parked in this general area within recent weeks. Evidently the police were keeping the place under surveillance, and we were obviously in for some questioning as to what we were doing there.

Dressed as we were for night beach-seining, we all looked like tramps, and I knew that any sort of wild alibi in this case would sound more convincing than the truth. Nonetheless, I gave the two officers a detailed account of the phenomenon of the singing sewers and of how disappointed we were that they were not in harmony that evening, and wound up by suggesting that they too might enjoy the music on some occasion when weather conditions were right and they had a little time to kill. By this time the first patrolman was leaning across the hood of the cruiser with his hands over his eyes, shaking his head. By now I was convinced that I would never be believed, but apparently they must have decided that anyone with an explanation that far-fetched must be telling the truth, so they good-naturedly let us off after cautioning us to beware of these isolated places after dark. I have often wondered if they ever did return to check on the veracity of my story.

The pygmy octopuses from Bear Cut, although too small and retiring in nature to make worth-while exhibits in the corridor tanks which were viewed by the public, did quite well in the 20-gallon glass tanks which I kept in my laboratory for the purpose of making observations on a few special specimens including pike blennies, young frogfishes, inch-long barracudas, newborn nurse sharks and stingrays, and, for a time, a large Gerrid or broadshad (*Diapterus plumieri*), whom we named "Bradshaw."

These laboratory tanks, which received their water supply from an overhead system of plastic pipes, were each fitted for overflow drainage with a glass tube standpipe forced through the center of a rubber stopper, which in turn fitted into a hole drilled in the bottom of the tank. I had learned from previous experience that larger octopuses could not be kept in these tanks, for although they might be covered with a screen lid to prevent their escape, they would invariably grasp the tube and pull out the stopper sooner or later. Although this procedure emptied the tank of water some time during the night (when these accidents usually happen) the flow of water from above was usually sufficient to keep the creatures alive, provided they remained in the tank and did not escape through the three-quarter-inch hole in the floor.

Actually, an octopus' ability to escape through small openings is nothing short of fantastic, and because of this Houdini syndrome it is sometimes nearly impossible to keep a restless octopus at home. A specimen with a lemon-sized body has little difficulty in squeezing through an opening of the size mentioned above, as he has no bones or other solid structures to stop him. Christopher Coates, Director of the New York Aquarium, relates an incident where ten small octopuses were individually placed in cigar boxes drilled with quarter-inch holes, and then the boxes bound tightly with fishing line before being placed and floated in a shipping tank being sent from Key West to New York. On arrival all had escaped.

The pygmies, however, seemed much less venturesome than the other species and in addition they were much too small to dislodge the stoppers in their tanks. Like all octopuses, they quickly learned to accept pieces of shrimp and other tidbits from one's fingers, "blushing" deep brown whenever they were first touched. One of their favorite tricks was to cling tightly either to the floor or side glass of the tank and cover themselves with one half of a small clamshell as a lid. In fact, *O. joubini* are frequently found living in the empty bivalve shells of scallops or small clams, and when disturbed they close these tightly to protect their tiny arms and grape-sized bodies. Often the shell will also double as a nursery for their eggs as well. Similarly, the larger reef octopus will frequently choose a large conch shell as a living or nesting site, and piles of discarded shells of the large edible pink *Strombus* conch, which are common refuse heaps along Bahaman shores, serve as veritable octopus "hotels."

One day, as I was sitting at my laboratory desk, I received a phone call from the boat dock, informing me that a shrimp fisherman had just pulled alongside with a very unusual octopus. A minute or so later I was aboard the craft, and as the fisherman lifted the lid of his live-well, I saw that it was a species unlike any I had ever seen previously. Its body was more elongate than the ones with which I was familiar, and the arms were exceedingly long and slender but almost squarish in cross section, and there was only a vestige of the membrane which usually connects their bases. But most surprising of all was its color—bright orange-brown covered with evenly spaced white polka dots! As the octopus slowly moved about the bottom of the well, these dots would vary from moment to moment in intensity, being brightest whenever it was touched.

The specimen was placed in one of the corridor tanks where it immediately took up residence in a hollowed-out slab of rock. Its graceful form and strange coloration attracted considerable public attention from the first. It was later identified by Gilbert L. Voss of the Marine Laboratory as *Octopus macropus*, the first of its kind recorded from the U.S. coast, although it is occasionally met with in the Bahama Islands and elsewhere in warm seas.

This individual lived for several months at the Seaquarium, eventually dying from a strange disorder which is fairly common among captive female

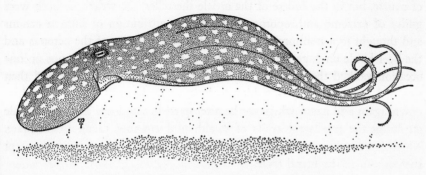

Whitespotted Octopus, *Octopus macropus.*

octopuses—hypertrophy of the ovary. The symptoms of this disease appear gradually over a period of weeks as the single ovary gradually enlarges until it crowds the other viscera to such an extent that the octopus eventually experiences considerable difficulty in breathing, and it usually dies shortly thereafter. The cause of this disorder is so far unknown.

Persons who view the octopus tanks at Marine Studios and the Seaquarium frequently see what look exactly like nearly transparent collar buttons floating around in the water, sometimes becoming as numerous as snowflakes. These are the horny caps which line the surfaces of the suction cups, occurring in a double row on the inside surface of each arm. Every so often these are shed, and during the shedding process the octopus will rub all his arms together in a constant, semi-rotating movement that is most peculiar to watch.

A question frequently asked by the public is, "How much pressure can a large octopus exert with his suction cups?" The answer is, of course, that an octopus exerts *no* pressure by means of the suction cups, nor does he press or squeeze with the arms, for they are for holding only. When an octopus takes hold of your hand or arm, as has happened to me many times in the course of my handling them, the suction cannot be felt unless you try to pull away from it. It is a fairly simple matter to free oneself from the hold of an average-sized octopus in a tank, but I have no doubt that it would be an easy possibility for an octopus with arms over 4 feet long to drown a swimmer, provided that the octopus also had a firm substrate, such as a smooth rock, on which to anchor itself. However, actual evidence that this has ever happened is based primarily on anecdotal stories which have a way of growing more spectacular with repetition.

I once read what was supposed to have been a first-hand account (as told to the writer of that article, of course) of a deepsea diver's hair-raising experiences with giant octopuses. The actual encounters may have occurred, of course, but in the course of the article the teller, the writer, or both were guilty of extreme anthropomorphism, or the attribution of human actions and thought to a nonhuman creature (see also the story of the octopus and the beer bottle on page 161). According to the story, a huge octopus on one occasion yanked the diver off his feet by tugging at his air line and then watched him, not bothering him so long as he lay still, but pulling him down again and again whenever he attempted to stand up. This sort of tale attributes the intelligent traits of stealth and cunning to an invertebrate, which is quite inaccurate. This is most unfortunate, as many persons accept such stories as the literal truth.

The largest species of octopus on the American coast, and possibly in the world, so far as is known, is *O. apollyon* which occurs in fairly shallow water off Oregon, Washington, and northward, and in much deeper water off California, since it requires low temperatures, from 40° to 50° Fahrenheit. The giant octopus is a very bulky species. The first one I saw was a 60-pound specimen in the refrigerated octopus grotto at Marineland of the Pacific. Its color was mainly dark red (the shade an ordinary octopus turns when boiled), and as it moved slowly about its rock-lined tank it presented a most impressive and majestic spectacle. I was informed by personnel there that some fishermen had recently caught an 80-pounder for the aquarium, but that it died before it could be placed on exhibit. One of the hardier species (so long as it is kept in water that is properly chilled), *O. apollyon* has been known to live for as long as two years in captivity. Unfortunately, the females tend to deposit eggs in the summer months, following which comes a three-month period of guarding them accompanied by fasting and eventual death of the specimen, even though the eggs be removed in the meantime.

John H. Prescott of Marineland of the Pacific and Cecil Brosseau of the Point Defiance Aquarium in Tacoma, Washington, recently reported in *Drum & Croaker* a method whereby the giant octopus may be chilled to the point of inertia (35°) by means of ice or other means and shipped considerable distances in ice-enclosed plastic bags inside a fiberboard drum with little or no water, and later revived. On arrival at its destination the octopus is placed in warmer water and if necessary given artificial respiration, which consists of massaging its body by hand until it commences to breathe normally. Formerly, it was necessary to ship them in a quantity of water at least equivalent to their own weight—a rather costly operation. According to Prescott and Brosseau, the largest specimen shipped to date weighed 70 pounds and the total shipping weight, including ice and container, was only 88 pounds.

The giant octopus is particularly abundant in Puget Sound, Washington, and I recently saw a 30-pound specimen from that area that was successfully sent by Murray Newman of the Vancouver (B.C.) Aquarium to the New York Aquarium at Coney Island. This species is certainly one of the finest and most impressive of aquarium animals and, thanks to the recent experimental work on shipping methods mentioned above, it is now available to any aquarium that has the facilities to keep it.

Although it may seem sacrilegious for an aquarist to mention anything concerning the culinary qualities of his specimens, I must say here that the octopus is one of the most delicious forms of seafood—provided that it is not only properly cooked but also tenderized in the process. I learned this the difficult way. While on training maneuvers aboard the U.S.S. *Audubon* during World War II, one of our crewmen hooked a fair-sized octopus which was swimming at the surface. After it had been killed, I removed two of its arms which I managed to cook on the stove of the sick bay kitchen, although my fellow hospital corpsmen were none too enthusiastic about the idea. The results of my effort at length gave off a highly savory odor but were quite inedible, having the consistency of a piece of rubber inner tube. To make matters worse, the two arms had curled into a tight spiral during the boiling process and though I unrolled them while attempting to bite off a portion, they quickly returned to their former position with a wet snap whenever they were released.

The Pacific Islanders pound fresh octopus meat with a club or mallet in order to tenderize it, or even allow it to slosh overnight in an old washing machine—according to Frank W. Lane in his book, *Kingdom of the Octopus*. However, in the years following my first abortive attempt at octopus cookery, I have discovered a fairly simple way of preparing them that does not require preliminary tenderizing—provided that the octopus is not a large one. For those who may be interested, I hereby offer my own recipe for *Octopus Experimentale,* to be prepared in the average laboratory:

| LAB EQUIPMENT * | INGREDIENTS |
|---|---|
| 1000-ml beaker | 1 octopus |
| Bunsen burner with ring stand | Seawater |
| Asbestos screen | Salt |
| Beaker forceps | Pepper |
| Shears | Bay leaves |
| Aluminum foil | Butter |

*Procedure:* Remove arms from octopus, place in seawater with bay leaves in beaker. Set on asbestos screen on ring stand over Bunsen burner. Light burner, adjust collar so that blue flame is produced. Bring to boil, then turn to low flame, allow to simmer for 20 minutes. Remove beaker with forceps, drain, cool, cut arms into short sections with shears. Wrap pieces individually in aluminum foil, place on asbestos screen under low flame, bake for approximately 10 minutes. Cool, unwrap, season with salt, pepper, and butter. Octopus may then be eaten with fingers or fork as desired.

An excited octopus will sometimes deliberately throw off an arm or two as he thrashes about, which often happens when one is captured by hand.

* Of course, a stove and conventional cooking utensils may be substituted, if necessary.

For a time the severed arm will move about actively, undergoing color changes, and clinging to whatever it touches. In the case of at least one species, the paper nautilus (*Argonauta argo,* which is a highly specialized octopus), the greatly elongated hectocotylized arm of the male may detach itself during the mating act and swim about with considerable activity, finally attaching itself inside the mantle cavity of the much larger female. In fact, this detached arm, when discovered in this place by early scientists, was long thought to be some sort of parasite until its true nature was later revealed.

On one occasion, when an octopus I had caught left one arm entwined about my wrist while he attempted to make off in a different direction, I removed it with some difficulty and finally tossed it into shallow water where it remained writhing about on the bottom. After I had finally recaptured the octopus and placed it in a sack, I happened to look at the lost member and discovered it wrapped tightly about a terrified and helpless large marine killifish, *Fundulus heteroclitis.* Evidently the fish, attracted by its motion and the scent of escaping juices, had paused to nip at it and had become quickly enveloped. Had I not released the fish it would probably have died in this condition.

Lost arms are normally regenerated by the octopus within a few weeks after they are lost, and captive specimens have been known to devour their own arms when they are particularly worked up over something.

The squids, close relatives of the octopuses, are much more active creatures, and in addition to the normal complement of eight suction-cup-studded arms, have two retractable tentacles with suckers at their tips, and sometimes recurved hooks as well. They also have a pair of movable fins toward the rear of the body and are free-swimming and capable of great speed in most cases. Unfortunately, most species do not take kindly to captivity and usually they will live only a few days, at best, in the aquarium.

One species of squid, *Sepioteuthis sepioidea,* which is fairly common in the Miami area, appears to be hardier than most. Two friends of mine, Mr. and Mrs. J. E. Nichols, once succeeded in keeping a 2-inch specimen in a 2-gallon glass bowl for almost a week, during which time it would shoot out its tentacles to seize small shrimp that were dropped in front of it. At the Marine Laboratory I once kept two slightly larger specimens in a 20-gallon tank under running seawater for approximately the same length of time. Both specimens soon developed the habit of sending powerful jets of water from their tank halfway across the room, especially when someone happened to be passing by. Sometimes the water was mixed with jets of ink, as I learned to my misfortune one day when a black blob suddenly appeared

on the front of a white shirt I was wearing, and all that subsequent launder-
ing accomplished was to change this to an attractive but still disfiguring
shade of blue.

The paired fins of squids vary tremendously in shape, size, and position
among the different species and are usually good characters for the purposes
of identification, each one developing his, as Norman Rockwell might say,
according to the dictates of his own conscience. In *Sepiateuthis* they run
along almost the entire length of the body, in this way somewhat resembling
the European cuttlefish (*Sepia*), to which this species, however, is not related.

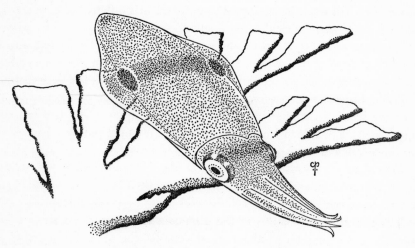

Reef Squid, *Sepiateuthis sepioidea.*

We often saw schools of them while we were skindiving on the reefs.
When approached too closely or too suddenly each one would blanch white
and dart off at tremendous speed, leaving behind a black "dummy" of ink.
At West End on the tip of Grand Bahama Island Fanny and I once discovered a large, foot-long *Sepiateuthis* swimming along the beach in fairly
shallow water and by carefully driving it ashore in such a manner as not to
frighten it, we were able to catch it by hand. Once caught, it wrestled with
our fingers, trying unsuccessfully to nip us with its beak, sending out pro-
testful jets of water with great force all the while, while the baleful look
in its great staring opalescent eyes was so heart-rending that we were eventually forced to release it.

Certain squids are reported to glide through the air for distances above
the surface of the sea in the manner of a flying fish, but I had never realized
what a remarkable sight this was until I actually witnessed it in person.

The place was a half mile offshore from Key Largo. Captain Gray and I were returning to Miami from a successful collecting trip to the Keys. The sea was quite calm on that day and there was little trace of the prevailing wind that we usually encountered on our northward journeys.

Gray was inside the cabin working on fishing gear while I was doing a stint at the wheel. As I gazed out over the water I suddenly saw a foot-long squid (*Sepiateuthis,* I am practically positive, as I saw the usual dark eye-like spots on either side of its back very clearly) shoot out of the water backward, flatten itself, and plane away at great speed for a hundred yards before disappearing beneath the surface. This occurred in the early afternoon, and I shall never forget the spectacle of this colorful invertebrate as it sped away, glistening in the sun.

By virtue of luck and coincidence, over a period of some three and a half years I chanced upon the only four specimens known up to that time of a new species of squid which grows to be only an inch in length when adult. This saga started during the fall of 1949 when I accompanied an ichthyological expedition from Miami to Cay Sal Bank, which lies roughly between the Florida Keys and Cuba. On the return trip our schooner ran into a storm and was disabled, so that it became necessary for a Coast Guard vessel to tow us back to Key West.

As we were brought alongside the dock, the searchlight of the Coast Guard cutter shone for a moment on the surface of the water between the two boats, and in the center of the beam swam two tiny squids, which I quickly scooped up with a hand net and dropped into preservative. Examining them later by daylight, I saw that they closely resembled the young of the common Gulf squid, *Loliguncula brevis,* except that the fins did not extend quite to the end of the body as they normally do in this species.

I presented the two half-inch specimens to Gilbert L. Voss, Cephalopod expert of the Marine Laboratory of the University of Miami on my return, and although he too at first thought them to be the young of some known species, an incident occurred the following year which proved them to be actually half-grown specimens. During the summer of 1950, I was again collecting with Gray off Key Largo. We were wading in 3 feet of water close to a channel, watching for small fish by means of a glass-bottomed bucket, when I happened to spot a squid approximately an inch in length swimming beneath a clump of green *Caulerpa* algae. When I netted it, it proved to be the same as the Key West specimens, and on dissecting it Voss found it to be sexually mature, thus establishing it as a dwarf species.

The fourth specimen, also an inch in length, came to light when I caught it by hand while swimming a year later at Crandon Park Beach on Key Biscayne at Miami! On the basis of these four known specimens captured years, and over a range of nearly 250 miles, apart, Voss in 1953 described *Pickfordia-teuthis pulchella* as a new species, genus, and even family of squid. Oddly enough, shortly after it was described, *Pickfordiateuthis* began to show up regularly at Bear Cut, and since that time we have seined a number of specimens at night along with *Octopus joubini*.

Dwarf Squid, *Pickfordiateuthis pulchella.*

# CHAPTER 14

# DANGERS, ODDITIES, AND DRAMA

*A Jewfish Spectacle and a Pelican Perplexity. Wild Theories, Quotes, and Misquotes. Moray Eels and a Televised Shark. Encounter with a Man-of-War. Squirting Crabs and Pistol Shrimps*

Odd things happen when least expected. On arriving at work one morning, I happened to pause before one of the windows of the main Seaquarium. Across the broad sandy expanse of the tank floor I could make out the shadowy form of a great 300-pound jewfish (*Epinephelus itajara*) facing me from the far wall. As I watched I saw his outline becoming perceptibly clearer, and I realized that this mighty sea bass was slowly headed in my direction. Like a suspenseful movie scene he drifted nearer and nearer, seeming to grow larger as he did so, until his disdainfully inscrutable face, backed by a massive bulk, all but filled my window. For a moment he paused reflectively, then rolled his eyes, opened his mouth, and spat out a pair of black-rimmed eyeglasses!

Just where the jewfish had found the spectacles and why he had picked up so inedible an object in the first place was a mystery, although large fishes, and sea basses in particular, will actually swallow odd things on occasion. Once, in an operation which the fish unfortunately did not survive, we removed a 3-pound lead weight which had been dropped some months before by one of the divers. One could only speculate as to what else might have been swallowed and successfully passed through the digestive tracts of this fish from time to time.

On seeing the eyeglasses so obligingly deposited before me by the fish, I summoned one of the feeding attendants and sent him to the floor of the tank in a diving helmet, and in due time he found them wedged partly beneath a large rock where the current had carried them. Disregarding the attendant's witticisms to the effect that the owner of the spectacles might still be inside the jewfish, I delivered them to our lost and found department, but they were never claimed.

Incidents of an oddball nature for some reason occur frequently enough to keep life from ever becoming dull for an aquarist. For example, one morning one of the maintenance men discovered a 5-foot diamondback rattlesnake swimming actively about in the Shark Channel. Fortunately for

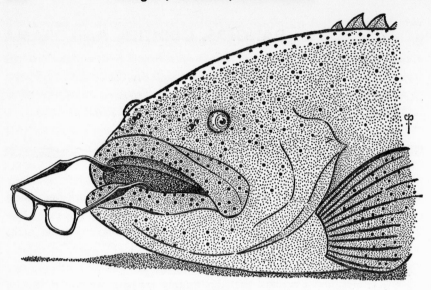

Spotted Jewfish, *Epinephelus itajara.*

the snake, there were few sharks in the Channel at the time, and he was subsequently rescued with a long-handled dipnet and conveyed to the Crandon Park Zoo in a sack in the back of my car. It is possible that the diamondback was placed in the channel by a prankster, but more likely he had fallen in during the night after having crawled across the highway from the uncleared northern end of Virginia Key.

Dealing with the public also has its unexpected twists. I once received a letter from a gentleman in England who wished to know how to distinguish between the sexes of pelicans. It seemed that a local zoo had gotten hold of two pelicans of the American brown variety, and some dispute reigned over their true gender, and would I be so good as to offer what advice and assistance I could. I admit that this question had never occurred to me before, and since the information was not to be found in any of my reference books, I put through a call to the Curator of Ornithology at the University of Miami.

He informed me that there was really no way that the sex of brown pelicans could be determined externally, so I relayed this information, along with my regrets, to my British friend. That would normally have been the end of our correspondence, but from time to time he sent me clippings and comments on the subject of the pelicans, as it appeared that more and more of the local people were becoming aroused over the question and fierce disputes were taking place between the zoo curators and various private individuals who all had their own suggestions and theories as to how to tell the males from the females, and the whole matter was rapidly approaching a crisis of some sort. Well, more than a year after I had sent my original reply, my friend informed me that my letter had been read before the House of Commons in London, so for all I know this argument may still be in full swing.

The specialized nature of my particular field of work has placed me in a position where I have undertaken to answer many letters of inquiry concerning the sea and its inhabitants. My first full-time occupation in this regard came in the fall of 1950 when I obtained a position on the staff of the Marine Laboratory of the University of Miami. In the course of this job I started the question-and-answer column *Sea Secrets,* which at that time was released each week to various Florida newspapers, besides answering questions which we received in the daily mail.

Answering the mail was more or less routine and repetitious at times, but there were interesting variations. One person wrote in to inquire what was the greatest and least possible profit to be made from commercial fishing. After due deliberation we were forced to inform the gentleman that his question, as he had phrased it, was unanswerable. Occasionally we would receive letters in the "crank" category, and two of these, received from different sources a year apart, were especially notable for the remarkable, if misguided, ingenuity the writers employed to attempt to explain certain natural phenomena.

The first of these letters had to do with the subject of plankton, a collective term for all the myriad forms of often microscopic free-floating and drifting forms of animal and plant life in the sea. Having expressed the partial truth that plankton by and large consists of lower forms of life, the writer followed this with the totally false statement that it was well known that plankton could not reproduce itself in nature. He then went on to explain that it was his firm conviction that planktonic creatures ("plankters," as they are called) were actually prehistoric forms of life that had existed for millions of years in a state of suspended animation in the polar ice caps, and as these ice caps progressively broke up into icebergs, and as the icebergs melted, new plankton was constantly being set free in the ocean. To clinch this, he pointed out that it is well known that plankton is found in greatest abundance in the polar seas, but neglected to mention the established fact that this is due to the constant upwelling of nutrient-rich bottom water in these regions.

The second letter had to do with the rise and fall of the tides, and began in a rambling fashion with the statement that, in the writer's opinion, Einstein was a fakir. This was remarkable information, indeed, and after briefly conjuring up a mental picture of Dr. Einstein writing his *Special Theory of Relativity* while reclining on a bed of spikes, I concluded that what this gentleman obviously meant was "faker." Following this with a concentrated attack on physicists and scientists in general, he then went on to say how ridiculous it was to assume that the tides were caused by the gravitational pull of the moon and the sun; they were obviously too far away.

His explanation ran as follows: the earth, it seems, is surrounded by a doughnut-shaped band of ionized gas far above its equator (note that this was written *before* the discovery of the Van Allen belts), and that this band of gas revolves about the earth on an eccentric axis. Gravitational forces emanating from this eccentrically rotating band of gas in turn cause the ocean floor beneath it to rise and fall (or to "breathe," as the writer put it), thus accounting for the daily tides. As a parting shot he then affirmed that if we would arrange for a public debate between Einstein and himself, he would prove to the world what a preposterous "fakir" the former was. Letters of this nature, though infrequently received, have a tendency to become treasured mementoes as time passes, though not quite in the manner that their writers intended.

During this period of time I was also engaged in a research project involving the investigation of various forms of Florida and West Indian sea life considered to be harmful to man, whether by attacking (as do sharks and barracuda), stinging or poisoning (as do jellyfishes, certain sponges, and certain corals), or by causing poisoning through being eaten (as in the case of a number of fishes that are found in the warmer regions of the ocean). My co-worker during this investigation was Winfield H. Brady, who was later to become curator of the Gulfarium at Ft. Walton Beach, Florida.

During the course of this project, Brady and I investigated all newspaper and medical reports, current and past, of shark and barracuda attacks that we were able to uncover, discovering incidentally that most incidents implicating the latter were undoubtedly caused by the former. As our work progressed, it was inevitable that we were sought out from time to time to render opinions on cases of reported attack. Now, one bane of the scientific person's existence is the ever-present bugaboo that he may be misquoted in print. This is seldom intentional; a journalist anxiously seeking professional confirmation of a point on which he has already made up his own mind will sometimes quote out of context or misquote subconsciously, and thus present a slanted set of "facts" in the first place. I do not mean to condemn either journalists or the tabloids by this statement, as they have been extremely helpful to me on occasion. Yet an unqualified statement to the press on the part of a scientist is fraught with pitfalls, as the following incident will attest.

In the course of our research on the subject of sharks and shark attacks, I received many calls from the local papers, asking me to comment on the validity of such and such a reported attack. Shark attacks do occur beyond question—perhaps more frequently than many people would like to believe —but a great many of these reported incidents are nearly impossible either

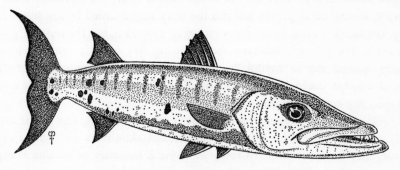

Great Barracuda, *Sphyraena barracuda.*

to prove or disprove, due to a lack of tangible evidence. Trying to establish which species of shark was involved, or whether it was a shark or a barracuda, is even more difficult, excepting in the rare cases where the attacker is subsequently captured (a very rare occurrence), or where recognizable teeth marks are left, or in the very rare cases I know of where a broken-off shark's tooth was actually removed from a wound.

Eyewitness reports are unfortunately unreliable. A great many sharks in the occasional-attacker class resemble one another so closely as to be recognizable only by an expert who has the specimen before him. Add to this difficulty the excited state of mind of the nonexpert, who may see only a shadowy shape in the water during the attack. Conversely, eyewitnesses to an attack, and most especially the victim himself, especially after some time has elapsed, often form a definite conviction that the attacker was a so-and-so and, if a person who was not present questions this, he becomes an inviting target for criticism, if not open hostility at times.

On this particular occasion I received a call from a reporter who informed me that a boy had been bitten on the foot by something while wading along Miami Beach at a spot known as Bakers Haulover, and did I think it could have been a shark, barracuda, or what? Being unable to obtain any further information about the case, I replied that if the boy were wading in shallow water it was unlikely that he had been attacked by either a shark or a barracuda, but more likely a small moray or one of the pugnacious toad-fishes that hide about rockpiles and coral heads near shore, or perhaps he could have stepped on a crab or broken bottle, as one recent report of "shark bite" had subsequently proved to be.

My statement was printed in the evening paper along with the information, contrary to what I had been told, that the boy was bitten while *swimming* off Bakers Haulover. This of course made a vast difference, as it appeared to be a genuine case of shark attack. Nonetheless, before I could stop it, several other papers had run the story accompanied by my statement that the attacker must have been a moray or a toadfish, but the *coup de grâce* to credibility was administered the following day when a central Florida paper quoted me as saying ". . . small moray or poisonous toadstool." What anyone could have had in mind while printing this gem is quite beyond my comprehension.

Although I had suggested a moray as a possible culprit, this fish is actually a much-maligned species, as experienced skindivers are well aware. True, they have needle-sharp teeth and have a tendency to become excited at the smell of blood, but so do many other predacious fishes. It is their snakelike build that is partially responsible for the manner in which they have captured the imagination of writers of the "woe betide" school of undersea adventure stories. In the Seaquarium community tanks, the morays become quite tame, and although they come out of the rocks readily to take fish from the hand of the diver, we have had no incident of deliberate attack on the part of any of them.

The largest species in the West Indies is the green moray, *Gymnothorax funebris.* This 6-foot monster is, as its name suggests, of a grass- or olive-green all over, but its skin is actually blue! The apparent green hue is produced by an amber-yellow slime which completely coats the body but may be scraped free with a knife, revealing the blue of the skin underneath.

The 3-foot spotted moray, *G. moringa,* often occurs among rocks and coral in quite shallow water. When disturbed, as when a rock is lifted from over it, this species, unlike the more philosophical green, tends to become hysterical. I have seen them rush madly this way and that at the surface, biting wildly at everything in sight with great vigor but with very little aim or purpose. After "blowing its top" in this fashion it usually becomes fairly relaxed and may be netted with little difficulty. The spotted moray has a "salt-and-pepper" pattern of black, brown, and yellow, and is quite attractive in appearance. Still smaller is the 1½- to 2-foot blackedge moray, *G. nigromarginatus.* It is marked with large pale spots on a tan body and the long dorsal and anal fins are edged in black. Unlike the others, this species appears to prefer muddy and grassy bottoms, and I have collected it in the mouths of estuaries where the water is slightly brackish.

Once, at the age of 11, I was bitten on the thumb by a blackedge moray I had discovered hiding inside a length of iron pipe lying in shallow water. As I recall it, the bite was exceedingly painful, and a lump appeared in my armpit shortly afterward, and my entire arm was sore for several hours. Since then, I have seen a fish die within a few minutes following what appeared to be a comparatively minor bite from this moray. Whether any actual poison is involved or whether this may have been due to bacterial or other infective agents is impossible to say without further study. Popular lore to the contrary notwithstanding, none of the local morays are known to be poisonous, and I have twice been bitten by other species of morays with none of the effects described above.

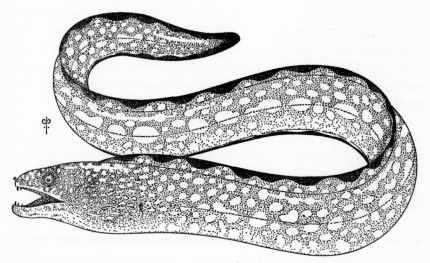

Blackedge Moray, *Gymnothorax nigromarginatus.*

Living about the reefs is the purplemouth moray, *G. vicinus,* which looks much like the spotted moray but is plain brown with an indistinct pattern. The most impressive one by far is the viper moray, *Enchelycore nigricans.* In this species the main color is a dark red-brown, and the jaws are hooked somewhat in the manner of a male sockeye salmon, so that the mouth cannot be completely closed. The teeth, which as in other morays grow in several rows in the upper jaw and two in the lower, are very long and sharp. Its table manners in captivity are most oafish, as it will seize a great chunk of fish in its jaws, bat it back and forth on the rocks before swallowing it, and scatter portions of it all over the tank with a sort of studied carelessness.

A quite different type of creature is the small chain moray, *Echidna carenata,* which has blunt, molarlike teeth for crushing the shells of crustaceans and small mollusks. Common along the Bahama shores but rare on the Florida coast, this species has a reticulated chainlike network of yellow over a brown or black ground color.

I have always been exceedingly fond of morays, which, despite their fearsome appearance, are nowhere nearly as savage under natural conditions as they are frequently thought to be. The same may be said for the barracuda, which, although proved to attack in rare isolated cases, is a much-maligned fish, frequently being blamed for attacks actually caused by sharks.

As I mentioned in an earlier chapter, while curator of the Seaquarium I would occasionally show live animals and discuss their habits on the weekly TV show *Let's Go Fishing,* which was presided over by Miami fishing expert Jim Dooley. On my first guest appearance I had with me a small nurse shark, *Ginglymostoma cirratum.* I brought the shark to the studio in a large, water-filled plastic bag inside a cardboard container, and at the last minute transferred him to a 20-gallon glass aquarium tank I had previously set up on a table in front of the cameras. He performed beautifully, and proved to be highly photogenic besides.

Needless to say, the shark was an instant hit, and several inquiring phone calls reached the studio before the program ended, one from a lady who wished to know if she might be able to keep a baby shark in with her goldfish!

On subsequent shows I was able to display a number of specimens simultaneously in a series of flat-sided glass bowls. Following the dangerous sea life theme, I brought along poisonous scorpionfishes with venom-tipped dorsal fin spines like slivers of glass; marine bristleworms whose myriad spines came off in anything they touched, causing considerable pain when left in the skin, but not truly dangerous; needle-spined *Diadema* urchins; yellow stingrays which inhabit the coral reefs, Atlantic stingrays which occasionally make their way into fresh water in southern Florida; small electric rays whose hexagonal-celled batteries can deliver a surprising jolt if stepped upon; the octopus which has a poisonous bite but which almost never bites humans, and the exquisitely beautiful but dangerous *Physalia,* or Portuguese man-of-war.

Commonly thought to be a jellyfish, the *Physalia* belongs instead to a group of jellyfish relatives called Siphonophores. The most distinctive thing about the Siphonophores is that they are not individual animals, but actually a whole colony of animals joined to form a sort of community body, dif-

ferent parts of which perform various functions, such as floating, swimming, feeding, stinging, and reproduction. The *Physalia* is the largest of
the Siphonophores and its most prominent feature is the large, clear blue
and pink gas-filled float that supports the colony on the surface of the sea.
Running along the top of the float is a stiffened but flexible sail which
catches the wind, but is so oriented that the Portuguese man-of-war usually
travels at an angle of approximately 45 degrees to the actual wind direction,
a device that is believed by some observers to prevent the colony becoming
entrapped in the long windrows of seaweed that form parallel to the wind
direction in a stiff breeze. The float is, oddly enough, quite muscular, and
on calm days may be seen to flop periodically from one side to the other,
wetting itself in the sea to avoid desiccation. From the bottom of the float
hang the elastic stinging tentacles like blue threads, sometimes trailing behind the *Physalia* for many feet.

Contact with these stinging threads with their intense, paralyzing poison
can be a most unpleasant experience, as I once learned the hard way. On
this particular occasion I was in the front of a boat dipping *Physalias* into
a bucket with a hand net while an assistant ran the outboard in the rear.
We were gathering them for a science film being made at the Lab, and
just before we started back with our specimens, I spotted an especially
large *Physalia* some distance away. I shouted to my assistant and pointed,
and in a few moments we were alongside it. Dipping it up in the net, I
signaled that we were ready to go back. My assistant turned the boat so
sharply that I was thrown off balance, and as I fell sideways onto the boat
seat my hand came down directly on top of the *Physalia,* whose float exploded with a loud "ponk." I hastily scrubbed the gloppy, burning jelly
off my fingers with a handful of floating seaweed as the boat sped toward
the dock, and as soon as we landed I poured alcohol over my hand to co-
agulate the remainder of the still-operating nematocysts, or stinging cells.
Within 15 minutes I was at a physician's office and he was covering my
hand with an anesthetic spray, which seemed to help but little. The pain
remained quite intense for two or three hours, when it gradually diminished,
although for some time I had a very painful lump in my armpit on the
afflicted side. Next day, aside from a slightly reddened hand, I had no
further evidence of my ordeal, but I can say that the memory of it is vivid
to this day.

The necessity for capturing a *Physalia* immediately before using it for
the purposes of television or photography is due to the fact that they do
not last long after capture. Whatever part of the creatures touches the side
of a glass or metal container, to say nothing of a net, sticks like watery

gelatin, and then commences to disintegrate. In plastic bags they fare somewhat better, but within days, sometimes hours, the stinging tentacles and
feeding organs almost invariably slough off. For this reason also, they are
worthless as aquarium exhibits, unless new specimens are collected each day.
In a tank they almost immediately drift against the sides and corners, where
they stick and remain until removed, showing little of their buoyant grace
as when found in the open ocean. I have thought about the possibility of
some day exhibiting them in a situation where they are kept away from
the sides by jets of air or water, but the problem remains unsolved for the
moment, especially since a very deep container is needed, as the stinging
tentacles may stretch downward for a distance of 20 feet or more on occasion.

On the TV shows, my *Physalias* were accompanied by specimens of the
remarkable bluebottle fish, *Nomeus gronowi*. Butterfly-like and silvery and
blue like the man-of-war itself, these delicate little fishes seek protection by
swimming in and out of the tangle of stinging tentacles, surviving because
in some as yet unknown way they do not appear to trigger off the stings
on contact. When forcibly brought against the stinging portions, as when
fish and *Physalia* are captured in a net together, the fish may be instantly
killed, but I have on certain occasions seen the fishes flopping unharmed on
top of the bunched tentacles of the *Physalia*. The bluebottle fish is not the
only species to seek this remarkable coexistence. Several times on netting
*Physalias* and their fishes, I have seen a few more active and thicker-bodied
fishes rush away, and on finally capturing several, I identified them as
young jacks or rudderfish of the genus *Seriola*. When in the company of
the man-of-war they were colored blue and silvery like the bluebottles, but
within a minute of being placed by themselves in a bucket they reverted,
chameleon-like, to the normal yellowish and brassy green pattern with
smoky black bars that these young fish have when captured around drifting
seaweed. While in the company of the *Physalia,* they appeared to me to
keep a slightly greater distance away from the tentacles than did the bluebottles.

When I first began arranging series of aquatic "performers" for the
shows, I worried lest some of them (e.g., the octopus, which is unpredictable
and obstinate to a degree out of all proportion to its primitive mental capacity) fail to respond properly or get out of hand in some way while on
camera. I quickly lost my fears in this regard, as some of the best sequences
occurred when something behaved in an unpredictable fashion. Once an
octopus, annoyed at the bright and hot lights which make human performers sweat, suddenly hit me full in the face with a stream of water from
its siphon, following this with a couple of jets aimed spitefully in Jim

Portuguese Man-of-War, *Physalia pelagica,* with:

(upper) Bluebottle Fish, *Nomeus gronowi,* and
(lower) Young Rudderfish, *Seriola sp.*

Dooley's direction, and then solved the problem of the objectionable lights by instantly opaquing the water in its tank with vast quantities of its natural ink.

Another star performer was the tiny snapping or pistol shrimp, *Alpheus.* These 1½-inch-long crustaceans are provided with one front pincer developed to an extreme size and consisting of a single large "tooth" or plunger on the movable part and a corresponding socket on the opposing part. When the plunger-bearing finger is opened at a 90-degree angle to the main part of the pincer, a situation is produced whereby two tiny, perfectly smooth surfaces are brought together, and these stick tightly in the same manner as will two wet, flat pieces of glass. When the shrimp finally exerts enough downward pressure with his tremendous claw muscle so as to overcome this suction, the plunger is suddenly driven into its socket with a loud pop and a water-hammer effect of surprising force. If the shrimp is on the bottom of a metal pail, the resonant "punk!" may be heard for a hundred yards or so. In a glass aquarium the noise can be quite sharp, and sounds as if the glass has suddenly cracked.

In large colonies, such as among oyster shells, barnacles, etc., on pilings of a wharf or in sponges and porous rock of a coral reef, these shrimps will set up a continuous crackle, familiar to skindivers or those who study magnetic tapings of undersea sounds. It has even been suggested that some of the acoustical mines used during World War II may have been detonated by nearby pistol shrimps who blew the mines and themselves to oblivion in what may have been history's most expensive form of self-annihilation.

As previously stated, the force of the concussion produced by *Alpheus* and its relatives is considerable. If a pencil point, glass rod, or similar object is moved toward one of these shrimps who has made itself at home in an aquarium tank by burrowing under a stone or similar object, the shrimp will usually fire away at a distance of one or two inches, and the force may be clearly felt through the fingers holding the pointer. I had always regarded this mechanism as a purely defensive function, but the fact that it may likewise be used to secure food is suggested by the following incident. I was keeping several pistol shrimps in a small glass aquarium, the bottom of which was provided with a number of short sections of glass tubing in which the creatures had set up housekeeping. Any small amount of sand, a pebble, or bit of debris which might accidentally find its way into one of the tubes was immediately ejected by the shrimp occupying it, and anything which moved close to an open tube end was first investigated, then vigorously popped at, sometimes several times in succession.

One day I introduced several half-inch baby triggerfishes into the shrimp tank, as I had nowhere else to put them at the time. The following morning I discovered all of them dead and partially eaten by the shrimps, and assumed they had been somehow caught and devoured during the night, since triggerfishes habitually rest close to the bottom during this time. Several days later I added another triggerfish, and this time watched to see if any of the shrimps would take notice. For a time nothing happened, but finally I saw the fish, attracted by curiosity, approach the open end of a shrimp-occupied tube. The *Alpheus* appeared presently, his popping claw

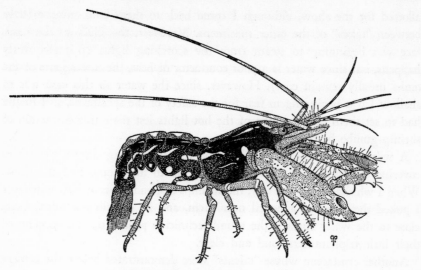

Pistol Shrimp, *Alpheus armatus.*

slowly assuming the "cocked" position. When the triggerfish had approached to within about two inches of the shrimp, the latter popped, as if to say, "Bang, you're dead!"

To my great surprise, the fish promptly rolled onto its side, obviously stunned by the concussion, whereupon the shrimp rushed forward, seized it, and dragged it into the tube and commenced to eat it! Although other fishes were subsequently eaten by the shrimps, this was the one and only time I actually witnessed this performance, although on several occasions a fish was "shot" at out of range, when it would immediately rush away as fast as possible, and eventually several remained in the tank for some time, since they learned through experience not to go near the shrimps at all.

Desiring to demonstrate the popping, if not the fish-killing, behavior of *Alpheus* on TV, I brought two pairs (a male and female frequently occupy the same burrow) of them to the studio in a 1-gallon glass bowl, which produced excellent resonance when half filled with water. Unfortunately, this first attempt was a complete failure, although they had performed beautifully an hour earlier at the Lab.

As was customary, my several marine displays were lined up on a table, and five minutes before show time the bright studio lights were turned on. Unexpectedly, this annoyed the shrimps, who began popping at random, building up to a perfect fusillade as the clock approached the "go" signal, and then falling perfectly silent as we went on the air, and nothing I could do would coax so much as one pop from them during the seven minutes allotted for the show, although I came back to them from time to time between "takes" of the other specimens. Moreover, the shallow water surface was beginning to steam from the scorching lights (this frequently happens, but since water is a poor conductor of heat, the lower parts of the tanks usually remain cool). However, since the water in this case was so shallow I was beginning to fear for the safety of the specimens, so I finally had to set them out of range of the hot lights lest their transformation to shrimp gumbo be complete.

A week later I repeated the attempt, this time using deeper water and covering the tank with a cardboard box up to the moment of the show. When I whisked the box away, the shrimps responded beautifully whenever I poked the point of a pencil near them, and by dangling a microphone close to the water surface, the sound technician picked up the popping of their little triphammers loud and clear.

Another crustacean whose "talents" were demonstrated before the camera in a novel way was the box crab, *Calappa flammea,* whose common name is derived from the fact that it can, when frightened, fold itself up in such a way that a would-be predator encounters only a continuous smooth surface lacking in any projections that can be easily seized. The body is smoothly rounded and somewhat bun-shaped, attractively marked with wavy brown streaks and spots, and both claws are greatly flattened and concave on the inner surface. When protecting itself, the crab will fold first the larger claw against the front of its body, covering slightly more than half of its front surface; then the smaller claw is folded to cover the remainder, slightly overlapping and fitting into a corresponding pleat in the large claw. At the same time the small and rather slender legs are folded into corresponding depressions on the underside of the body, so that complete protection is achieved.

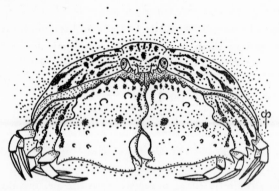

Box Crab, *Calappa flammea.*

Despite the small size of its legs, the box crab is quite nimble-footed, and scurries about rapidly in the aquarium, and, as many crabs do, occasionally buries itself in the sand with only its eyes visible above the surface. Biologically, *Calappa* belongs to a group known as the Oxystomaceous crabs, who have their mouth parts narrowed into a sort of vertical gutter, which gives them an odd, petulant expression when viewed full in the face. Fishes normally breathe by taking water in through the mouth and expelling it through the posteriorly located gill openings, but in crabs this process works in reverse. Water is taken in through two slits located in the "armpits" where the pincer-bearing appendages join the body, is circulated through the voluminous gill chambers located just beneath the carapace or back shell, and is finally expelled at either side of the crab's mouth. Motile power for this operation is supplied by the rapid beating of jointed appendages known as "gill-bailers," which are located close to where the water streams make their exit. Due to the narrowness of the mouth region in the Oxystomaceous crabs, the two excurrent streams are combined into a single upwardly directed one of restricted diameter but of considerable force.

*Calappas* are in the habit of prowling about in shallow water at low tide, and at such times their little water jets often betray the crabs' location by rippling the surface as they move along. In the laboratory I noticed that if one of them is placed in a shallow container of water so that only the intake portion of its gill apparatus is submerged, once the gill-bailers get full steam up, a curved stream of water several inches in length is produced.

To demonstrate this, I placed before the TV cameras a large glass ashtray which I had previously filled to the proper depth with seawater. Lighting a cigarette, I puffed on it once or twice, then carefully set it on the rim of the tray. From a nearby bowl I then selected a large *Calappa,* dried it off, and then placed it in the center of the ashtray and aimed it in the proper direction. After a few seconds the stream appeared, growing in intensity, until the cigarette was extinguished to the accompaniment of a slight hiss of steam. I repeated this demonstration on several occasions, sometimes requiring several trial shots due to initial misjudgment of the range of the stream or the crabs' natural tendency to shift their position before and during the squirting procedure.

Although this and other "stunts" were occasionally employed for the purpose of providing a visual demonstration of a particular character or ability on the part of an animal, the main objective of the shows was to acquaint the viewers not only with the great variety in form, but also with the varied behavioral patterns and traits of sea creatures in adapting to their particular mode of life. Unfortunately, many of these traits—particularly those associ-

ated with the procurement of food—could not be demonstrated due to the
animals' reluctance to perform in a natural manner under the bright lights,
restricted space, and other artificial conditions met with in the studio. However, because of the vast number and variety of living sea creatures available in the area, new material was never wanting, and, as before stated, the
very unpredictability of certain animals often enhanced the programs in
unexpected ways. The future possibilities of science and natural history
education, I am convinced, are really quite unlimited through the medium
of television.

# THE RARE AND THE UNUSUAL

*Rediscovery of the Stars and Stripes. First Cherubfish Seen*
*Alive. The Magnificent Royal Gramma. Glowing Colors from*
*the Twilight Zone. Luminous Sea Life. The Golden Gar from*
*Boynton Beach. Sea Snakes. The Coelacanth, Most Sought-After*
*Fish. Whalebone Whales in Captivity*

"The Strange Stars-and-Stripes Fish," read the caption under an artist's
drawing of a most unbelievable-looking sea creature, "one of the rarest
fishes in the world, having been photographed once from a diving bell in
the Bahamas, but never captured!"

I put aside the newspaper and thought that, of all the ridiculous half
truths in the occasional sensational natural history items that one encounters
in the Sunday supplements, this one certainly took the top prize. It was easy
to see what had actually happened. One of the early pioneers in underwater
photography had come up with a blurry and distorted picture of some reef
fish, and filed it away. Years later, it had been picked up by a team of
writers engaged in turning out a Sunday panel having to do with all sorts
of natural phenomena, and in redrawing it, the illustrator had allowed his
imagination free rein. For one thing, it seemed to lack a head, and in study-
ing the figure closely I could deduce that in the original photo, the fish had
had its head pointing away from the camera. The fish, whatever it was,
had evidently had a pattern of alternate horizontal stripes of light and dark,
while its large dorsal fin was solid dark with light dots. Using this as a cue,
the artist had illustrated it in the brilliant colors of the American flag!

This sort of thing I have always deplored, mainly because our world and
the sea spread over it are filled with such an array of genuine wonders that
it has always seemed to me completely unnecessary to try to invent things
that don't exist. I was on the point of tossing the paper in the wastebasket
when a dim memory of something I had once seen began to stir in my
brain. I took another look at the garish outrage. Could it be possible that
the stars-and-stripes fish actually existed? And could it be further possible
that somewhere, some time, I had seen it with my own eyes?

The colors as represented were, of course, ridiculous. But the pattern itself,
changed slightly, was believable, and although no head was visible, there

was something vaguely familiar in the foreshortened body form. The dorsal fin appeared to be divided into two parts, the forward portion high and bannerlike, the after section long and flowing, following the contour of the back . . . Suddenly, I remembered! I *had* seen this fish once. Like the early cameraman, I had gotten just a glimpse of it, and it was only because of the fact that the illustrator, in copying the photograph, had made it nearly unrecognizable, that I had not recalled the incident immediately.

It happened during my very first aqua-lung dive a number of years ago. A friend had invited me to join him on an exploratory sojourn at Carysfort Reef off Key Largo, some 50 miles south of Miami. I had investigated the reefs previously with face mask and swim fins, but this was a new experience, and quite a breathtaking one, in which I could go as deep as I wished and never have to leave any spot of particular interest for the necessity of taking a breath of fresh air. One of the delights of aqua-lung diving is the feeling of total weightlessness one experiences, and, instead of being strapped to a couch like an astronaut, one is free to move through his watery space at will, for the slightest movement of a hand or flipper causes you to turn or roll in any direction, as one flies in a dream.

I was about 40 feet down on the far side of the reef, noting the vast numbers of fishes, who, unafraid of me now that I had in effect become one of them, were swarming about on all sides. I was quite amused at one 4-inch beau gregory (*Eupomacentrus leucostictus*), which darted at me repeatedly and nipped me here and there on the arm and legs whenever I approached too close to a certain coral outcropping, indicating that the little creature probably had a tiny nest of eggs somewhere thereabouts. I had discovered a cave, or rather a tunnel, big enough to stand in, entering an undersea cliff. Swimming into this, not without a certain feeling of apprehension, novice that I was, I saw that 10 feet in front of me was a chimneylike opening in the roof, through which I could see the silhouettes of dozens of small silvery sweeperfish (*Pempheris schomburgki*) that flitted back and forth across the opening. Just beneath the chimney I made myself as narrow as possible and, fluttering my fins ever so slightly, I rose like an arrow as the sweepers parted ranks to let me pass.

Once in the open, I spied a large patch of white sand, in which there were a number of tiny round holes as if someone had repeatedly poked a pencil into the sand, and hovering over each, head uppermost, was a little yellowhead jawfish, *Opisthognathus aurifrons,* who darted into his burrow on the slightest disturbance. I lay on my stomach on the sand, or rather, hovered on it as weightless as a blimp at its mooring mast, to watch for the reappearance of the jawfish, when my attention was suddenly taken by a

Glassy Sweepers, *Pempheris schomburgki.*

large horizontal cleft in a rocky wall that rose vertically from the far end of the sand patch.

Filled with curiosity, I swam over to the fissure and peered inside. Hardly had I done so when the most amazing fish swam slowly and majestically toward me out of the dark recesses of the fissure, leisurely turned around, and glided back out of sight. I must have seen it for less than five seconds, but the impression of its form and color pattern were stamped indelibly on my mind. I have a good eye and memory for momentary detail, and after my dive I made a sketch of the fish, which subsequently proved to be surprisingly accurate.

The fish was one of the miniature drumfishes of the genus *Equetus,* known as jackknife fishes because of the high, bladelike first dorsal fin which rises in a high curve behind the head. This one, however, was marked in a fashion quite different from any I had previously seen. It was about 8 inches long and the first dorsal was black, broadly edged with white posteriorly, and the second dorsal and tail were solid black, marked with round white polka dots. The body was a rich dark chocolate with a series of parallel curving white stripes that swept downward from the region of the head and first dorsal toward the tail, and the whole creature resembled an abstract painting come to life. Later, I was able to identify it as the rare and elusive *Equetus punctatus,* the spotted jackknife fish or, as the papers had it, the stars-and-stripes fish. It was not until 1959 that the Seaquarium finally obtained one in the flesh, and it remained one of our prize exhibits of all time.

Stars-and-Stripes Fish, *Equetus punctatus.*

Some of the fishes in the sea are so rare, or so difficult to find, that they are known to science only from one or two specimens, and these may have been collected a number of years (and sometimes a considerable distance) apart. Then all at once they may unaccountably turn up, sometimes in surprising numbers, in an area where it is difficult to see how they could have been missed all that time. When the fish turns out to be a particularly unusual and colorful one besides, only the true biologist-adventurer can fully appreciate the thrill and elation that such a discovery brings. I was rewarded by such an experience in the summer of 1957.

Captain Gray, Emil Hanson, Philip Case, and I were collecting fishes from the shallow reefs just south of the island of Bimini, and our live-wells were rapidly filling with specimens that we would soon carry across the

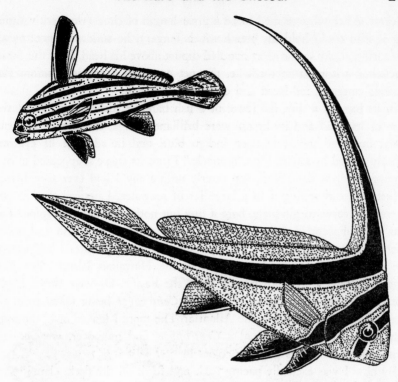

Coral reef relatives of the Stars-and-Stripes Fish:

(upper) Cubbyu, *Equetus pulcher.*
(lower) Jackknife-Fish, *Equetus lanceolatus.*

blue Gulf Stream to the Seaquarium. After a brief and hurried lunch on this particular day (for we didn't wish to waste a moment's collecting time), we moved our collecting boat the *Sea Horse* out into deeper water, where the bottom, although clearly visible, was 40 feet beneath our keel.

Here the coral grew somewhat sparsely and the ocean floor appeared relatively barren, but we knew from experience that there were a host of small things among the rocks. So Phil Case donned a face mask and fins and dropped below for a quick survey. Presently he reappeared, breathing hard, and with a look of excitement on his face. "There's a fish down there I've never seen before!" he announced.

These were magic words to us, and they sent us into all sorts of imaginative speculation. This time we were not to be disappointed. Phil submerged as soon as he had been handed a dipnet of the specified size, and we all leaned over the rail watching his activities through our glass-bottomed buckets. After what seemed to be a great length of time (we were wondering if Phil could hold his breath much longer), he suddenly shot toward the surface, holding the short-handled dipnet above his head. Like the sword Excalibur arising from the lake, the net appeared a moment before Phil himself emerged, red-faced and quite out of breath.

In its bag lay a tiny, flat jewel of a fish barely 2 inches long. The lower part of its head and its breast were brilliant orange, the rest of its head, body, fins, and tail were deep indigo blue, and in addition its eye was heavily ringed by a dark blue "monocle." From its shape it appeared to be a Pomacentrid, or damselfish, but utterly unlike any I had ever seen before.

Just before dropping it in a large jar of seawater, I noticed that its preopercle, or forward gill-plate, bore a tiny but noticeable flat blue spine. This was no Pomacentrid. It had to be a Chaetodontid, or angelfish and, moreover, its shape and coloring strongly reminded me of pictures I had seen of the *Centropyge,* or pygmy angelfish of the Hawaiian Islands. But *Centropyge* species were known only from the Pacific. Or were they? Had I not read a year or so before of a single *Centropyge* being taken from the stomach of a fish caught in the Atlantic? The more I looked at it, the more convinced I was that we had a *Centropyge,* and moreover, we were the first ever to behold its glowing colors in life!

By now I was excitedly pacing back and forth on the deck, clapping my hands and muttering to myself as I have a tendency to do on such occasions, when Phil added, matter-of-factly: "By the way, there's at least four more of them down there!" I was now in seventh heaven. After an hour's activity on the bottom, using Desco masks and a gasoline air compressor, Emil and Phil had succeeded in collecting a total of seven of these little treasures, and next day we took them, along with our several hundred other specimens, back to Miami.

At the Seaquarium I lost no time in checking on all available references to *Centropyge.* These and a hurried phone call to Loren Woods, curator of fishes at the Chicago Natural History Museum, established beyond a doubt that my identification of them had been correct. Woods himself had, in 1951, co-authored the original description of *Centropyge argi* Woods & Kanazawa, which was named for the Argus Reef off Bermuda, where the original specimen had been taken from the stomach of a deep-water grouper in 1908. Later, in 1952, a second one had been found in the stomach of a snapper caught at Campeche, Mexico. But until our collections at Bimini, roughly halfway in between, no further specimens had come to light. Evidently this pygmy angelfish or "cherubfish," as Woods appropriately suggested we call it, has a rather considerable range.

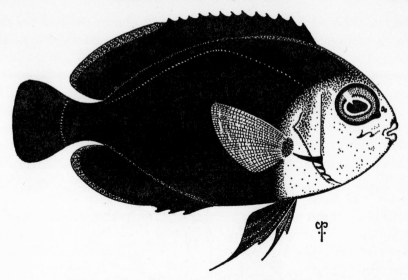

Pygmy Angelfish or Cherubfish, *Centropyge argi.*

The seven original specimens survived for some time at the Seaquarium, and when they eventually died they were preserved and later distributed to the Chicago Natural History Museum, the National Museum in Washington, and the reference collection of the Marine Laboratory of the University of Miami.

From this time on, others have taken the cherubfish at Bimini, and Captain Gray has brought additional specimens to the Seaquarium from time to time. It is difficult to say whether this fish had suddenly extended its former range (whatever that might be) to invade the reefs at Bimini, or whether it had lived there all along but for some reason had managed to escape detection the entire time.

The reefs at Bimini also gave up another exquisitely beautiful little fish, the fairy basslet or royal gramma. I would be hard put to name, or even imagine, another fish, no matter from what section of the world, that could outdo this 4-inch Serranid or sea bass, *Gramma hemicrysos,* in sheer loveliness. The forward half is bathed in the most brilliant orchid-magenta imaginable, and actually appears to fluoresce in the sunlight, although this may be an optical illusion (I will explore this subject at greater length shortly). The rearward portion is by contrast a brilliant orange yellow. The first sight of one of these fish, hovering over a coral crevice with slightly drooping tail as it customarily does, will never be forgotten by the undersea explorer.

Fairy Basslet or Royal Gramma, *Gramma hemicrysos.*

A curious phenomenon regarding the royal grammas displayed in the Seaquarium dioramic tanks under fluorescent lighting is that each one appears to be actually glowing, with a violet haze or "ghost" bathing its upper side, much like a picture printed with its colors slightly out of register. Many visitors have commented on this, and whether it is an actual glow induced by the lighting or merely an illusion of water refraction I am not sure, but I believe it most likely to be due to the latter. I recall having read somewhere that a violet light, because of the particular nature of its wavelength, does not focus sharply on the retina of the eye as other colors do. Anyone who has noticed violet-tinted neon signs or similarly hued tail-lights of cars at night will recall the eerie fuzziness of this particular color.

That some sea creatures actually do fluoresce in the normal light in which they live is a fact of which I was long unaware, but which I recently saw demonstrated in a most dramatic way at the aquarium at Scripps Institute of Oceanography at La Jolla, California.

As is generally known, light will penetrate the sea only to a depth of a few hundred feet, even in the clearest water. The warm colors of the spectrum are very quickly eliminated, in the first hundred feet or so, until only a blue light is eventually left. Living organisms of this blue-bathed "twilight zone" are often brightly colored, as flashlight photographs and examination of the creatures themselves will prove. However, it has long been generally assumed that colors such as red, orange, yellow, and yellow-green are naturally invisible at this depth, appearing merely as altered shades of brown, mustard, and bluish in the dim illumination. However, in some instances at least this is definitely not the case.

In one of the tanks at the Scripps aquarium I saw a collection of living invertebrates recently dredged from the twilight depths of the sea, and they were being displayed together in a tank that was illuminated only by an ordinary dim blue light bulb, but under this illumination they could actually be seen glowing with soft, pastel colors. I particularly remember a small, branching sponge that glowed faintly green; a colony of Alcyonarians or soft corals whose stalks were bluish and expanded polyps pale pink; and a tube-dwelling anemone that gave off an orange-yellow glow. This scene of the utmost beauty I can compare only to the exhibits one sees in museums of fluorescent minerals displayed under "black light" (ultraviolet), but it must be remembered that these sea animals were displayed under plain blue light, and evidently have the ability to absorb light of one particular wavelength and to re-emit it in other ranges of the spectrum!

In the totally dark abyssal depths of the sea (and this includes the major portion of the undersea world) many creatures, including fish, produce their own light through the phenomenon of bioluminescence. This light may be of various colors; it may be diffuse or in the form of sharply defined spots and blotches, and it is either produced directly by the organism, or else by colonies of luminous bacteria that live in a symbiotic relationship with it. Among the invertebrates particularly, there are many luminous forms that live near the surface of the sea and produce their light at night, in the manner of fireflies. The most frequently observed of these are the single-celled dinoflagellate *Noctiluca,* which light up the sea at night like a myriad of tiny sparks, and the 2- to 4-inch Ctenophores, which are distantly related to both jellyfishes and the planarians or flatworms, but more closely resemble the former in being much the size and shape of a lemon and quite transparent.

The Ctenophores light up with a brilliant whitish to greenish light for a second or so in duration, and I recall during my Navy service aboard the *Audubon* seeing the surface of the Pacific lighted up in the wake of our ship for a considerable distance by *Noctiluca* and Ctenophores churned into activity by the propeller. Also, during this particular interval when I happened to leave one of the ship's "heads" (which happened to be unlighted at the time)

I couldn't help but notice a greenish glow as the water cascaded out of the room's main fixture.

For a moment I was startled at this unexpected display from an improbable source, until it occurred to me that all Navy ships use seawater in the plumbing wherever possible, and these bioluminescent organisms were apparently unharmed by their forced journey through the intricacies of the ship's piping system. Repeated flushings brought further pyrotechnics, and in due time I introduced a number of my shipmates to this spectacle, which was always attended by a certain degree of mirth. On reminiscing about this incident, I think that we should have organized ourselves formally into an appropriate club, such as the *"Audubon* Flush-Watchers' Society."

Bioluminescence, or cold light, whether it be produced by fish, fireflies, Ctenophores, bacteria, or *Noctiluca,* is always brought about in the same manner: a chemical, luciferin, is combined with an enzyme, luciferase, in the presence of moisture and oxygen. This process can be duplicated in the laboratory, but bioluminescent organisms have also the power to separate the chemicals in some mysterious way so that they may later be recombined again and again. This cold light is highly efficient, virtually all of the chemical energy being converted directly into light, while in an ordinary light bulb (which we have grown to accept as highly practical), fully 90 per cent of the electrical energy going through it is converted into heat, light being produced by the remaining 5 to 10 per cent.

I have tried keeping various bioluminescent sea creatures alive in the aquarium with varying degrees of success. Most rewarding of these were some Ophiurids (brittle starfishes) that Fanny and I chanced to find one evening at Card Sound between the Florida mainland and the upper Keys, the only place we have found this particular species to date. We discovered them quite by chance one evening just at dusk. They were living in large chunks of rock honeycombed with holes, and after dark the starfishes would extend their arms from the holes, searching for food particles in the passing current. When touched, they would flash with a brilliant greenish light, which lasted for a couple of seconds.

By chipping carefully at one of the rocks by the light of a gasoline lantern we were able to obtain a couple of starfishes nearly intact, but the process was slow and laborious. Moreover, brittle stars can move quite actively, and these would seek to withdraw and bunch their arms in the recesses of the rock the moment they were disturbed. However, we made the fortunate discovery that if one of the rocks was rolled out on shore and left unmolested, the starfishes would emerge on their own accord within a few minutes so that they could be gathered up and dropped into a jar of seawater. In this manner we collected about a dozen of the larger specimens, which we took with us back to Miami.

We placed them in a 10-gallon saltwater aquarium fitted with a sub-sand filter in our living room. Here they lived for several months, and at night it was often only necessary for a person to stamp his foot on the floor in front of the tank to cause the starfishes to flicker their lights in unison. In this case the actual light source, as in other luminous starfishes, was thought to be luminous bacteria in their skin, with the starfishes apparently having the power of somehow "triggering off" the bacteria at will. The light in this case took the form of bright bands or waves which ran along the arm toward its tip, much like a tiny advertising sign, and creating quite a spectacle as it did so.

It often happens that aquariums obtain desirable specimens from private individuals who discover something out of the ordinary and manage to capture it for identification. One of the remarkable trains of circumstance that sometimes arise involves the memorable golden garfish from Boynton Beach.

Boynton Beach is an East Coast town about 40 miles north of Miami. One day in 1957 a farmer happened to be walking along the banks of an irrigation canal that ran through his property. In this canal were a number of Florida spotted garfishes, *Lepisosteus platyrhincus*. These predacious and primitive fishes are uniformly abundant throughout the Florida Everglades. Generally scorned by the white angler, they are nevertheless relished by the Seminole Indians, who split and remove the hard-scaled hide before cooking.

As the farmer surveyed the canal and its contents, he suddenly noticed a garfish that was strangely different from the others, for instead of being a mottled olivaceous brown like the others, this one was a bright golden orange! Desiring to obtain it as a curiosity, he hurried to his house and presently returned with a 22-caliber rifle with which he proceeded to shoot the unfortunate gar. However, possibly due to an error of aiming caused by light refraction in the water, the shot was a near-miss and succeeded in only stunning the fish, which was then prodded to within reach with a long pole. It was then carried the distance of a half mile to the house by hand, an ordeal that few but the tenacious gar could have survived, and then placed in the gentleman's bathtub, where it revived and started to swim about. We were then notified by telephone of the find and I drove to Boynton Beach and purchased the specimen for the Seaquarium.

The fish turned out to be a xanthic specimen, or, more precisely, a mutation in which almost the only pigments in the skin were the orange and yellow ones. This particular type of color abnormality is occasionally found in a number of fishes, the best example being the ornamental goldfish, *Carassius auratus,* which in the wild state is normally a brassy brown with a silvery sheen like its near relative the carp. Besides xanthism, various other color abnormalities are occasionally observed in fishes (and other animals as well). These include melanism, where the skin is suffused with black pigment, and albinism, where the black pigment is completely lacking. Albinos are usually white or nearly so, and their eyes appear pink because the blood vessels in the back of the eyeball are not obscured by dark pigment as is normally the case.

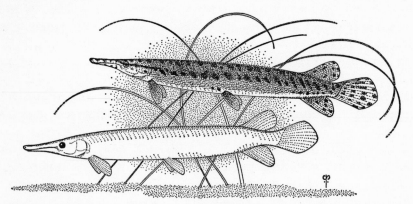

Golden and normally colored Florida Garfish, *Lepisosteus platyrhincus.*

One most striking thing about our golden gar was the fact that, while its back and sides were a brilliant orange and its underside pure white, its eyes were as black as two shoe buttons! In a normally colored gar of this species, the eye is olive brown like the rest of the fish, and a dark stripe that normally runs along the side of the head continues through the eye as a horizontal bar (this particular type of marking is found in many fishes, amphibians, and reptiles as well, and it appears to cause the eye to look less conspicuous through "masking" the pupil). Here was a fish whose body totally lacked the normal dark pigments, and yet these pigments completely suffused the eyeballs, giving it a most striking appearance.

Back at the Seaquarium, I was most anxious to secure some color photographs of our rare gar, and I set about to obtain these immediately, as in matters such as this I have an intuitive fear that something might happen to our specimen, should we wait too long. In this case I proved to be right, and through a most unfortunate circumstance I failed to get any good pictures of it at all. Our photographer at that time was about to embark on a trip, but I managed to persuade him to shoot two entire rolls of film of the gar before he left, one in color and the other in black and white. While on his trip the photographer made the disconcerting discovery that his camera had actually been empty of film when he made the color shots, but by the time he returned it was too late for good pictures. The gar, roughly handled during the time he was carried from the canal to the bathtub, quickly developed a peculiar fungus disease of the skin which caused it to break out in black patches. Although the fish became very tame and would eat from my fingers, the fungus responded to no medication and continued to spread.

At length, with the help of the staff of the Marine Laboratory of the University of Miami, I was able to identify the fungus and decided as a last measure to treat it by gradually changing the gar's tank over from fresh to salt water, as these fish can tolerate a considerable concentration of salt, and I doubted whether the fungus would survive this change. I proved to be right about this—the fungus patches on the skin soon disappeared, but by this time it had worked down under the gar's scales where the salt could not reach. Almost three months after his capture, our precious golden gar-fish finally expired.

It was most unforunate that we had obtained no color photographs, since these golden gars are quite rare. I had seen only one other previously—one that had been speared and extensively mutilated in the course of retrieving it from a canal in the Everglades west of Miami, but at the time of writing I know of at least two which are now in other aquariums. One has lived for several years at the aquarium at the Ft. Worth, Texas, Zoo, and the other is at the National Fish Hatchery Aquarium at Welaka, Florida, a public attraction which I later helped to design for the Government.

Occasionally, I have had noteworthy specimens collected for me on request by persons who happen to be traveling to some particular place. A memorable collection of this sort was made for me in the winter of 1958 by Mr. Al Pfleuger of Miami. Mr. Pfleuger, one of the world's best-known and most accomplished taxidermists (I sometimes refer to him as "The king of the royally mounted") was about to make a trip to the Pacific side of the Panama Canal Zone, and in a telephone conversation he asked me if there was anything I especially desired from that region. Without hesitation I asked him if he might be able to obtain some specimens of the yellow-bellied sea snake, which he agreed to attempt to do.

All my life I have been inordinately fond of snakes. Fanny, who shares my enthusiasm for them, has reared an Indian Rock python to its present length of 14 feet from the time eight years ago when it was left, literally a doorstep baby, in a basket at her home some time before our marriage.

Although circumstances have unfortunately prevented our ever getting in touch with the donors, we know this much about them: they were a young Air Force couple, and the husband was about to be transferred to Alaska, a not too suitable environment for pythons. After offering the specimen to a local animal compound in Vero Beach, Florida, and being turned down, they were finally given Fanny's address along with the assurance that she would be delighted to receive it. Since she was not at home at the time, the basket containing the baby python was left with her father, but in their haste to depart the young couple neglected to leave a forwarding address.

I had always wanted a chance to observe a living sea snake at close range ever since I had seen them basking on the surface of the sea from the deck of the *Audubon* along the coast of New Guinea and the Philippines during the final months of World War II. All the true sea snakes belong to the family *Hydrophidae* and are poisonous, being a highly specialized offshoot of the cobra group. Despite their poisonous nature, most of them are reluctant to bite, hence the comparative rarity of snakebite data from these creatures.

The yellow-bellied ones I hoped to obtain from Panama were the same species I had seen in the Philippines, *Pelamis platurus*. It is the only true sea snake to reach the Western Hemisphere (all others are restricted to the Indo-Pacific region) and has what is evidently the greatest known range of any living snake, being found from Madagascar through the Indian Ocean northward to Siberia and across the Pacific to Panama and Mexico.

A few of the more primitive sea snakes are capable of leaving the water and crawling about on land, as they have the typical cylindrical snake shape, although their tails are flattened vertically, but the greater majority of them never leave the water and are in fact quite helpless when out of the water, as the entire body is vertically compressed (as are some eels) and in some the belly forms a pointed keel as well. The sea snakes that do leave the sea to climb about on rocky islets are egg-layers as are their cobralike relatives, while those that lead a strictly marine existence bring forth their young alive. Although one sea snake reaches a length of over 8 feet, most of them are much smaller, the yellow-belly not exceeding a yard and averaging about 2 feet.

Some weeks went by and I had all but forgotten my initial conversation with Al Pfleuger when one afternoon he showed up at the Seaquarium with two galvanized pails over which cloth covers had been bound with heavy cord. I knew at once what the pails contained, and my hands fairly shook as I unbound the twine and whisked off the covers to have a look. The snakes, 25 in all, resembled a tangle of colorful spaghetti in the bottom of the two containers. After admiring them briefly, I prepared one of the 500-gallon dioramic tanks for them.

The overflow drain of this tank was fixed so that the water line rose only two-thirds up the front of the glass, and here the snakes could be easily viewed as they floated about on the surface or submerged to twine among the rocks in the corners of the tank. Once inside, they began to swim about in all directions, and I marveled at their sublime grace and flowing movements, which are quite different from those of ordinary water snakes, which are merely a land form with part-time swimming habits. Because of their flattened paddle tails, sea snakes obtain most of their "push" from the rear, and because of this some species have their necks attenuated in the form of a whiplash surmounted by an unbelievably tiny head, a design which enables them to strike at their fish prey with great speed and accuracy. The yellow-bellied sea snake, although one of the species most highly specialized for swimming, has a more or less normally proportioned head and neck, but the belly forms a deep continuous keel and the body is slightly bowed so that if one were stretched out on its side with the head and tail at the same level, the midsection of the body would be somewhat beneath this.

The backs of these snakes were uniform dark brown, almost black. Some of them had a side band of brown between this and the clear yellow of the underside, while in others the black and yellow met on the sides in a continuous sharp line of demarcation. This line ran almost straight until shortly before the tail, when it began to undulate, finally breaking up into alternate bars and sometimes spots of black and yellow on the tail proper.

As in all sea snakes, the nostrils were located on the top of the snout and were capable of being tightly closed against the water by means of small valves. As they swam or rested on the surface, they had a tendency to droop their necks and wave their heads from side to side as they peered this way and that, searching, or so I thought, for food. Although I was fully aware of their poisonous fangs, they appeared so docile and languid in nature that at length I picked up several by the tail, keeping an eye on their heads meanwhile. I was surprised to find them quite limp and flabby when out of their native element, and when placed on a flat surface they were quite unable to crawl, but lay on their sides and flipped about in an aimless way. (Like all the more specialized sea snakes, the yellow-bellies have no enlarged ventral crawling scutes as land snakes do, but are covered all over with small, hexagonal scales which do not overlap.) Returned to the water, they commenced active swimming at once.

Although they showed no inclination to strike at any object moved toward them, I noticed that several would bite sideways if touched or rubbed with

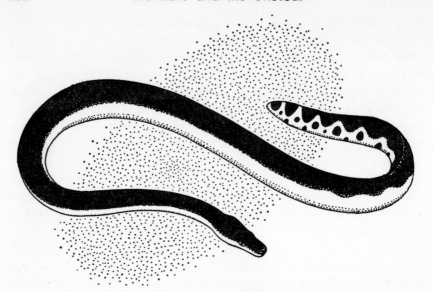

Yellowbellied Sea Snake, *Pelamis platurus*.

a stick on the side of the head. Thinking that this might be a good way to start them feeding, I secured several small killifishes, and after killing them, injected their stomachs with a small amount of air from a hypodermic syringe so that they would float. When I placed one of these on the surface of the water and moved it against the side of a snake's head, he seized it at once and swallowed it entire with rapid movements of his jaws, followed by a convulsive movement in which he spat out a small quantity of loose scales (a procedure which, I was to discover later, normally followed feeding in these snakes). I also discovered that, once they had settled down to their tank existence, they were mostly ready feeders and often showed considerable dexterity in catching living fishes in the water.

Several of the snakes appeared to be quite young, about a foot in length, and I took the two smallest of these home with me and set them up temporarily in a half-filled 10-gallon glass aquarium tank fitted with a subsand filter. Here they thrived very well for a time, feeding on various small fishes which I placed in the tank from time to time. In this connection I noticed a difference in the size of the fish they would eat as compared to morsels swallowed by ordinary snakes. Snakes are proverbial for the great size, by comparison, of the prey they can swallow, since their lower jaws are in two halves connected by elastic tissue, and by working each side of their face independently, they engulf their food by pulling themselves over it stocking-wise, one half at a time. These sea snakes apparently possessed

Bluebanded Sea Snake, *Hydrophis cyanocinctus.*

much lesser powers of jaw distension; they fed only on moderately sized fishes, and these were always captured and swallowed quite rapidly, followed by the inevitable ejection of loose scales.

Although all the yellow-bellies thrived for some time, their numbers were decimated after some months. It may be that they weren't getting quite the right diet, though I doubt this. It may have been due to close-quartered confinement, or possibly due to some as yet unknown factor. One possibility is that, since in nature these snakes rest for long periods at the sea surface, they must be used to receiving a tremendous amount of direct sunlight—in fact much more than it would take to kill the average snake, which cannot endure more than a few minutes of full sunlight at any one time. Under indoor captive conditions during which they were deprived of all but artificial light, they may have suffered something like a Vitamin D deficiency which interfered with their metabolism. For any aquarist who desires to keep *Pelamis platurus* in the future, I would recommend the placing of an ultraviolet lamp over their tank.

Since this time I have seen some blue-banded sea snakes (*Hydrophis cyanocinctus*) at the New York Aquarium. These beautiful and graceful creatures come from the Indo-Pacific region, and a closely related form has adapted itself to a freshwater existence in a lake on the island of Luzon, in the Philippines. The blue-banded sea snake is quite different from the yellow-belly in form and behavior, being very long (about 5 feet) and slender, with a surprisingly small head. Instead of floating mainly at the surface, they spend most of their time swimming slowly and majestically near the bottom of their tank. Although quite hardy in captivity, they are slow to take food under artificial conditions.

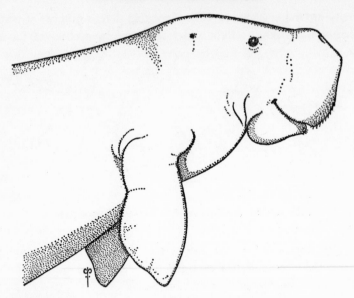

"EUGENIE," the captive Dugong at the Steinhart Aquarium.

I am frequently asked: "What is the one specimen an aquarium would most like to have?" This is a difficult question, since preference differs among individual aquarists. I have already stated that two of my major preferences would be the boutu or Amazonian freshwater dolphin (*Inia geoffroyensis*), and the giant ocean sunfish (*Mola mola*), and to these I will add a third, the dugong (*Halicore dugong*). All of the above have been kept in U.S. aquariums, though with no lasting success at the time of writing, either through difficulties in providing them with their proper diet, or else due to injuries suffered by the specimens during the course of their capture. Any one of these would make a truly first-rate exhibit and be valuable as well from the standpoint of scientific observation.

I cannot speak for all other aquarists, but I think I can make a couple of fairly accurate guesses as to what specimen or specimens are most generally desired at present.

Among the fishes, the answer is most obviously the Coelacanth. This fish, long believed to have gone the way of the dinosaurs and to exist only in the form of fossilized remains, was suddenly resurrected from its 100-million-year-old grave and added to the list of twentieth-century species with the discovery of a living specimen trawled off East London, South Africa, and subsequently named *Latimeria chalumnae* by Dr. J. L. B. Smith of Rhodes

University in Grahamstown in 1939. Since that date, a number of additional Coelacanths have come to light and a few have been observed for a short time in a living state, but thus far none have survived for long due to the manner in which they were captured or the lack of facilities to handle them in a saltwater environment.

The principal significance of the Coelacanth is that it stands in an evolutionary position very close to what must be the common ancestor of the present-day fishes as well as the amphibians, who in turn gave rise to the reptiles, the common ancestor of birds and mammals. The present-day lungfishes (*Dipnoi*) are also in much the same position on the evolutionary ladder. Like the latter, the Coelacanth has paired fins that are remarkably limblike in form.

I have little doubt that in the future, perhaps the very near future, a living Coelacanth will find its way into some aquarium where the public and scientists alike can observe it. In 1957, I had the good fortune to talk with Dr. Smith in person when he visited the Seaquarium. He informed me, among other things, that he had talked with a skindiver who was quite positive he had seen *Latimeria* on a shallow-water reef off South Africa, and he felt certain that a specimen could eventually be secured for aquarium study.

I found Dr. Smith to be a highly dedicated person and still all-absorbed in the subject of the Coelacanth. I will never forget his intense manner as he looked into the 80-foot circular tank and remarked in all sincerity: "If I could but see *Old Fourlegs* [his pet name for the Coelacanth] swimming in your Seaquarium, I could die happy the next day!"

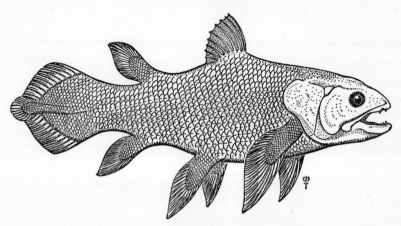

The Coelacanth Fish, *Latimeria chalumnae.*

*Latimeria* has shown us that a real possibility exists of the eventual discovery of other previously unheard-of sea creatures, some of which may be suitable for exhibition in the aquarium. For instance, a 6-foot larval eel has been found, though no one knows how large the adult form may grow. Certain rare whales are to date known only from dead specimens that have washed ashore; and, had their bodies sunk instead of floated, we might still be unaware of their existence. And, it is whales, moreover, that offer what is perhaps the greatest challenge to the aquarist at the present time.

Although pilot whales and white whales are exhibited in various aquariums at the present time, these animals are comparatively small when compared with what the average person envisions when the word "whale" is mentioned, nor do they bear too great a resemblance to the great whales of commerce, such as the right whales, rorquals, humpback, and sperm whales. Will it ever be possible to exhibit one of the giants alive, feeding, and swimming, at an aquarium? Well, surprisingly enough, one species already has, and more than once. But before going into this, let me briefly cover some of the problems that will have to be overcome in this venture.

First, there is the matter of capture and transportation. A whale more than, say, 20 feet long, would be exceedingly difficult if not impossible to raise from the water, once captured, without the risk of seriously injuring it, due to its great bulk. It would almost be necessary to construct a "swim-in" tank or enclosure such as the Seaquarium Shark Channel. Secondly, a tank or enclosure would have to be provided which would allow the creature ample room to swim. The largest aquarium tank today, about 100 feet long, would just float a really large whale, but wouldn't allow him room to turn around. Problems of water circulation, conditioning, and clarity would be increased accordingly. Finally, there is the problem of food. A sperm whale (*Physeter*) would quite likely thrive on squid, provided that he would eat the smaller available kinds and provided that something like a ton of them could be supplied at each meal. As to the great whalebone whales (*Mysticeti*), there is a different problem, for most of them feed exclusively on small, planktonic organisms, mainly shrimplike creatures known as Euphausids which they strain from the sea in vast numbers by means of their brushy sieves of baleen, or whalebone.

To attempt to supply them in captivity with this natural food, and in sufficient quantities, seems totally untenable, unless a sort of hamburgery substitute in the form of some kind of ground-up meat acceptable to the whale can be devised. The impossibility of obtaining a natural plankton diet has spelled doom for specimens of the giant manta ray (*Manta birostris*) that have been tried as aquarium specimens to date and it undoubtedly would do the same for the 40-foot basking shark (*Cetorhinus*) and that largest of all fishes, the 45-foot whale shark (*Rhincodon*). All of these have feeding habits similar to those of the great whales, and are provided with supplemental plankton-straining structures in their gills.

To my knowledge very few, if any, direct observations have been made on the actual method whalebone whales use to obtain the vast amount of food that they require each day, but from the form of their jaws and throat structure we obtain some interesting clues which suggest that two quite different methods may be employed, by the right whales (*Balaenidae*), and the rorquals or finner whales (*Balaenopteridae*) respectively.

The right whales derive their common name from the early days of whaling when they were the "right" whales to kill, since they yielded the most oil and especially since their carcasses would float after death and so not be lost as in the case of the rorquals, which are not so buoyant and tend to sink. The rights have tremendous heads (one-third their total length), their jaws are curved, and the upper jaw fits into the lower in such a way that a vast trough or gutter is formed when the mouth is open. Undoubtedly they swim through clouds of plankton with the mouth open in the manner of the basking shark and manta, continuously filtering the water and concentrating the plankton against the baleen until enough has been gathered to be swallowed.

The rorquals (which include the 90-foot blue whale, *Balaenoptera musculus*, which is the largest of all whales) have no such trough arrangement, the jaws simply being straight and fitting together in a continuous line. However, the throats of the Balaenopterids as well as of the related humpback (*Megaptera nodosa*) are fluted by a large number of longitudinally arranged grooves which allow the throat to expand to a considerable extent, as can be seen when their bodies are pumped full of compressed air, as is done to float them in the course of modern whaling operations. On contemplation of this arrangement it appears likely that these whales feed in much the same manner as a pelican securing small fish, that is, by engulfing a vast amount of plankton-rich water until the throat balloons to considerable dimensions and then allowing it to flow back out through the baleen along the sides of the mouth, trapping the plankton in the process. Whether or not these two probable methods do in fact occur may be established as whales are studied more extensively in the future.

Although plankton animals appear to form the bulk of the food of whalebone whales, some of them also feed on small fishes to a considerable extent. Chief among these is the 30-foot piked whale or lesser rorqual, *Balaenoptera acutorostrata*. This is the species that has been kept in captivity at the Mito Aquarium in the suburbs of Numazu City, some distance from Tokyo, in Japan. A total of three have been impounded in a netted enclosure at the aquarium. The first was captured during the middle 1930's and survived for nearly three months, according to the report of Seiji Kimura and Takahisa Nemoto in *The Scientific Reports of the Whales Research Institute,* No. 11, 1956. During the latter half of its confinement it is said to have fed, but no further information is given. The second lesser rorqual was a calf several weeks old that died after two weeks in captivity in May, 1954. Finally, on November 26, 1955, a 20-foot lesser rorqual was taken in a large pound-type net trap and towed to the aquarium between two boats. It was described as being quite docile the whole time. In the netted enclosure it swam about slowly, usually in a counterclockwise direction, and would rise to breathe, usually in the same spot, after every second or third circle of the enclosure.

Captive 20-ft. Lesser Rorqual, *Balaenoptera acutorostrata.* (Drawn from underwater photographs of specimen.)

Mr. Hanajima, Director of the Mito Aquarium, attempted to feed the whale on anchovy flesh from time to time, but it apparently took no interest. However, a number of mackerel also shared the pool, and their numbers gradually dwindled, and they were frequently seen to leap from the water surface in an agitated manner, so presumably the whale was feeding on them, though water conditions never permitted any actual feeding to be observed.

Finally, toward the end of December, three bottlenosed dolphins, *Tursiops truncatus,* were placed in the pool with the whale, and during the night of January 2nd the whale escaped by breaking through the net after a total of 37 days in captivity. It may be presumed that the presence of the dolphins caused the whale to become restless or alarmed, although no visible change had been observed in the rorqual's behavior following the arrival of the dolphins.

I am indebted to Curator F. G. Wood, Jr. of Marine Studios for a copy of the *Norsk Hvalfangst-Tidende* in which the article by Kimura and Nemoto was reprinted. The article contains several photos of the whale, most of which were apparently taken underwater by skindivers. The photos are not of good quality (water turbidity appears to be mainly responsible for this), but they permit positive identification, one showing the light-colored band on the flipper which is the lesser rorqual's trademark. I also note with some amusement that in closeups of the whale's face there appears that same expression of serene contentment that characterizes the bottle-nosed dolphin with which I have become so familiar.

Certainly a properly constructed tank of the oceanarium type would be most suitable for the lesser rorqual, as well as the killer whale mentioned in Chapter 7, and any aquarium that is so fortunate in the future as to acquire and successfully maintain either of these cetaceans may well find that they have obtained the ultimate aquarium specimen.

# CHAPTER 16

# AQUARIUMS AND THE FUTURE

*Aquariums and Their Universal Appeal. The New Oceanarium
Concept. Public and Private Aquariums in the United States
and Abroad. The Rising Tide of Aquariums and Their Future
Potential in the Fields of Education and Research*

For some time now I have held a firm conviction that, of all those
institutions devoted to the display of natural objects living or otherwise,
the aquarium holds the greatest interest for the greatest number of people.

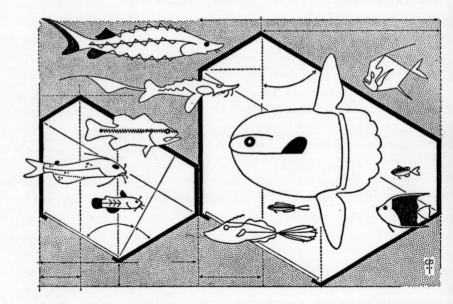

Certainly, at the present time, there exists no other institution having to do
with the natural sciences that can match the aquarium in its universal appeal
and the fascination which it evokes in persons of all categories—young and
old, biologists and laymen, alike.

The reason for the immense popularity enjoyed by the aquarium exhibit
probably has as its psychological basis the natural attraction that a strange
and unfamiliar world holds for the human imagination. For, behind the
dividing glass panel, is a world that man may view but may not enter—

excepting ever so briefly, and then only by virtue of cumbersome mechanical devices that enable him to breathe, to travel, and even to see, for without some sort of glass-imprisoned air space between him and the surrounding liquid medium the human eye cannot obtain anything better than a distorted and blurry picture of the world beneath the surface. Here, behind the glass panel, may be seen living creatures, creatures whose forms vary far beyond anything inhabiting the terrestrial sphere, perfectly adapted to a world in which gravity means practically nothing, moving, feeding, reproducing, and spending their lives in the liquid that gives them life and from which all earthly life came, but which would deprive man of his own within a few short minutes on entering it unaided.

Although the aquarium as an institution has existed in this country for nearly a hundred years, the present-day ones are all products of this century, and it is only within the past two and a half decades that real scientific and mechanical progress has been made in this regard.

In 1937, Marine Studios introduced the principle of the Oceanarium—the giant multilevel tank which displays various species of large and small fishes and other forms of marine life together, much as they are found in the open sea. In the period following World War II, several additional aquariums based on the design pioneered by Marine Studios have appeared, and several others are scheduled to follow. The need for scientific research on the sea and its inhabitants has to date played only a secondary role in this development, the primary motivation being that aquariums of the oceanarium type are good business ventures in the field of public entertainment, owing first and foremost to the tremendous popularity which the public has accorded the bottlenosed dolphin and other trainable cetaceans (which may be appropriately maintained only in aquariums of this type) as "show" animals.

Before I close my story I would like to introduce the reader to some of the more successful and better-known aquariums of this country and elsewhere, beginning with those that fall into the category of "public" aquariums—in other words, maintained by aquarium societies or foundations rather than by private corporations.

The John G. Shedd Aquarium of Chicago is perhaps the best-known public aquarium in the United States, and it was built at a cost of over $3 million and opened to the public in 1930. Located near the Chicago Natural History Museum (formerly the Field Museum), the Shedd Aquarium is housed in a large marble building 300 feet in diameter and octagonal in shape. In the center of the building, under a skylighted dome, is a 40-foot pool simulating a swamp, which is decorated with ferns and other plants requiring a moist environment. It contains turtles, frogs, fish, and other typical swamp denizens. From the rotunda surrounding the pool radiate six main galleries, along both walls of which are a total of 132 exhibition tanks, half of which are marine and the rest for freshwater species. The tanks hold a total of nearly 14,000 gallons of water, and the largest of them are 30 feet long, 10 feet wide, and 6 feet deep. In the building's basement are four large reservoirs which hold a total of 2,000,000 gallons of water, half of which is fresh and the rest salt. Each reservoir is partitioned in half and operated in such a manner that one-half of its contents is "working"— that is, being pumped through the exhibit tanks, drained, filtered, aerated, collected, and returned continuously—while the other half is idle or "resting," which helps to restore its clarity. "Working" and "resting" parts of each reservoir are reversed on the first and fifteenth of each month.

The public galleries are so arranged that both they and the work space behind them are continuous, but are separated from one another. An overhead tram rail such as one finds in machine shops allows portable holding tanks to be moved with a minimum of effort from any one part of the work space to another, and the manner in which work space and galleries are laid out makes the Shedd Aquarium the most efficient one from the standpoint of operation of any I have seen to date. In addition to the six main public galleries with their rows of large tanks is one room, with an Oriental motif, devoted to the display of freshwater tropical fish and plants.

The success that the Shedd Aquarium has experienced through the years with its marine exhibits has proved that a saltwater aquarium need not be located near the sea, and salt water, if properly handled, need only be replaced in small quantities. The original seawater for the aquarium was transported from Key West, Florida, in 160 railroad tank carloads, and since then make-up has consisted largely of water brought in along with new specimens, plus a certain amount of artificial seawater, several formulas for which are now available.

In collecting specimens, particularly the marine forms, use is made of a specially constructed railroad car named the *Nautilus*. This car, which was built by the Pullman Company for the aquarium, carries its own air-compression, water-circulating, and filtering systems, besides space for a number of portable tanks. In periodic collecting expeditions to the Bahamas, the tanks and water-handling machinery are transferred directly to a barge alongside the railroad dock in Miami. The barge is then towed across the Gulf Stream to the collecting grounds and later the specimen-filled tanks are returned to Miami where they are loaded aboard the *Nautilus* and carried to Chicago, being under the close surveillance of the collecting crew all the while. The original *Nautilus* has now been replaced by another car of more modern design.

Since the wartime closing of the old and famous Battery Park Aquarium in New York City, the first unit of a projected $10 million aquarium to replace it has been built at Coney Island by the New York Zoological Society. This aquarium effectively combines tanks of more or less standard design with several large community pools for mixed species. Due to its location on the northern Atlantic Coast, this aquarium is especially well suited for the display of northern marine mammals, including Atlantic and Pacific walruses, sea lions, seals (of which it has several species), and the now-famous white whales, *Delphinapterus leucas,* which were captured in Alaskan waters and transported to New York by plane.

The most notable specimens at the New York Aquarium to date have been two young walruses, "Olaf" and "Ookie." "Olaf," a male of the Atlantic species, soon demonstrated an interesting fact to his curators: that of all the Pinnipeds (the group of marine mammals that includes the sea lions, seals, and walruses), the walruses are the most lovable, gentle, and trustworthy in captivity.

I made friends with "Olaf" during two recent trips to the aquarium and discovered that he loves to be petted and most particularly that he likes to nuzzle people with his great "Mr. Glencannon" mustache, an experience much the same as having a street sweeper's broom shoved in one's face. Of all the aquarium and zoo animals I have met to date, "Olaf" is one of the two I have found to be the most charming, the other being "Winston," an immense male manatee (now deceased) at the Sea Zoo near Daytona, Florida.

"Ookie" is a female Pacific walrus, and much younger than "Olaf." Both animals live in outside pools along with the various other Pinnipeds which are supplied with 54-degree salt water, winter and summer, from a deep well along the beach front. Both walruses enjoy playing with large rubber balls for hours at a time and they have learned the habit of spitting a small jet of water high into the air, a feat also practiced by dolphins and white whales. Reared at first on a special milk formula, "Ookie" and "Olaf" are now fed large quantities of fish and fresh-shucked clams.

The Steinhart Aquarium at Golden Gate Park in San Francisco is noted particularly for its collection of Pacific Ocean fishes and invertebrates as well as unusual freshwater tropicals, many of large size. A natural history museum and a planetarium are located in buildings adjoining the aquarium and all are under the auspices of the San Francisco Academy of Sciences. The aquarium also maintains a scientific research laboratory and, in addition to the display of marine life, a collection of unusual reptiles and amphibians.

Completed in 1923, the Steinhart Aquarium is actually located some distance from the ocean front, but in recent years it has been able to flush and recharge its saltwater reservoirs by means of a long pipeline extending to the sea. Through its many research activities, this aquarium has contributed considerable knowledge, not only on matters pertaining to sea life, but also to the operation of aquariums. Included in this latter category are recent studies on filtration techniques, ultraviolet sterilization of seawater, and the rearing and breeding of "difficult" species in captivity. Experiments at the aquarium have also led to the development of a practical means of drying and storing *Artemia* (brine shrimp) eggs so that they may be easily shipped and hatched whenever desired, furnishing a ready source of live food for young fishes. This accomplishment alone has been of inestimable value to aquarists generally and to breeders of tropical fishes in particular.

In 1963, a program of renovating the Steinhart Aquarium was completed, in which the public traffic-flow pattern was improved and the original tanks were replaced with those of more modern design, including a number of vanishing-side-wall tanks that were first introduced by Dr. Garnaud at the Monaco Aquarium in 1950. These tanks have a trapezoidal shape, being wider in the rear than in front, with the result that the side walls flare outward. When filled with water the additional light refraction causes the slope of the walls to appear to be greater than it actually is, with the result that they disappear altogether when the tank is viewed from the front in the normal way. If the angle is just right and a fish happens to lie close to the wall, the fish may still be seen while the wall cannot, giving the illusion of great spaciousness in a tank of ordinary size.

The distinction for being the oldest aquarium in the United States goes to the National Aquarium in Washington, D.C. Actually, this aquarium has had several different locations, the first one being at Woods Hole, Massachusetts. In 1873 it was started as a summer project, closing down during the winter. Shortly thereafter, the first National Zoo was founded on the grounds of the present Washington Monument. Along with the zoo animals, which we are told included monkeys, deer, turtles, an eagle, and several dozen English sparrows (evidently something of a curiosity at that time), were a number of holding ponds known as Babcock Lakes, where the new Federal Fish Commission was investigating the artificial propagation of shad, buffalofish, and other commercially important species. Eventually, this operation was moved to the basement of a Washington building known as Central Station, and in 1886 the National Aquarium was set up in a special annex.

A saltwater addition to the aquarium was built in the following year, and both sections operated on the "closed" system, with the water being circulated continuously through the tanks by means of pumps and piping. The steamer *Fish Hawk* periodically brought replacement supplies of seawater up the Potomac River from Chesapeake Bay to maintain the marine exhibits. William P. Seal, the first director of the National Aquarium, at this time developed what was probably the prototype of the modern "aquarium stone," a device that breaks up an airstream into myriads of tiny bubbles for the purpose of oxygenating the water. His method, an ingenious one, was to force small disks made of sections of porous grapevine into the ends of rubber tubing.

In 1932, the National Aquarium, which is now under the Branch of Fish Hatcheries of the U.S. Fish and Wildlife Service, was relocated in the basement of the newly constructed Commerce Building. At the present time it displays only freshwater fishes, reptiles, amphibians, and crustaceans in tanks ranging up to 2,000 gallons, but plans are presently under way to replace it with a multimillion-dollar new National Aquarium and Fisheries Research Center to be located in Washington.

One of the finest aquariums in the country for its comparatively small size is devoted to the display of marine specimens of the U.S. Pacific coast. This is the T. Wayland Vaughan Aquarium-Museum of Scripps Institute of Oceanography, situated at La Jolla, California. Here the glass-fronted tanks are located along one wall only, eliminating the disturbing influence of cross-reflection which is met with to some degree in all other aquariums which have tanks on opposite walls with no light barrier in between. Besides the fishes, many Pacific invertebrates, such as abalones, spiny lobsters, crabs, sea slugs, and the various deepwater fluorescent organisms (such as were discussed in the preceding chapter) are exhibited here from time to time.

The Cleveland Aquarium in Ohio occupies a building that was formerly a bathhouse for Lake Erie beachgoers. Although most of its tanks are of modest size, considerable ingenuity has been employed in the setting up of its exhibits, and its staff has spared no pains to procure all manner of strange and unusual life with which to stock them. By means of a carefully worked out formula for artificial seawater which its makers call "Instant Ocean," the Cleveland Aquarium has managed to keep octopuses alive and in good health for longer periods of time than do many aquariums located on the seacoast, and these animals are among the most finicky of all marine creatures in regard to their environmental water tolerances.

Another interesting accomplishment of this aquarium has been the rearing of a number of the so-called home tropicals to considerable size in its larger tanks, proving that available space has much to do with the size eventually attained by many fishes. (For instance, several young tarpon brought from Florida and kept for a number of years in a medium-sized tank at the Shedd Aquarium are now not much over a yard long, about half the size they would be had they remained in the wild.)

The largest tank, which is half filled, is the home of a collection of Atlantic harbor seals; and other unusuals include a Potamotrygonid or freshwater stingray from South America, as well as an Arapaima or pirarucu (*Arapaima gigas*) from the upper Amazon region. This latter fish has the reputation of growing to be the largest of all the world's freshwater fishes, specimens of 15 feet having been reported, though as yet unverified. The shape of the Arapaima is somewhat elongate with the fins crowded to the rearward portion of its body and the scales are very large. Quite variable in color, the young are marked with flushes of red and orange or they may be plain greenish and silvery. The largest I have seen alive is a 6-foot specimen at the Shedd Aquarium, and this one is quite dark, with each scale broadly outlined with violet. It feeds on smaller live fish which it engulfs entire by snapping its great gill-plates apart, creating a strong vacuum and emitting an audible "thump" as it does so. I once saw a foot-long carp disappear down its throat too rapidly for the eye to follow, and then the Arapaima made several convulsive swallowing movements and continued its leisurely gliding progress around the tank which it shared with a large lake sturgeon and several alligator garfishes from the Mississippi. Plans are now in progress for the construction of a much larger aquarium to replace the present one in Cleveland, and experimentation in effective means of artificially lighting tanks, as well as a new tank design based on the vanishing-side-wall principle, are being carried on toward this end.

The James R. Record Aquarium, which is part of the Ft. Worth Zoo in Texas, exhibits its specimens geographically—that is, according to that portion of the world where they occur. In common with several other aquariums, including those at Cleveland and New York, the "charge" of the electric eel and various other fishes having electrical powers is effectively demonstrated to the public with the aid of an oscilloscope and a microphone (which turns the electrical impulses into sound) attached to wires set in the ends of the tank. The pink boutus (*Inia geoffroyensis*) which were received in 1962 from the upper Amazon River are now the James R. Record's main attraction, and will no doubt continue to be for some time to come. At the present time, plans are under way to add a saltwater section to the exhibit.

At Stanley Park, Vancouver, B.C., is the Vancouver Public Aquarium which specializes in sea life of the northwest Pacific coast. This section of the Canadian coast, which lies just north of the U.S. border, abounds in a particularly rich assortment of marine invertebrates which inhabit the cold waters there. Collectors have transported considerable numbers of these to the exhibit tanks, giving the Vancouver Aquarium one of the finest collections of living marine invertebrates and notably of an almost endless and most beautiful variety of starfishes, to be found anywhere in the world. This aquarium is also the main source for the giant octopus (*Octopus apollyon*), which is being shipped to various other aquariums around the country. Fishes included are salmon, sculpins, rockfishes, spiny lumpsuckers, marine sticklebacks, besides many other little-known northern species. In the summer of 1962 the aquarium staff assisted the Canadian Department of Fisheries in capturing a 2-ton basking shark, *Cetorhinus maximus,* in the waters of Barkley Sound. Lifelike casts of this monster are now being prepared for the new Hall of Ocean Life at the U.S. National Museum as well as for the proposed Hall of British Columbia Fishes later to be added to the exhibits at the Vancouver Aquarium.

The Toledo, Ohio, Aquarium which is connected with the Toledo Zoo, while not large, maintains a particularly fine collection of native fishes of the Great Lakes. This is one of the few aquariums that has successfully maintained the odd and particularly delicate paddlefish (*Polyodon spathula*) in one of their large tanks for a number of years.

The "big three" among the privately operated aquariums today are Marine Studios, Marineland of the Pacific, and the Miami Seaquarium. The first of these, Marine Studios (better known to the public as "Marineland" from the name of the town where it is located) is by now the world's best-known aquarium. Opened to the public in 1937, it soon made famous (and was itself made famous by) its jumping and performing bottlenosed dolphins. In its original concept, Marine Studios was not planned as an aquarium, as such, but as a place where realistic underwater movies could be made. At first, the plan was to enclose a suitable cove or cleft between two cliffs in the California coastline by means of a wire net extending from the sea floor to above the surface and to photograph the sea creatures impounded therein from a diving bell. Later this plan was abandoned due to the danger of storms and other inherent disadvantages, and it was then decided to build two great tanks with portholes in their sides for the purpose. Although California was still the originally favored site, Marine Studios was eventually built on land acquired near the Matanzas Inlet, some 18 miles south of St. Augustine, Florida.

The Studios consist of two three-level tanks, a circular one 75 feet in diameter for the dolphins, jewfish, groupers, and other large fish, and a rectangular tank approximately 100 feet long by 25 feet wide for sharks, rays, sawfish, and the various kinds of reef fishes, large and small. Although many movie shorts and sequences from certain movies such as *The Creature from the Black Lagoon* series have been filmed at Marine Studios, its success in this regard was greatly overshadowed from the first by its wide acclaim as a public attraction.

The great success of Marine Studios resulted in the opening of Marineland of the Pacific on Palos Verdes Peninsula near Los Angeles, California, in 1954. Here is located the largest aquarium tank ever built, a four-level oval oceanarium 100 feet long by 50 feet wide, 20 feet deep, and holding approximately a million gallons of water. A second tank, circular in shape and 80 feet in diameter, is the home of the great "potheads" or Pacific pilot whales (*Globicephala scammoni*) that have been tamed and trained with considerable success here. Two of these which were captured offshore near Marineland were recently shipped by air in great canvas cradles to Marine Studios in Florida, where they are now part of the show. In addition to their large tanks, both oceanariums exhibit a number of smaller reef fishes in smaller aquariums of conventional shape and design, those at Marine Studios being provided with dry dioramic backgrounds to increase their apparent depth.

The Miami Seaquarium was opened on Virginia Key in 1955, a year after Marineland of the Pacific. Owing to its subtropical location, the Seaquarium exhibits specimens that are primarily from the Florida Keys and the Bahaman region in two 14-foot deep circular tanks, one 80 and the other 50 feet in diameter with a total capacity of about a million gallons, plus a circle of 26 corridor tanks of from 300 to 500 gallons capacity each. Additional displays include the two Lost Islands with their surrounding tide pools, the 750-foot ring-shaped Shark Channel, and the other exhibits already described.

A smaller aquarium of the oceanarium type called the Gulfarium was built at Ft. Walton Beach, Florida, on the northern shore of the Gulf of Mexico in 1955. Although a major portion of this section of the Gulf is muddied from the constant outflow of large rivers, the water in the Ft. Walton area has a remarkable clarity rivaling that of the Florida Keys, and the beach sand is amazingly white—in fact, a local story has it that some enterprising person once sold a barrel of it as sugar during the wartime shortage! The Gulfarium has a three-level main tank 70 feet in diameter and the water level is set at only halfway up the top row of windows which encircle it, allowing visitors to watch the complete leaping sequence of the trained dolphins as they race across the tank floor and precipitate themselves high into the air for a proffered fish.

A smaller "reef tank" of a most unique design is 30 feet long by 20 feet wide and approximately 7 feet deep. The front of this is walled by a series of glass panels which run from its surface to the floor and which are separated for strength by narrow partitions of metal. The effect on the viewer is quite remarkable and gives the feeling of actually walking on the bottom of the sea. Other aquariums are already planning tanks based on this design, which gives an effect that has not been achieved by other means.

The devastating hurricane that hit the Keys in the fall of 1961 resulted in the shutdown of the Theatre of the Sea which had been in operation since 1946 at Islamoralda, Florida. This exhibit could be described as the only "natural" aquarium in the United States, for it originally consisted of a group of pits from which Key limestone had been quarried. Owing to the natural porosity of the remaining rock, these pits eventually became filled with seawater which seeped into them and even had a tendency to rise and fall with the tide. Their walls and floors became carpeted in time with a rich growth of algae, and when fishes, sea turtles, and dolphins were placed in the pools as an experiment, they thrived and could be readily seen through the clear water by the public. Eventually, as more and more specimens were added and their average size increased, it became necessary to install a system of pumps in order to keep the water moving at a faster rate than that which the tides provided. Before this happened, the Theatre of the Sea was unique in being an aquarium maintained, aside from the necessity of collecting and feeding the specimens, entirely by natural means.

Today new large private aquariums are projected for various locations, including San Diego, Tacoma, Boston, Providence, St. Petersburg, and Galveston. One has been opened in Philadelphia. A recently opened public aquarium of the oceanarium type is the Seven Seas Panorama, located at the Brookfield Zoo in Chicago, Illinois. Since it maintains only marine mammals, including the bottlenosed dolphin, its tanks, including the 180,000-gallon main one, make use of filtered well water containing a 4 per cent solution of high-grade commercial salt. Although no marine fish would survive for long in this "shortcut seawater," the dolphins, sea elephants, seals, and sea lions thrive in it with no apparent discomfort.

Despite the fact that each of the four dolphins in the main pool produces about 9 pounds of waste material per day, the water quality is exceptionally good for a large aquarium of this type. This is partly due to the rapid turnover of the filter-pump system (almost once an hour) and an efficient chemical system similar to those employed by industrial water-treatment plants. Because of its being subjected to a cold winter climate, the main tank of the Seven Seas Panorama is enclosed by a concrete shell which supports the viewing gallery and is surmounted by a removable plastic skylight.

While the accent in aquariums of the United States has been to display as many species and specimens as is feasible in the space allotted, those in Europe and elsewhere tend to be more conservative in theme, often displaying only one or two specimens in a tank of several hundred gallon capacity. On the other hand, great artistic care has gone into the exhibits. In Frankfurt, for instance, considerable effort has been expended on the backgrounds so as to make them as realistic as possible. This aquarium also has the best mechanical equipment of any aquarium now in existence—in fact, it is automated to the point where the system operates without a single engineer on its staff, with emergency systems taking over automatically should anything go amiss in the operation at any time. Visitors are allowed to see the mechanical equipment as well as the tanks themselves, a novel idea in itself.

The Bergen Aquarium in Norway, which is located next to the Institute of Marine Research, features a circular room around the walls of which are nine large tanks of the vanishing-side-wall type with the specimens grouped by families and species. Upholstered benches in the center of the room and luxurious carpeting make this rather unique among existing aquariums. On a lower floor are additional tanks in which such biological principles as evolution, camouflage, symbiosis, and regeneration are illustrated by means of living specimens. Considerable care has gone into all of the exhibits so that a feeling of naturalness is conveyed throughout.

The aquarium in Munich separates its specimens geographically, with South American, African, Asian, and European species assigned to different sections. In Hamburg, aquatic life is incorporated into a new building called the "Troparium" which forms a part of the Hamburg Zoological Gardens and is devoted to the display of various kinds of tropical mammals, birds, reptiles, amphibians, and fishes.

The Berlin Aquarium, which was rebuilt after suffering wartime damage, now has what is said to be the largest collection of living fishes of any aquarium in the world. The building, which is four stories high (split-level aquariums seem to be the rage in Europe) houses not only fishes, but also reptiles, amphibians, and an insectarium consisting of large glass cases for living insects of the world.

The Plymouth, England, Aquarium, which was recently rebuilt, has installed vanishing-side-wall tanks and in lieu of filtration has its reservoirs arranged in such a way that water upwelling to the top of one is immediately conducted with a minimum of turbulence to the bottom of the next, so that the water is cleared by the process of natural sedimentation.

The previously mentioned Monaco Aquarium is now planning to add an oceanarium-type tank for dolphins and other large species. It is planned to build this tank in a cantilevered manner so that it will extend from the present oceanographic building out over the sea.

The foregoing mentions just a few of the world's better aquariums, and no attempt has been made to list them all. If the present trend continues, the next few years will see the development of a number of new aquariums, both in the United States and abroad. Undoubtedly, many of these will be of the "porpoise-show" type, but this particular theme is now approaching the point of being repetitiously overdone. On the other hand, many other possibilities remain to be tried. The "limnarium," or freshwater oceanarium, has yet to be built in full-scale form, and many creatures, such as freshwater dolphins of the genera *Sotalia* and *Orcaella,* the four related Platanistids, freshwater sharks, sawfishes, sting rays, giant sturgeons, the Arapaima and African tigerfish, giant Nile perch, Amazonian manatee and large softshell turtles of the tropics would be ideally suited to this type of tank. In the smaller tanks, experimental modifications of the vanishing-side-wall principle may make the exhibits even more realistic in appearance, and new methods of lighting can be developed to bring out the colors of the specimens to better advantage.

It also seems desirable that future aquariums begin to place less emphasis on "show business," featuring such things as flag-raising whales and sea lions that blow horns. True, these items are popular with the public and they have their place, but such natural wonders as bioluminescence, animal sonar, color-changing, protective mimicry, and convergent and divergent evolution may be similarly exploited in educational exhibits.

The aquarium also affords an opportunity for more scientific study than is being carried on at the present time. Investigations in fish ecology, behavior, genetics, growth and longevity, nutrition, pathology, poisons and antibiotics produced by aquatic organisms, may all be carried out at laboratory-equipped aquariums.

The aquarium should maintain a fully equipped staff of scientific personnel, including not just aquarists and ichthyologists, but also research biologists concerned with behavior, physiology, biochemistry, etc. Ph.D.'s and M.D.'s should be included for the purpose of carrying out veterinary and medical studies on the specimens, and for these purposes the most modern laboratory facilities and equipment are indispensable. Man's world is rapidly growing smaller, and today his attention is turning toward the sea and its inhabitants more than ever before. Such island nations as Japan have for centuries relied upon the sea for a major portion of their livelihood, and in the years to come the rest of the world will have to do the same.

Finally, the aquarium can perform an important role in the field of conservation management. Our terrestrial wildlife is retreating before the advances of civilization, and it is inevitable that our fishes and other aquatic life will eventually follow suit; in fact, this is already happening. Whole populations are being wiped out through increasing impoundment and pollution of our rivers, lakes, and streams, the introduction of foreign species which compete with native fauna and cause unforeseen ecological changes, and the indiscriminate use of pesticides, a fact the seriousness of which the public at large is just beginning to comprehend. Through its educational exhibits and research facilities, the aquarium can help to emphasize to the public the importance of maintaining a natural balance of our aquatic resources and preserving the rarer forms from eventual extinction, as well as acting as a repository for those species for which extinction is already an immediate possibility.

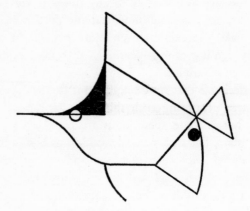

# INDEX

(Numbers in boldface type refer to illustrations.)

273

# CRAIG PHILLIPS

was born in Buffalo, New York, in 1922 but at the age of three, when his father, P. Craig Phillips, Sr., took over the City Editor's desk at the St. Petersburg *Independent,* the family moved to Florida. He grew up in that city to become a Floridian of a special breed—a "beachcomber." Not only did he spend all his spare time collecting animals along the shore but he also displayed considerable talent as a poster and cartoon artist, in which fields he won several contests. By the age of eleven, he had his own column in the St. Petersburg *Times* entitled "Exploring Nature's Shores and Shoals."

Graduated from high school in 1940, Phillips went into the Navy in 1942 and spent four years on active duty. During the war, he was in the Pacific theater, but he still managed to collect reptiles and fishes! Discharged in 1946, he took a job as assistant collector at the famed Marine Studios, but then entered college and was graduated from the University of Miami in three years with a major in Biology and a minor in Art. He then joined the staff of the Marine Laboratory and wrote for the press and technical publications and did art work for both. In 1954, he was appointed curator of the Miami Seaquarium.

In 1959, he joined the U.S. Fish and Wildlife Service as staff specialist for the purpose of helping plan and design the new National Aquarium and Fisheries Center in Washington, D.C. Phillips' wife, Fanny, is also a marine biologist who aids him in his work and researches.